THE FOOD
Dictionary

Denis Bodenham

REDCLIFFE
Bristol

First published in 1993 by
Redcliffe Press Ltd
49 Park St, Bristol

© Denis Bodenham

ISBN 1 872971 18 0

British Library Cataloguing-in-Publication Data.
A catalogue record for this book is available
from the British Library.

Typeset by Mayhew Typesetting,
Rhayader, Powys
Printed by The Longdunn Press Ltd, Bristol

Contents

Introduction

The reader may well ask why a retired surgeon should be writing a dictionary of food.

A lifetime working as a surgeon reinforced for me the importance of an enquiring mind in the pursuit of knowledge and the solving of problems. When I took up cooking as a hobby, after retirement, it was natural for me to approach it in a scientific way using my interest in medicine, chemistry, physics and engineering, despite the fact that my wife and some of our friends regarded this attitude as eccentric.

Just before my retirement in 1979 I was presented with a sum of money to start a charity to carry on my work on skin cancer, particularly malignant melanoma, and so the Skin Cancer Research Fund (SCARF) was set up at Frenchay Hospital. When retirement came it was suggested that I should write a book to raise funds for the charity. The idea of yet another collection of recipes was unattractive but there seemed to be a gap in the market for a comprehensive reference work on food and cookery; hence the seed was sown for this book.

It did not seem unreasonable to me to expect cookery books to explain what really goes on in the cook-pot and oven, and why things can sometimes turn out badly. I was disappointed when I was unable to find readily available answers to many questions and so began to build up my own databank some ten years ago. Personal experience of ill health and major surgery prompted me to extend my enquiries to include health aspects of food and cookery, and food-related diseases. Many of the health issues have been subjects of controversy in the past but there is now a considerable measure of agreement amongst experts. (Currently held views have been presented in a clear and unequivocal way in a series of publications issued by the Ministry of Food, Agriculture and Fisheries and the Department of Health.)

The task has been considerable and the preparation of a text with 2,700 entries free of ambiguities and inconsistencies is time consuming. Although I have made every effort to present as factually correct a text as possible it is important to emphasise that all food has a natural origin and as with all biological products is variable in quality and composition. Bearing this in mind any figures given, such as nutritional and energy values, can only be used as a working guide. To avoid the book being too long it is extensively cross-referenced and I hope the reader will find this useful in order to obtain full information on the subject of interest.

If this work enjoys any success it will be largely due to the help and time given freely by many friends and organisations to whom I am enormously grateful. Because of this there have been no production costs up to the point of handing over to the publishers and all royalties will go to the charity, SCARF.

Acknowledgements

This work has depended heavily on a number of experts and institutions who have willingly and freely given me the benefits of their knowledge in fields beyond my capability.

At an early stage Dr James Dunlop, Director of Public Health, Hull, inspired me with his wide and, to me, unusual knowledge of food and health matters.

Two years ago I sent parts of an early draft to Caroline Waldegrave, Chairman of the Guild of Food Writers and Principal of Leith's School of Food and Wine to ask her for her opinion. She gave me very sound advice regarding the construction of the book and encouraged me to pursue it to the end. I am very grateful for all the help she has given me and for agreeing to write the foreword.

I cannot overstate the help I have had from my colleagues, Professor William Gillespie, Emeritus Professor of Microbiology, with the microbiology and organic chemistry and Dr Martin Hartog, Consultant Physician, with advice on disease; he also impressed on me the importance of consistency. They both read the whole work and had a major influence on the final version.

I am grateful to Dr Charles Kangi of Blueneck computers and Max Murison, Surgical Registrar at Frenchay Hospital, for help with integrating two computers and assistance in programming.

Dr Anthony Jephcott, Director of Public Health Laboratories, Bristol, for his contribution on food poisoning and food borne diseases, Dr John Cummings, of the Medical Research Council's Nutritional Research Unit in Cambridge, for his contribution on dietary fibre.

Dr David Reeves, Consultant Microbiologist, for his help with his considerable knowledge of wines and spirits.

I also wish to thank Dr Malcolm Campbell, Consultant Neurologist for his help on the neurological consequences of alcohol consumption, particularly scrumpy, and Dr Gaston Pawan, Emeritus Consultant in Nutrition, Middlesex Hospital for providing important information on carbohydrates.

David Smith, Master Fishmonger, who has answered many questions with patience and understanding, helping me on the entries concerning fish.

The Association of Medical Microbiologists has kindly supplied me with its up to date leaflets from their 'Facts About' series which has ensured accuracy in relevant entries.

Tate and Lyle and British Sugar have provided information on artificial sweeteners. The White Fish Authority, Edinburgh and the Torry Research Institute, Inverness for their help with fish and with fish parasites.

I am particularly grateful to Her Majesty's Stationery Office for allowing me to use copyright material for the tables in the index and the current list of food additives.

This work could never have been freed of many imperfections in my choice of words and punctuation without the enormous amount of help I have had from my cousin, June Pasley. She has spent her life-time working in English and French and has been able, over many weeks of continuous effort, to bring a polish far beyond my ability; spotting omissions and rephrasing sentences which were quite clear to me, but would have been confusing to others.

My wife, Anne, who is virtual co-author, but declines to accept such a title, has spent endless hours researching nutritional values in reference works and on super-market shelves, and checking, with June, the many cross references. During the last 12 months she has learnt to use a computer and accepted responsibility for translating my cousin's corrections on to disk and in doing so she too has found a number of passages that needed clarification, spotted even more omissions. All this time working on the book has dominated her life, taking precedence over her many other activities.

I must acknowledge my gratitude to John Sansom, of Redcliffe Press, who had the courage to take on a new author writing on an unlikely subject and who has given every assistance during the last 15 months of its gestation.

A work like this is never finished, new knowledge seems to come to hand almost daily in a rapidly changing world and omissions become apparent, but there comes a time when a halt has to be called, however dissatisfied the author feels. In researching the many reference works, differences of opinion and fact are always coming to light and some issues will remain unanswerable as they lie beyond the frontiers of knowledge. The author must accept final responsibility for the facts and opinions expressed.

Denis Bodenham
Bristol, September 1993

Foreword

Denis Bodenham sent me a first draft of his book in 1990 and I realised then that it was unique. He has worked on it for a further two years. I do not know how he ever decided it was finished. I have found it completely fascinating and absorbing. The only drawback is that every time I read an entry I want to find out more about other subjects, too. I have no doubt that this objective, scientific and authoritative approach to a subject steeped in controversy and confusion will prove invaluable to cooks, teachers of home economics, doctors and nutritionists alike.

On each page you find yet another surprising snippet of information. Did you know that cyanide accounts for the most serious effects of excessive consumption of scrumpy, that a berry contains seeds and that therefore a strawberry isn't a berry at all, or that the word marmalade comes from the Portuguese word for quince and has nothing to do with oranges?

I love the way that Denis puts us health food fanatics into place with the accurate and chemical meaning of organic, that is, a chemical substance that contains carbon, an essential component of all living matter. I wonder how many would describe a pig as an omnivorous ungulate ...

This book has been written because Denis felt he needed much more data when he is cooking, which is something he loves to do. His book, too, is clearly a labour of love. All royalties go to the Charity SCARF. I commend it to you.

Caroline Waldegrave

A

abattoir A public slaughterhouse. The premises must be registered with the local authority and the operators conform to rigid codes of practice, in the interests of the animals and of public health. Religious and ethnic practices are allowed when carried out responsibly.

abalone A flattened, edible marine **mollusc** also known as ormer or sea-ear. Varieties include *Haliotis tuberculata*, *lamellosa* and *assinina*; rare off the south coasts of the UK, more common in Australian waters and off the Pacific Coast of North America; the largest may reach 250 mm in size. As with all aquatic animals which live by filtering water, they must be taken from pollution-free waters and cooked.

NUTRITIONAL VALUE: protein 19%, carbohydrate 3%.

ENERGY per 100g: 100 kcal, 418 kJ.

USES: it is usually canned for sale.

abrasive A substance which wears down, used for grinding and sharpening cutting instruments and cleaning where gentle methods are inadequate. Care should always be taken to use the finest grade of abrasive, whether in solid, liquid or powder form, to minimise scratching and wear. Abrasives can remove protective coatings from work tops, laminates, painted and varnished surfaces and plated metals. Abrasives will usually scratch ceramics and glass, should never be used on silver, and on copper and brass only as a last resort. Special liquids are available which contain very fine or soft abrasives designed for specific use, but even these, will, in time, wear the surface and damage the article. See **carborundum**, **pumice**.

absinthe A green-coloured liqueur made of a bitter extract from the leaves and tops of the hardy perennial herb, *Artemia absintha*, also known as the common wormwood. It is not drunk today as it is poisonous, and even in the quantities normally consumed in the past, can cause convulsions.

accelase A mixture of **enzymes**, based on *Streptococcus lactis*, used to speed up the ripening of **cheese** and enhance its flavour.

accidents Always keep a good first aid manual at hand. The most important injuries which can occur in connection with domestic appliances are as follows:—

Burns and scalds. Due to contact with hot surfaces, to spilling of hot fats and liquids, or steam. Steam is invisible until it starts to cool, and is intensely hot: even brief exposure can cause serious injury.

First aid. Plunge the affected part in cold water or put under the cold tap to cool the skin (immediate cooling diminishes the depth of the damage and lessens the pain), then cover with a sterile non-adhesive dressing or, if not available, with a clean, freshly-ironed, cotton cloth. If the damaged part was covered by clothing at the time of the accident this must be removed immediately, as it will retain the heat of the liquid and increase the intensity of the burn.

Flame burns. These are generally serious. The victim must be moved from the source of the fire and burning clothing or fat extinguished by excluding air with a fire-blanket, woollen coat, damp towel. Damaged clothing is best left on, and any exposed damaged skin covered with a sterile non-adhesive dressing. Hospital treatment should be sought as quickly as possible for all but small burns.

Electrical injuries. Due to the passage through tissues of an electrical current, which always takes the shortest path between the points of contact, which may be water, a damp floor or conducting material linked in any way to the earth. Almost always due to faulty mains wiring or equipment, loose wires or damaged plugs. The current instantly causes muscles to contract, preventing the victim from letting go, or causing them to be hurled violently across the room. Electricity passing through the heart or brain can cause sudden death. The current may cause serious damage or kill living tissue without, at first, showing visible signs if the damage is in deep tissues. Local damage may show as an obvious burn with destruction or loss of tissue.

First aid. Do not touch the victim until the source of electricity has been disconnected by switching off the current or pulling out the plug. If this is not possible, put on rubber gloves and move the victim. If the victim has stopped breathing, or the heart has ceased beating, immediate artificial respiration or heart massage should be carried out in accordance with instructions in a first aid manual. Treatment in hospital is necessary for all but the smallest injuries.

Cuts. Serious injuries can occur when the hand slips opening a tin, a glass container breaks, when sharp knives and bread or meat slicing machines are being used. Some of these can be penetrating and sever nerves and tendons. Simple superficial injuries can be satisfactorily treated by stopping the bleeding, using local pressure with a clean, readily available pad of kitchen tissue, and holding the part up as high as possible until bleeding ceases. If there is any risk of a penetrating injury, a piece of glass left in the wound, or a wound that gapes, medical advice must be taken.

acetic acid (**E260** and related substances **E261–263**) Acetic acid is the essential ingredient in **vinegar** and is found in fermented liquids, such as beer, wine and cider, which have become infected with *Acetobacter aceti* (vinegar bacillus). It is made naturally by fermentation or synthetically from alcohol. In the pure state, it is known as glacial acetic acid which becomes solid below room temperature. It is strongly caustic and can cause burns of the skin and mucous membranes.

USES: as a **preservative** in pickles and chutneys, flavouring in soups, sauces and a tenderising agent at a concentration of 4–5%.

acetoin *Acetyl methyl carbinol*. A chemical substance produced by **bacteria**, which changes to **diacetyl** during the souring of **milk**. It is responsible for the characteristic flavour of **butter**.

acids Sour substances, the opposite of **alkalis**, with a pH of below 7. Acids are present, to some extent, in all fresh foods and are a feature of most fruits. They have a wide range of functions in **digestion**, and in preparation of food. A degree of acidity is essential for freshness and to conserve **vitamin C** in **fruit** and **vegetables**. **Wine** and fruits contain a mixture of acids, the correct balance of which is one of the factors responsible for their subtle characteristics.

Acids control **enzyme** activity and preserve the colour of red fruits. **Acetic** and **lactic** acids limit the growth of **bacteria** and **moulds** and are used as food **preservatives**. For measurement of acidity see pH.

The most important acids found in food are as follows:—

Acetic acid. Vinegar.

Ascorbic acid. Vitamin C. High in citrus fruits, sweet peppers. Present in most fresh vegetables including potatoes and germinating seeds.

Citric acid. Citrus fruits.

Lactic acid. Sour milk, hard cheese, yoghurt.

Malic acid. Rhubarb, plums, apples.

Oxalic acid. Spinach, rhubarb, beetroot tops and sorrel.

Tannic acid. Tea-leaves, red wine.

Tartaric acid. Grapes and wine.

See **hydrochloric acid**.

acid and **base foods** Following **digestion**, and towards the end of **metabolism**, some foods form weak **acids** and some **alkalis**. The former are known as acid and the latter as basic foods. Generally those which contain a greater proportion of **sodium**, **potassium**, **calcium** or **magnesium**, such as milk, fruits and some vegetables, produce alkalis even though they may have an acidic taste. Those in which **chlorine**, **sulphur** and **phosphorus** predominate as in meat, fish, cereals and cheese, produce weak acids. Fats and carbohydrates are generally neutral.

acidophilus The bacterium, *Lactis acidophilus*, is a normal inhabitant of the large bowel. Ingestion of this organism is harmless in moderation and may be beneficial.

USES: variants of this bacterium are used in souring of milk, and cream, cheese and yoghurt-making.

acitron A form of candy made from *Echinocactus grandis*, a native cactus of Mexico.

acrolein A pungent and irritating gas produced by the overheating of fats.

ackee Pear-shaped, red, edible fruit of the tropical tree, *Blighia sapida,* related to the **lychee**. Only the whitish flesh is eaten; the rest is poisonous, as is the flesh when the fruit is under- or overripe.

USES: mainly for cooking with fish. Not usually available in the UK.

additives Substances used to alter, enhance or improve the colour, flavour, appearance and keeping qualities of food. They have a major role in commercial cooking and the preparation of processed foods, but only a

very small place in home cooking. There is now a move away from additives and fewer are being used.

The EEC recognises about 500 substances that are considered safe in the quantities permitted. Each additive must be recorded on the label of the goods by the full name, or by code, using the letter E followed by a number, and by the number only if it is awaiting full approval. Exemptions are at present made for all drinks, including wines, snacks and food sold in small packets. The regulations are rather loosely interpreted; for example, manufacturers who include in their product ingredients from another source do not necessarily have to disclose the additives in these, nor does the quantity of additives used have to appear on the label, although the quantity of other ingredients such as fat, sugar, must appear.

The quantities of additives consumed in a mixed diet are generally safe. Those who subsist solely on convenience foods could run a slight risk of taking an excess.

Additives can be broadly classified according to their intended function; many however, have more than one function and occur in more than one classified list. A full list, which changes from time to time, of recognised additives with their code numbers and full names is published by the Ministry of Agriculture, Fisheries and Food and is available from HM Stationery Office. There are also more detailed books on the subject. See appendix pages 257–263.

USES:

1. To compensate for loss of **colour** in food processing or enhance natural colours; some are dyes, others are chemicals which increase the intensity of natural colour.

2. To prolong the shelf-life of products, by limiting deterioration that occurs in natural foods by the action of **bacteria**, **moulds** and **enzymes** and by the action of the **oxygen** in the air. To prevent or delay fats going rancid. The

most frequently used are based on **toco-pherol**, a naturally occurring **antioxidant** known as **vitamin E** and listed E306−309.

Fungicides are used on the surface of fresh fruit, particularly apples, **citrus fruits**, to reduce spoilage; these can only be partly removed by washing.

3. To enhance flavour in meat products, jams, fruit drinks. The additives include **acids, sugar, salt, monosodium glutamate, yeast extracts, hydrolysed vegetable protein, artificial sweeteners**.

4. To change the character of the food by the use of **bulking agents, emulsifiers, thickeners** and stabilisers which inhibit changes after manufacture, as in sauces, ice-cream and processed dairy products which may result in the product separating out.

5. To increase the bulk and weight, and improve succulence, of products such as chicken, ham, prawns and processed cheeses by raising the water content.

adipose tissue Tissue in which **fat** is stored in specialised cells and which may account for around 15% of body weight and more in some animals. It is particularly located under the skin, around the kidneys and in the abdomen. The fat content in domesticated animals is always greater than in the wild equivalent. In all warm-blooded animals it is mostly saturated.

adlay *Coix lachrima-jobi*, also known as Job's tears, a tall tropical grass, grown in Asia and Africa for its hard bean-like seeds.

NUTRITIONAL VALUE: protein 15%, fat 5%, carbohydrate 30%, vitamin B complex, iron.

ENERGY per 100g: 360 kcal, 1506 kJ.

USES: ground and cooked as a **gruel**. The seeds are also used as beads.

adulterate To debase food by the addition of cheap substances or materials. In the high standards set in the EEC countries, adulteration is rare.

adzuki or **aduki** *Phaseolus angularis*. Small dark-brown or red beans of the Orient which are sold dried. They must be washed, soaked, and cooked by boiling for at least 10 minutes, to destroy the poison **lectin**, then simmered until soft for up to 30 minutes. See **pulses**.

NUTRITIONAL VALUE: average: cooked: protein 9.6%, carbohydrate 26%, dietary fibre 5.7%

ENERGY per 100g: average: cooked: 135 kcal, 565 kJ.

USES: in salads, soups, stews, as a source of protein in vegetarian dishes.

aerobes. The group of **bacteria** which grow best in the presence of oxygen, though some are able to grow slowly in its absence, as compared with **anaerobes**, which can only grow in the absence of oxygen, though some will remain viable in its presence. Most pathogenic bacteria (capable of causing disease) are aerobes, hence the advantages of excluding air by vacuum-packing, which not only deters the growth of **moulds** and bacteria, but also lessens deterioration by **oxidation**. There are some beneficial aerobic bacteria, which inhabit the large intestine, involved with the breakdown of **dietary fibre** and the manufacture of **vitamin B6**. See **food poisoning**.

aflotoxins A group of **toxins** produced by a **mould** which can grow on dried **figs**, **peanuts** and other **nuts** and are capable of causing serious liver damage. All suspect figs and nuts should be destroyed.

African corn See **sorghum**.

agar (E406) Also known as agar-agar. A natural product obtained from red seaweeds. Chemical variations with similar properties are listed as **additives** E400−406.

NUTRITIONAL VALUE: none; it cannot be digested.

USES: as a gelling agent, for thickening and as a stabiliser. Much used in commercial food processing, such as ice-creams. Valuable in place of **gelatine**, which would be destroyed by natural proteolytic **enzymes** present in some fresh fruits, such as **pineapple** and **paw-paw**. Agar sets at a higher temperature than gelatine but the resultant gel does not melt so well in the mouth and has a different feel.

agave A subtropical member of the lily family, *Agarista pulchra*, which grows to a large size and exudes a sweet sap from cut stems.
USES: the sap is fermented to produce the national drink of Mexico, known as **pulque**, distillation of which produces **tequila**.

agglomerated flour Flour which has been blown into a jet of steam causing it to reform in very small granules, and which is then dried in a stream of hot air. In this form it mixes easily with water.
USES: the basis of instant thickening powders for soups, stews.

ageing In **wheat**, a process of oxidation, which occurs naturally and improves the baking quality of flour used for bread-making. See **flour improvers**.
The term also refers to the mellowing of taste and development of bouquet in wines and spirits which takes place slowly with storage. For this reason some of the finest brandies and whiskies are stored for up to ten years or more. See **congeners, fusel oil, gluten**.

aioli A speciality mayonnaise from the Provence region of France, flavoured with garlic and vinegar or lemon juice.

ajowan *Carum ajowan*. Also known as omum and bishop's weed. The seed is strongly-flavoured and related to **caraway** *(Carum carvi)*.
USES: as a flavouring in Indian cooking.

akavit A Scandinavian **liqueur** flavoured with **caraway** seeds.

à la carte A list of dishes priced separately on a menu, as opposed to **table d'hôte**.

à la mode de or **à la** After the style of.

à la russe See **russe**.

albacore *Thummus thymmus*. A form of tunny fish usually canned and sold as **tuna**.

albedo The white **pith** of **citrus fruits**.
USES: commercially as a source of **pectin** and important in the manufacture of **marmalade**.

albumen A naturally occurring water-soluble **protein** present in **egg**-white, muscles and blood. It is transparent until it coagulates and becomes opaque at a temperature of 70°C (158°F). When there is a 10% content of other similar proteins called **globulins**, as in egg-white, the mixture can be whisked to form a stable foam for foods such as **meringues**. See **hydrogen bonds**.

albumen index A measurement of the quality of an **egg**. The white is separated from the yolk and poured on to a flat plate. Freshness is determined by the ratio of the height of the mass against the width of the spread. The fresh egg retains the greater height and spreads less.

alcohol The name given to a group of chemical substances, based on **carbon**, hydrogen and oxygen (see **gas**), varying from the very simple to complex; the latter, known as higher alcohols, may be solids. Generally the term means **ethanol** (ethyl alcohol), produced in the **fermentation** of sugar solutions by yeast. It is the characteristic feature of fermented and distilled drinks. Beer usually has a concentration of 3–5%, wines vary, from 7–8% for light German wines, up to 14% for the heavy red wines and champagne, and 30-60% for spirits and liqueurs. Traces of other alcohols, known as **congeners**, are usually present.
Contrary to popular belief, alcohol is not a stimulant but acts by suppressing self-

control. It also dilates blood-vessels and increases heat loss; it should never be given to treat shock or injury. Ethanol taken in excess over a long period leads to liver damage (cirrhosis) and deterioration of brain function. Women have a lower tolerance than men and should consume less.

ENERGY per g: 7 kcal, 29 kJ (nearly twice that of carbohydrate).

USES: any alcoholic drink may be used in cooking, for its flavour or to bring out other flavours which are only soluble in alcohol. Extracted flavours are retained in the water present after the alcohol has been evaporated in cooking. Alcohol is retained when used in cold foods, as in **brandy butter, trifles** with **sherry, kirsch** with fruits. See **beer, brandy, cider, fusel oil, lager, perry, spirits, wine.**

alcohol safe limits Alcohol is quickly metabolised, but the rate of absorption is very variable depending on the strength of the medium and the amount of food ingested with it. It is now customary to quantify alcoholic drinks in terms of units; one half pint of beer (approx 300 ml), one glass of wine (approx 100 ml) and one measure of spirit (approx 25 ml) equal one unit. Men should not exceed 21 units per week and women 14.

Regular weekly consumption of approximately 50 units for men and 35 units for women carries a high risk of long-term damage to the liver and nervous system. One unit, under conditions of rapid absorption, can raise the blood-level above the legal limit for driving. Consumption of alcohol should be reduced in pregnancy. Hepatitis is a disease which damages the liver and alcohol should not be taken during the acute phase. Alcohol tolerance may be reduced if liver function does not fully recover.

al dente 'To the tooth'; an Italian term meaning cooked firm enough to bite but neither too soft nor too hard.

aldrin One of the early synthetic pesticides now banned because of its persistence in the soil.

ale See **beer.**

alecost *Chrysanthemum balsamita*. A hardy perennial **herb,** also known as bibleleaf and costmary.

USES: widely used in biblical times in stuffings and soups, but rarely today. Has been used to flavour beer.

alesander *Smyrnium olustratum*. Also known as alesanders, blackspot leaf and horse parsley. Cultivated as a salad crop but generally superseded by the superior quality of celery.

alfalfa *Medicago sativa*. More commonly known as lucerne. Probably the most widely cultivated forage crop in many countries.

NUTRITIONAL VALUE: has a small but useful content of vitamin C.

USES: the seeds may be germinated and used in the cotyledon stage in **salads.**

alga The generic name for aquatic plants which do not have separate roots, stems and leaves. The most important are seaweeds and many are edible. They have a high mineral content.

NUTRITIONAL VALUE: negligible except as a source of **calcium, iodine, potassium.**

USES: commercially as a source of **agar** and other gelling agents. Used as fertiliser on farms by the coast, and as a mineral supplement for animals. See also **carrageenan** and **lava.**

alginates Salts of alginic acid found in seaweeds. They are **polysaccharides** and widely used as food **additives,** listed within the range E400-E406, in commercial food production as thickeners, gelling agents and stabilisers in food such as ice-cream, sauces, pie fillings. Unlike **gelatine** they are not destroyed by **proteolytic enzymes** and melt at a higher temperature.

alginic acid (E400) A natural extract from seaweed. Also related compounds E401–405. See **agar**.

USES: gelling agent, stabiliser and thickener.

alkali A substance, which when dissolved in water, is the opposite of **acid** and has a pH above 7 (see **pH**). An alkali present in the **duodenum** is essential for the function of the enzyme **trypsin**. Natural food substances which are acid, tend to become alkaline when they deteriorate. Some **mineral waters** are alkaline.

alkaloids Chemical substances, widely distributed in plants. Many have powerful medicinal properties such as **digitalis**, **quinine**, **morphine**, or are highly poisonous such as **cocaine**. The alkaloid content of plants is variable, and for this reason, **herbal remedies** are unreliable, without scientific assay to check for strength.

Two alkaloids are important in cooking: **solanine**, found in green potatoes is poisonous and resistant to heat; **lectin**, found in small quantities in many vegetables is destroyed by ordinary cooking, but for the high concentration in red, brown and black beans boiling for at least ten minutes is necessary.

alkanna *Alkanna tinctoria*. A perennial herb of Southern Europe, related to borage. The flowers are blue.

USES: the roots are used as a source of dye to colour foods, such as sausages, meats and wines. Acidic food will turn red or pink and alkaline food will turn bluish.

alkannet The colouring substance extracted from the roots of **alkanna**.

allergen See below.

allergy A state of the body when it over-reacts to the presence, by contact or ingestion, of any substance, called an allergen, which is generally tolerated by the majority of people. It may manifest as a skin rash, swelling of a part of the body, fainting or collapse. Examples of allergens are primula leaves, nickel, bee or wasp stings, mosquito bites, milk, eggs, shellfish, strawberries. Once sensitivity is established, the reaction may be triggered by very small quantities of the allergen. Medical advice must be taken if sensitivity develops. It may be possible to desensitise the sufferer. See **mites**.

allgood See **Good King Henry**.

allspice The berry of *Pimenta officinalis*, a native shrub of Jamaica; also known as Jamaica pepper and myrtle pepper and in the north of England sweet pepper, but it is not the same as the sweet pepper of the *Capsicum* family. The dried berries have a flavour suggestive of mixed spices.

USES: to flavour meat dishes, soups, casseroles, cakes, desserts and puddings.

allumettes Pieces of potato cut like matchsticks and fried.

almond The **kernel** of the fruit of *Prunus amygdalus*, a Mediterranean tree related to peach and apricot. The flavour is due to **amygdalin**. The best varieties come from sub-tropical areas; those grown in the South of England produce nuts which are small and bitter. In their shells they keep well in dry conditions for many months but once shelled and skinned they start to deteriorate and should be refrigerated or frozen. See **benzaldehyde, fat**.

NUTRITIONAL VALUE: protein 16–17%, fat 50% of which only 10% is saturated, vitamin B complex.

ENERGY per 100g: 565 kcal, 2334 kJ.

USES: for flavouring and decorating biscuits, cakes, desserts, sweetmeats, fish and a variety of savoury dishes. The skin is usually removed by brief immersion in boiling water. They can then be split, chopped or flaked. The flavour may be enhanced by light roasting. Ground almonds are used with flour in baking and in **almond paste**.

almond essence An oily liquid extracted from **almonds**. Cheap substitutes may be prepared from the **kernels** of **peaches** and **plums**, sometimes with the addition of synthetic **benzaldehyde** which is responsible for much of the characteristic flavour.

USES: as a flavouring for biscuits, cakes, desserts and sweetmeats.

almond paste See **marzipan**.

alpha-tocopherol (E307) Vitamin E and related compounds E308–E309. Synthetically produced.

USES: as an **antioxidant** to retard deterioration in **fats** and processed foods containing them.

aluminium A metal which is generally not affected by substances used in cooking and has largely replaced copper. It is light in weight, relatively inexpensive, soft, will take a high polish and is an excellent conductor of heat and electricity; it is resistant to acids but attacked by **alkalis** and **salt** if left in contact with them. The possible toxicity of aluminium in the diet is still under investigation but no firm evidence is at present available to justify restricting its use, although it has been suggested that it may be linked with **Alzheimer's disease**.

It is easily machined but containers made from it need to be thick-walled for strength. It can be rolled out into paper-thin sheets.

USES: for saucepans, frying pans, pressure cookers, disposable containers. It is used in the form of aluminium sulphate for the clarification of water supplies, but this is being replaced by iron chloride. See **aluminium foil**.

aluminium (Ĕ173) Permitted metallic food colouring for coating foods only; used as an alternative to the much more expensive silver.

aluminium foil The metal prepared in paper thin sheets and much used to wrap food, to exclude air, and to retain flavour during cooking. It is destroyed by **salt** and should not be used to wrap salty foods. It should not be used in a **microwave oven**.

Alzheimer's disease A progressive wasting disease of the brain, usually affecting the elderly and associated with loss of memory and later dementia. The origin is unknown and the link with **aluminium** is unproven.

amino acids Weak organic acids from which **proteins** are made in plants and animals. Eight of the twenty known are essential to life and cannot be synthesised by the body; they are present in foods of high nutritional value such as **milk** and milk products, **cheese, eggs, liver** and **kidneys**. The others can be synthesised by the body from proteins present in a mixed **diet**.

Vegetarians can take in sufficient amino acids from a mixed diet of **pulses, wheat** and wheat products supplemented by **yeast**. Proteins are broken down into amino acids during digestion and built up again in the liver for growth and natural repair processes. Amino acid supplements are not required and should only be taken on medical advice. See **gelatine, melanoidin, phenylketonuria**.

ammonia A noxious **gas** made only of **hydrogen** and **oxygen**. It is formed in small quantities by certain **bacteria** breaking down **protein**, as in soft cheese when overripe, and urea in babies' nappies when wet. The gas is used in some commercial refrigeration plants.

ammonium alginate (E403) Similar uses to **alginic acid**.

ammonium chloride A simple chemical substance with a salty taste, used as a salt substitute where a **low-salt** diet is required.

ammonium pectate (E440) See **pectin** (E440).

amontillado A medium or dry **sherry**.

amygdalin A **glycoside** (glucoside) present in **almond**, peach and apricot kernels from which the flavour and smell are derived as they change to a mixture of **glucose**, **benzaldehyde** and **cyanide**. The small quantity of cyanide consumed is destroyed by a healthy liver.

amylase A natural **enzyme** secreted by the salivary glands and the pancreas which converts **starch** into **sugar**. It occurs in two forms which together are known as **diastase**. Salivary amylase is also known as **ptyalin**.

anabolism The chemical process of building up living tissues. Certain drugs and anabolic steroids can stimulate anabolism, promoting muscle strength, and have been illegally used by athletes with a risk of long term dangers. See **metabolism**.

anaemia A state in which there is a reduced concentration of the oxygen-carrying substance, **haemoglobin**, in the blood. It may be due to causes such as, excessive blood loss and a failure to form blood because of dietary deficiencies. See **iron**, **vitamins (B12, folic acid)**.

anaerobes A group of **micro-organisms** which are able to grow in the absence of air, such as *Clostridium botulinum* which produces one of the most potent nerve **toxins** known. This is the cause of serious or fatal **food poisoning** from canned food which has become contaminated during manufacture or later by damage to the container. See **aerobes**, **antibiotic**, **bacillus cereus**, **blown**, **botulism**, **canning**.

anchoor Dried slices of green or ripe **mango**, with a sweet-sour flavour.
USES: in **curries**, **chutneys** and **marinades**.

anchoiade A paste made with pounded **anchovies** and **olive oil**. There are many variations using added ingredients such as **onion**, **tomato**, **herbs** and **spices**.

anchovy *Engraulis encrasicholus*. A small, oily **fish** of the **herring** family with a strong flavour; found in the Mediterranean and off the Atlantic coast of southern Europe, sometimes migrating to coastal waters of southern Britain. Very similar fish are found in tropical waters, all of the same family. Anchovies are usually salted and canned in olive-oil.
NUTRITIONAL VALUE: protein 18%, fat 18% most of which is polyunsaturated. vitamin A, vitamin D, minerals.
ENERGY per 100g: 234 kcal, 979 kJ.
USES: for fish-pastes, flavouring **pizzas**, in **hors d'oeuvres**.

andouille A speciality French **sausage** made in Normandy and Brittany.

angel cake A very light, fatless, sponge-cake.

angelica The flat ribbed stalk of a perennial **herb**, *Angelica archangelica*. It is usually crystallised and dyed green.
USES: for decoration on cakes and desserts.

angels-on-horseback A savoury, originally of **oysters** wrapped in **bacon** and fried but now the term is generally used for a variety of fillings wrapped in bacon.

angostura bitters A proprietary concentrated bittering agent named after the town of Angostura in Venezuela where it originated. Although the formula is a trade secret it is known to contain a number of spices, peel of mixed citrus fruits and **quinine**.
USES: for flavouring of fruits, cocktails, ice-cream, gravies and soups.

anisakiasis See **fish worms**.

anise or **aniseed** *Pimpinella anisum*, an annual plant, hardy in temperate zones.

USES: the seeds are used in soups, condiments, liqueurs, sweetmeats and savouries. The leaves may be eaten fresh in salads.

anisette A **liqueur** flavoured with **anise**, **coriander** and **fennel**.

anithole Essential oil contained in the seeds of **anise** giving it its characteristic flavour.

annatto (E160b) A naturally occurring yellow/orange dye obtained from the covering of the seeds of the tropical South American tree, *Bixa orellana*.

USES: for colouring chocolate, cheese, smoked fish.

anthocyanins See **colour**.

anthoxanthins See **colour**.

antibiotics A group of substances, extracted from cultures of various **moulds** and **bacteria**, having the property of being well tolerated by man, and retarding or destroying **micro-organisms** which cause disease in man and animals. Indiscriminate use of antibiotics in animals to increase **meat** production, and their presence in meat and dairy products in small quantities has seriously impaired the medical control of human diseases, by encouraging resistant strains of micro-organisms. They can also interfere with the production of foods, such as **cheese**, which depend on the action of certain bacteria.

The first true antibiotic was **penicillin**, extracted from the mould *Penicillium notatum*, a close relative of the blue mould *Penicillium roquefortii* which gives blue cheeses, such as Roquefort and Stilton, their character. The only antibiotic which is now permitted in food preservation and in animal feeds is **nisin** (234) because it is not used medicinally. Certain antibiotics used in the treatment of disease interfere with the function of beneficial bacteria present in the large bowel. See **anaerobes**.

anticaking agents Powdery substances which interfere with the natural tendency of the grains of foods such as salt, icing sugar, to stick together. They are classed as food additives and examples include magnesium carbonate (504), magnesium oxide (530), potassium ferrocyanide (536), calcium silicate (552), magnesium trisilicate (553a), aluminium sodium silicate (554), aluminium calcium silicate (556), bentonite (558), kaolin (559), stearic acid (570), magnesium stearate (572).

antioxidant Any chemical substance able to prevent **oxidation** which causes deterioration of food. Commonly used examples are **ascorbic acid (vitamin C)**, **sulphur dioxide** for fruits and drinks (**Campden tablets**), **tocopherol (vitamin E)**, for fats and products containing them. Found within the range E 300-321 of food **additives**. Some of these have additional properties in commercial food production. Evidence is accumulating that the antioxidant vitamins C & E may play a part in the prevention of some cancers and other disease.

antipasto Italian form of **hors d'oeuvres**.

antiseptics See **disinfectants**.

apéritif A drink taken before a meal to whet the appetite.

apollinaris A **sparkling**, slightly **alkaline**, natural spring **water** from the Rhine valley in Germany.

apothecaries' weights An obsolete system of weights used in compounding medicines and now superseded by the metric system. Over the years there have been several standards but the last, in use until World War 2, was as follows:−

437.5 grains = 1 ounce.
7000 grains = 1 pound.
15.5 grains = 1 gram.

apple *Malus pumila*. A hardy fruit widely dispersed in nature and cultivated in all but the hottest climates. Available in many varieties and ripening between August and October in the UK. Some keep well in cold storage and are available all the year round. Related to the **pear, quince** and **medlar**.

NUTRITIONAL VALUE: variable with variety: vitamin C content up to 30mg per 100g.

ENERGY per 100g: average: 46 kcal, 196 kJ.

USES: eaten raw as a dessert fruit, in a wide range of cooked dishes, in sauces. It is one of the most versatile fruits. Also for **cider**, apple drinks and **Calvados**.

apple strudel A rich Austrian speciality made with a very thin sheet of pastry dough layered with breadcrumbs, apple, mixed nuts, sultanas, sugar and spices, rolled into a sausage-shape and baked.

apricot *Prunus armeniaca*, a stone-fruit smaller than a peach and earlier to ripen, with a full flavour. Often sun-dried, when it needs to be soaked before being cooked. Some sun-dried apricots are exposed to **sulphur dioxide** to preserve their natural colour and then labelled sulphited; when not treated they are dark brown, both types are available. The high sugar content in the dried fruit acts as a **preservative** so that it keeps well at room temperature in an airtight container. Also available canned.

NUTRITIONAL VALUE: average: fresh, protein 0.5%, carbohydrate 8.0%, vitamin C. Dried and canned fruit have no vitamin C. Fruit canned in syrup has up to 30% carbohydrate.

ENERGY per 100gm: average: fresh: 30 kcal, 126 kJ. Dried: 182 kcal, 761 kJ. Tinned in syrup: 106 kcal, 452 kJ.

USES: as a dessert fruit, cooked in a variety of desserts, in **preserves**.

aqua vitae Ethanol (ethyl alcohol). A name for pure **alcohol**.

arachis oil See **ground-nut oil**.

arame Edible seaweed found in the Far East and dried. It is soft and sweet and can be used in soups.

arborio rice See **rice, arborio**.

arctic roll A **swiss roll** covered in ice-cream.

argol See **tartar**.

armagnac Prestigious **brandy** distilled from grapes grown in the Armagnac region of Gascony.

arrack A spirit distilled from the fermented sap of the coconut-palm.

ALCOHOL CONTENT: 30−40%.

arrope See **geropiga**.

arrowroot A very pure form of **starch** prepared from the root of a tropical South American plant, *Maranta arundinacea*. It forms a clear **gel** when heated to boiling point with water. The gel can reverse if it is boiled too long.

NUTRITIONAL VALUE: almost pure carbohydrate.

USES: for savoury jelly containing pieces of **meat, fish** or **vegetable**, general thickening purposes. Made up with **milk** as a food for invalids. See **tapioca**.

arsenic An **element** for which no essential role has yet been identified. In the past it was used medicinally but it is highly toxic and can cause skin cancer, even in small doses. At one time it was an impurity in **lead** and **pewter**.

arteriosclerosis (atheroma) A disease associated with deposits of fatty substances, particularly **cholesterol**, in the lining of blood vessels, leading to blockage known as thrombosis. It is a common cause of strokes and heart attacks and may cause gangrene of the feet or legs. The high **fat** consumption in modern society has played a part in the much higher incidence of the condition in affluent countries than in those where the diet is low in fat. Fat should not provide more than 35% of energy requirements and half should be in unsaturated fats, mainly of **vegetable** origin or from **fish**. A low-fat **diet** together with regular exercise and avoidance of obesity and smoking are important ways of reducing the risks.

artichoke, globe *Cynara scolymus*. A member of the thistle family, grown for the edible flower-head. It should be soaked in salted water before use, to remove any earth or insects.

NUTRITIONAL VALUE: negligible.

ENERGY per 100g: 7 kcal, 29 kJ.

USES: cooked and usually served as a separate course with melted butter and/or a sharp sauce. Only the bases of the leaves and the central heart are eaten. Care must be taken to remove the 'choke' or hay, a tight pad of inedible fibres above the heart.

artichoke, Jerusalem. *Helianthus tuberosus*. A member of the sunflower family grown for its edible tubers, somewhat like the potato but fully hardy, and with a distinctive flavour. Contains a **polysaccharide**, **inulin**, which cannot be digested but is broken down by normal intestinal **bacteria** to produce gases which can cause flatulence and diarrhoea.

NUTRITIONAL VALUE: carbohydrate 1.5%.

ENERGY per 100g: boiled: 18 kcal, 75 kJ.

USES: as a vegetable boiled or baked and for flavouring soups or stews. Should be eaten only in small quantities, because of side effects.

artificial Made by man in imitation of the real thing. Particularly refers to flavouring agents and colouring substances. Generally poor substitutes for the naturally occurring and are best used to supplement natural colours and flavours.

artificial sweetener A **sugar** substitute. The first artificial sweetener was used by the Romans and made by boiling **lead** in grape juice, known as sapa. The practice of putting lead shot in wine bottles existed until recent times. Lead is a long-term poison and is now banned from all water-pipes, solder in cans, pewter, paint.

Artificial sweeteners should fulfil certain criteria; they should be:–

1. Entirely safe for human consumption including diabetics.
2. Taste like sugar.
3. Free of any aftertaste.
4. Reasonably priced.
5. Stable for the use required.

Artificial sweeteners cannot fulfil the role of sugar in providing the same sensation in the mouth due to bulk and viscosity, and the osmotic pressure required when it is used as a **preservative**. **Polydextrose** is sometimes added to artificial sweeteners to give them some of the physical characteristics of **sugar**. It has also been found that a mix of sweeeteners may have a better taste than a single one.

Four sweeteners are now licensed for sale and two additional ones may soon be licensed.

Acesulphame K. 130 times as sweet as sugar and chemically related to **saccharine**. It is stable and can be used for cooking. The taste differs slightly from sugar and it has limited acceptance; used in chewing gum, drinks and some processed foods.

Aspartame. 20 times as sweet as sugar; it is unstable in fluids and cannot be used for cooking. There is a small chance of adverse reaction in sufferers from **phenylketonuria**. It is now the most widely used artificial sweetener, and for ease of application, is usually mixed with a sugar such as maltodextrin.

Cyclamate. 30 times as sweet as sugar; it was synthesised in 1937 and considered safe until a potential risk of causing cancer led to its withdrawal. It is now becoming accepted again as the risks are insignificant and approval is expected in the UK soon. It is stable, can be used in cooking and has a good taste.

Saccharine. O-sulphobenzidimide, the first commercially produced artificial sweetener; it is 500 times as sweet as sugar and stable, but some find it has a bitter or metallic taste. Inexpensive, it is widely used in soft drinks and processed foods in order to lower the calorie value.

Sucralose. 600 times as sweet as sugar; it is made by modifying a sugar molecule, is stable and has a good taste. This sweetener probably has the greatest potential for future use. Approval has been granted in Canada and is expected in the EEC soon.

Thaumatin. Also known as Katemfe and Talin and 3000 times as sweet as sugar; it is prepared from the fruit of a tropical tree *Thaumatococcus danielli*. The onset of taste is slightly delayed and it tends to linger on, for which reason it has not been widely accepted. Its stability in cooking is variable and generally better in an acid medium. It has the property of enhancing flavours and may be used to increase the sweetness of low-sugar products. Used in chewing gum and in animal feeds to enhance appetite and weight-gain.

asafoetida A gum extracted from the roots of the umbelliferous herb, *Ferulula asafoetida*, which grows to 3–4m in South West Asia. It is white or grey at first, then darkens with age. It is a powerful flavouring agent and used in minute quantities to give a hint of onion flavour.

ascorbic acid (E301, vitamin C and related compounds **E302–E304)** Present in most fresh **fruits** and **vegetables**, including **potatoes**. **Blackcurrants** and **sweet peppers** have a high content, significantly more than **citrus fruits**. An adequate intake is assured with a mixed diet containing fresh fruits, salads, leaf and root vegetables. The vitamin is progressively destroyed by cooking and is also destroyed by sunlight, so that milk in bottles should be taken inside as soon as possible. **Scurvy** used to be a common

and most serious problem during long sea voyages, due to a lack of ascorbic acid in the **diet**.

USES: as an **antioxidant** to prevent discoloration of fruits which do not have a high vitamin C content, such as apples, pears and peaches. To limit natural oxidation processes in foods, and enhance the **protein**, **gluten**, in **flour** for breadmaking.

asparagus A hardy member of the lily family; *Asparagus officinalis* is the variety most often grown, for its delicate young shoots cut before the buds burst. Originally known as asparagrass or sparrow-grass.

NUTRITIONAL VALUE: negligible.
ENERGY per 100g: 14 kcal, 59 kJ.
USES: cooked as a vegetable, and often served separately with melted butter.

asparagus bean *Vigna sesquipedalis*. A subtropical or tropical climbing annual, and a member of the **pea** and **bean** family. The beans develop in long pods up to 1m in length; it is also known as the **yard long bean**. Eaten mainly in India.

NUTRITIONAL VALUE: the mature seeds have a high food value. See **pulses**.
USES: shelled and cooked fresh or dried and used as pulses.

asparagus lettuce See **celtuce**.

asparagus pea *Tetragonolus purpureus*. An annual **pea** of Southern Europe; the whole pod may be eaten when young, or later, the shelled peas. The ripe peas have been used as a substitute for coffee.

aspartame See **artificial sweeteners**.

aspic A clear form of **gelatine** made from fish-bones, swim-bladder or chicken and animal bones.

NUTRITIONAL VALUE: negligible.
USES: for savoury moulds containing fish, meat, vegetables, as a glaze or garnish, in sauces, particularly the classic **chaudfroid**.

aspirin Acetylsalicylic acid. The most widely used of all drugs with a range of medicinal properties for relieving pain, reducing fever and reducing the risk of recurrent heart attacks and strokes. It is generally safe but can produce bleeding and allergic reactions. It is closely related to salicylic acid which was used until replaced by aspirin. Until recently salicylic acid was used as a food preservative but it is now banned in most countries because of the risk of allergic reaction.

astaxanthin An oil-soluble and stable pigment related to **carotene**. It is responsible for the colour of **salmon**, but absent from farmed salmon unless food **additives** are used.

asthma A state in which the bronchial tubes, responsible for carrying air into and out of the lungs, pass into a state of spasm and the flow of air is restricted. It can be brought on by exposure to an **allergen** present in the air, such as pollen, or in certain foods; some **additives** can precipitate an attack. Foods which have been found from experience to bring on an attack must be avoided. The list of additives which have been associated with asthma in susceptible individuals includes colouring agents and **preservatives**.

astringent A substance present in some fruits, such as cider apples, the skin of red grapes, and strong tea, which has a characteristic effect on the mouth known as astringency. Astringents tend to coagulate **proteins**, but in the quantities usually present they are responsible for some of the desirable qualities of drinks such as red wine, tea. Most are related to tannic acid.

aubergine *Solanum melongena ovigerun*, also known as the egg-plant or blue tomato, a fruit related to the **tomato**, **capsicum** and **potato**. Now widely available, it is grown in hothouses or warm climates.

NUTRITIONAL VALUE: protein 0.7%, carbohydrate 3.1%, vitamin C approx 5mg per 100g, calcium, sodium.

ENERGY per 100g: raw: 14 kcal, 59 kJ.

USES: as a vegetable, usually baked or fried, sometimes stuffed, an essential ingredient in **moussaka** and many Mediterranean dishes.

au four Baked in the oven.

au gratin A dish made with sauce, topped with breadcrumbs and/or grated cheese and browned in the oven or under a grill. See **melanoidin**.

au jus Meat dishes dressed with their own juices.

au naturel Food cooked simply, such as potatoes boiled in water.

autolysis The breaking down of dead plant and animal tissue by the action of naturally occurring or developing **enzymes**. The tenderising of meat by hanging is a controlled autolysis, which is stopped by cooking. See **tender**.

avocado pear The fruit of the evergreen tropical tree, *Persia gratissima*, from South America, which is now extensively cultivated for its dark-skinned, pear-shaped fruit with a large central stone. The fruit is unusual in that it only ripens after it is picked. The pulp is buttery when it is ripe, with a rich flavour.

NUTRITIONAL VALUE: average: protein 4.2%, fat 20%, mainly monounsaturated, carbohydrate 1.8%, vitamin C, calcium.

ENERGY per 100g: 220 kcal, 920 kJ.

USES: eaten dressed with a vinaigrette sauce, mixed with peppery spices or chopped and used in salads and in cooked dishes.

azarole *Crataegus azarolus*. A hardy, deciduous tree of the *Rosaceae* family, related to the hawthorn and apple. It produces small, edible, seeded fruits and is cultivated in Southern Europe.

azo dye See **colour** (synthetic colours).

B

baba or **rum baba** A small **yeast**-cake baked in a mould and then soaked in syrup containing rum. Similar to **savarin**.

babaco *Carica pentagona.* A seedless variant of the *Carya papaya* (**papaya** or paw-paw). A large fruit, long and fluted in shape, which has a soft edible skin, is seedless and has a pleasantly acid flavour. A native of Ecuador but now grown in hothouses in Guernsey.

NUTRITIONAL VALUE: average: carbohydrate 8%, vitamin C.

ENERGY per 100g: average: 30 kcal, 126 kJ.

USES: eaten as a dessert fruit, in fruit salads.

baby foods Proprietary foods, for reconstituting with sterile water, made from modified cow's milk and containing similar concentrations of **proteins**, **fats**, **carbohydrates**, **minerals**, **vitamins** and water to those in human breast milk. These foods all lack the naturally-occurring human antibodies present in the mother and secreted by the mammary glands. Manufacturer's instructions must be accurately followed; new-borns, with their delicate digestions and restricted range of tolerances, are easily disturbed by any deviation and even slight excesses of protein, fat, **salt** and other minerals can have serious consequences. Less than optimum amounts can lead to deficiencies. Medical advice should be taken for any persistent bowel disturbance, vomiting or rash.

bacillus One of a group of rod-shaped **micro-organisms**. The group includes those most dangerous to man such as *Bacillus anthracis* (anthrax), *Clostridia botulinus* (**botulism**), *Clostridium tetani* (tetanus); several of them are capable of growing in the absence of air (**anaerobes**).

bacillus cereus A **bacillus**, which causes **food poisoning**, widely present in the soil, and capable of contaminating **vegetables** and other foods. Growing under favourable conditions in food it produces a **toxin** in a similar manner to **staphylococcus**, causing nausea, vomiting, abdominal pain, **diarrhoea** and, in some cases, collapse.

baclava A dessert made with flaky pastry, layered with nuts and covered with hot syrup or honey. Of Turkish origin.

bacon Pig meat, traditionally taken from the sides of the animal, that is cured and sometimes smoked. The product has developed from a farmhouse industry to present day large-scale factory production. The type and quality of bacon depends on selection of the original meat and the methods of **curing**. See **gammon, ham, smoking**.

NUTRITIONAL VALUE: raw: protein up to 20%, fat 20%—40%, 50% of which is saturated, the rest unsaturated, vitamin B complex, minerals.

ENERGY per 100g: raw: variable according to fat content, 260—440 kcal, 1088—1841 kJ.

USES: sliced as rashers for the traditional British breakfast, to serve with poultry, boiled or baked as a joint, cubed in casseroles and risottos, as a flavouring for soups.

bacteria Single cell **micro-organisms** which may be round (cocci) or rod-shaped (bacilli) and which, unlike plants, do not depend on chlorophyll. They are found singly or paired and some have movable tails. Some have a **spore** stage when they are resistant to destruction by heat or chemicals. They can multiply rapidly under favourable conditions. Most require oxygen (**aerobes**), but some can multiply without oxygen (**anaerobes**).

They are widely dispersed in the air, soil, water and in all forms of animal life. They have wide-ranging capability; some, essential to health, are normal residents in the large bowel, aiding the breakdown of food and **dietary fibre** and manufacturing **vitamins** of the B group. **Herbivores** depend on bacteria, not present in man, for the digestion of **cellulose**. Bacteria are essential in nature for maintaining soil nutrition and work in close harmony with many plants. Some are used in **cheese-**making, others for **yoghurt**, **vinegar**, and some cause food to deteriorate. Bacteria cause diseases and are responsible for outbreaks of **food poisoning**.

Bacteria are becoming of increasing economic importance and some can be used for manufacturing essential substances, for commercial purposes, in the pharmaceutical industry. Their uses are expanding rapidly and they are now being introduced for removing, or making safe, noxious substances. See **antibiotics**, **microwave ovens**, **sterilisation**, **vinegar, yoghurt**.

badoit A natural French spring-water, slightly **alkaline**. See **mineral waters**.

bagaceira The Portuguese version of **marc**, which is **brandy** made from the residue of grapes after wine has been made.

baguette The traditional long, French, **loaf** of **bread**.

bain-marie A dish or pan of simmering water into which a container of food is placed to allow cooking at a temperature of just below boiling-point. Used especially for sauces and dishes that are likely to curdle if boiled. A bain-marie can be used on top of the stove or in the oven.

baked beans There are many versions of this nutritious food, popular with children. They are said to have originated in Boston, USA, from a Red Indian recipe. Traditionally they were made with **brown dutch beans** baked very slowly in an oven with a piece of salt pork or streaky bacon, molasses, sugar, water or stock, mustard, bay leaves and sometimes tomato puree. Haricot beans are probably more commonly used now. More familiar than home-cooked beans are the canned varieties which are usually in tomato sauce.

NUTRITIONAL VALUE: average: canned, protein 4.8%, fat 1%, carbohydrate 15%.

ENERGY per 100g: average: 81 kcal, 339 kJ.

USES: served on toast as a lunch or supper dish, as a vegetable to accompany meat dishes, with bacon and egg and sausage.

bakelite One of the first plastics to be widely used for handles, light switches, plugs and sockets. Once set, it cannot be melted. It is a good insulator of heat and electricity but will not stand oven temperatures and becomes brittle after repeated immersion in boiling water.

bakewell tart A traditional open tart made with shortcrust **pastry**, spread with jam and topped with an almond sponge-mixture.

baking One of the oldest forms of cooking. The process of cooking in an **oven**, heated by **gas**, oil, electricity or solid fuel, where the food is exposed to hot air and also heated by radiation from the sides of the oven. The temperature is today controlled by a **thermostat** to within close limits. The degree of heat is matched to the time of cooking in order to achieve the best result for the particular ingredients. The food to be cooked is placed on a baking-tray or dish of suitable size, covered or uncovered for all or part of the time. The temperature, at some stage, can be high enough to cause **browning** which is a feature of **oven** cooking and gives it a special character. Special care needs to be taken with **poultry** and large joints of **meat** to make sure the inside reaches the necessary temperature to kill any **bacteria** which can cause **food poisoning**.

baking additives A range of **additives** which, when mixed with **flour**, enhance its qualities, retard the rate of deterioration and improve the quality of the product. The group includes bleaches, oxidising agents to 'age' the flour, **fats** and **preservatives**. Most flour sold already contains some of these. Home bakers can add **ascorbic acid** to enhance the **gluten**, fats to improve the keeping quality and **acetic** or **lactic** acid in small quantities to retard the growth of **moulds**. See **ageing**.

baking powder A preparation designed to release **carbon dioxide** into cake mixtures and soda-bread to produce a sponge-like texture. All brands contain **bicarbonate of soda** (500) and an **acid**. A common mixture is 1 part bicarbonate of soda and 2 parts **cream of tartar** (potassium hydrogen tartrate). Other acid-forming substances are also used, such as acid phosphates (E336, E450a), which react slowly as the mixture is heated. **Starch** is usually added to give bulk and make it easier to dispense small quantities. It must be kept dry in storage. Self-raising **flour** already contains the optimum quantity of such ingredients.

balachan A speciality flavouring of South-East Asia made from dried and salted **shrimps** and **prawns**. Used in a variety of local dishes.

balachong A pickle prepared in Southern India based on **prawns, mangoes** and **spices**. It is usually eaten with **curry** dishes.

balanced diet A diet which contains all the essential requirements of **carbohydrate, fat, minerals, vitamins** and **dietary fibre**. Current studies of requirements for all nutrients, including vitamins and minerals, confirm that a generally mixed diet contains quantities in excess of the minimum for health, growth and repair. Supplements are required only when there are dietary restrictions due to causes such as age, illness, ignorance or poverty and then only on medical advice. See **diet**.

ball A state in the boiling of sugar with water which is reached as the water evaporates, and the temperature rises, to the point when a little of the syrup taken out and dropped into cold water forms a ball. Soft ball is reached at 115°C (239°F) and hard ball at 120°C (248°F).

ballotine A leg of **chicken** or whole small bird, boned, stuffed and coated with Madeira sauce. It is served cold and may be glazed with **aspic**.

balm A variety of **mint**, *Melissa officinalis*, with a smell of lemon.

balsamic vinegar An expensive traditional vinegar, from Modena in Italy, with a long history. It is dark brown, pleasantly acidic with a fruity flavour and aroma. It is made from grape juice which is slowly concentrated over a low heat, then mellowed and acetified for a period of years in wooden barrels. See **vinegar**.
USES: in salad dressings, sprinkled over hot grilled, fried or boiled meat, raw vegetables, with sugar on fruit, particularly strawberries.

bamboo shoots The shoots of *Bambusa vulgaris* and *Phyllostachys pubescens*, edible bamboo grown in Eastern Asia. The young shoots are large, up to 10cms in diameter, and harvested before they show above ground. In the West they are only available canned, whole or sliced, in water or brine and ready to use. Once opened any unused shoots will keep in a refrigerator immersed in water, changed daily, for 10 days.

NUTRITIONAL VALUE: protein 2.3%, carbohydrate 6%.

ENERGY per 100g: 35 kcal, 146 kJ.

USES: in salads, in many Chinese and Japanese dishes.

banana *Musa paradisiaca sapientum*. The fruit of the common banana is seedless, with a soft sweet, almost white pulp. When fully ripe it is aromatic and the flavour distinctive. There are many varieties differing slightly in size, shape, colour and flavour but these are generally only available in the tropical countries of origin. *Musa cavendishii* is a dwarf variety introduced into England from China and grown in hothouses in the early 19th century and now widely cultivated in the Canary Islands and tropics. The large variety known as a **plantain** requires cooking. Bananas ripen quickly but are sensitive to cold. Fruits that feel soft and have discoloured skins should be avoided. They should not be stored in a refrigerator. They are available dried, often sliced, when they keep well. See **banana figs**.

NUTRITIONAL VALUE: average: carbohydrate 25%, vitamin A, vitamin B complex, vitamin C, minerals, particularly potassium.

ENERGY per 100g: average: 94 kcal, 393 kJ.

USES: as a dessert fruit, in fruit salads, cooked or raw in a variety of desserts, split or sliced as an accompaniment to curry dishes, fried with chicken and bacon.

banana figs The name given to split dried bananas; where all the starch has been converted to sugar.

Banbury cake A small spiced fruit-cake or bread made either with pastry or a leavened dough; there are a number of variants.

bannock A small cake of Scottish origin made with wheat flour, barley or oatmeal, sour milk, and yeast or baking powder. The Selkirk variety also contains mixed dried fruit and candied peel.

bap A soft bun made with a **bread** dough using milk and water or all milk, usually dusted with **flour** after baking. The recipe makes a good base for **pizza**.

barbary pears See **cactus**.

barbecue The term originally used to mean **roast** whole over a fire. Now usually implies cooking food on a grid over charcoal, hot coals or wood embers with little or no smoke and generally carried out in the open. **Gas** is sometimes used as fuel for convenience. Permanent barbecues are made of brick, with a grid to support the food over the heat source. Small portable barbecues are made of steel or cast iron and charcoal is usually used for fuel. Some have rotating **spits**, for roasts, turned by a small electric motor and some have rests for **kebab** skewers.

barbecue sauce A piquant sauce based on tomato puree, onion, spices and vinegar. Used with sausages and meat cooked on a barbecue.

barding A method of keeping lean meat and poultry moist during **roasting** or **braising** by covering it with slices of pork fat or bacon.

barley *Hordeum sativum*. A hardy member of the grass family and probably the first crop cultivated by man. It has a low **gluten** content and **flour** made from it makes a heavy **bread** unless mixed with **wheat flour**. **Pearl barley** has had the bran and germ removed, taking with it most of the **minerals**, **protein** and **vitamins** leaving mainly **starch**.

NUTRITIONAL VALUE: average: protein 9%, fat 1.4%, carbohydrate 75%.

USES: in the production of **malt**, in

'Maltings', where the barley seeds are germinated, kept warm to allow the **diastase** present to convert starches to malt, then dried and heated to stop the process, followed by roasting; the whole procedure is carried out under precise conditions of temperature. To make pearl barley.

barley sugar Amber-coloured crystalline sweetmeat made by boiling sugar with barley water and forming into small squares or sticks.

barley water The product of boiling **pearl barley**. It has a high **starch** content and this gives lemon drinks a pleasantly bland flavour.

barm The froth on top of fermenting **beer** or **wine**.

barnacle *Branta leucopsis*. A form of crustacean which lives stuck to rocks. The Atlantic barnacle, *Pollicipes cornucopia*, has a long edible stalk.
NUTRITIONAL VALUE: variable, similar to **mussels**.
USES: cooked by boiling and eaten as other shellfish.

baron of beef A double **sirloin** joined across the spine and traditionally served at City Banquets.

barrel Also known as **cask**. A strong vessel traditionally made of oak staves shaped precisely to fit together and held by iron hoops. When the dry wood is soaked in water, it expands and the barrel becomes water-tight. Used for transporting and storing liquids such as **beer**, **wine**, **spirits** and, in the days of sailing ships, for storing dry goods and salted beef and pork. The standard capacity is 36 gallons (163 1) but barrels and casks are also made in a range of sizes; a firkin holds 9 gallons and a hogshead 52.5 gallons. Some barrels may hold up to several hundred gallons. Barrels used for **sherry** are later used for maturing

whisky. Traditionally they are sterilised by burning sulphur inside them. Barrels today tend to be made of **aluminium** or stainless steel and some plastic.

basal metabolic rate Usually abbreviated to BMR. The basic amount of energy used by the body when fully rested. The BMR is greatest (weight adjusted) for infants and generally falls with age. It falls slightly in women after puberty. It is influenced by the thyroid gland and by fevers (infections). The average is 1600 kcal per day for men, 1300 for women. See **metabolism**.

basil *Ocium basilicum*. A tender annual **herb**, having a strong characteristic aroma. The fresh leaves are best for use. It freezes well but loses some flavour if dried.
USES: it is used widely, particularly with tomatoes and is an essential ingredient of **pesto** sauce.

bass *Labrax lupus* or *Murone labrax*. A European non-oily marine **fish** with firm flesh and a good flavour; it is almost bone free. Bass is a name also used for other, similar, marine and freshwater fish.
NUTRITIONAL VALUE: average: protein 15–18%, fat 1–2%.
ENERGY per 100g: average: 75 kcal, 314 kJ.
USES: lends itself to most methods of cooking.

baste To spoon **fat** and pan juices over **meat** being roasted, to keep it moist and preserve the flavour.

Bath bun First made in Bath, a large bun of rich **dough** containing **sultanas** and **candied peel**, and sugar-coated after baking.

Bath chap The cured and smoked cheek of a **pig**; it may be cooked like a **ham**.

Battenberg A cake made of multiple

squares of pink and yellow sponge, sand-wiched together with jam and covered with **marzipan**.

batter A mixture of flour, milk and egg used for dishes such as **pancakes**, **fritters** and **yorkshire pudding**.

bay *Laurus nobilis*. A moderately hardy ever-green tree, the leaves of which have a distinctive flavour and aroma. They can be used fresh or dried.

USES: to flavour soups, meat and poultry dishes.

bay salt Coarse sea-**salt** made by evapor-ating sea-water in large pans or bays.

bazargan An Eastern dish of **bulgar wheat** made into a form of salad with onion, tomato, olives, and spices such as coriander, allspice; there are many varia-tions.

beachwheat See **buckwheat**.

bean curd See **tofu**.

beans A large number of leguminous plants with kidney-shaped seeds contained in elongated pods. Some are eaten fresh and many are used in their dried form after allowing them to reach a natural maturity in the pod. Dried beans have a high nutri-tional value and are an important source of **protein** in **vegetarian** diets and in the third world countries where **meat** is in short supply or unavailable.

All dried beans contain an indigestible **polysaccharide** called **inulin** which can cause flatulence when excessive quantities are eaten. This effect can be lessened by adding a pinch of **bicarbonate of soda** to the cooking water and rinsing in fresh water after cooking. **Salt** impedes the soft-ening process and should not be added until after cooking is complete.

All dried beans should be soaked for up to 8 hours (depending on age and size) prior to cooking in fresh water. All red, brown and black beans contain **lectin**, a

poisonous **alkaloid** which is destroyed by boiling for at least 10 minutes. Simmering or 'slow' cooking is not sufficient for safety. Dried beans kept for over a year may become resistant to soaking and then not soften with cooking. See under separate headings.

Those used fresh include – **broad beans**, **french beans**, **runner beans**.

Those used dried include – **adzuki**, **black**, **black eye**, **brown dutch**, **butter**, **flageolets**, **ful medames**, **haricot**, **mung**, **pinto**, **red**, **soya**. See **inulin**, **lectin**.

bean sprouts See **sprouted seeds**.

béarnaise sauce A variation of **hollandaise sauce** with white wine, shallots and tarragon.

beat Generally implies to amalgamate two or more substances, such as sugar and fat, egg-white and egg-yolk, and incorporate air into the mixture by agitation. Implements used range from a fork or spoon to an attachment on a **food processor**. See **whisk**.

béchamel A basic white sauce made with milk which has been infused, when warm, with onion, carrot, bay leaf, and various **spices** such as cloves, mace and peppercorns.

beef The **meat** of the ox; that from the young calf is called **veal**. Beef used to be the principle source of animal protein but the long time it takes to bring an animal to maturity, and the high cost of feed, have made beef expensive and reduced its consumption in the UK. Much of the **fat** in beef is located between the muscle fibres and cannot be removed; it can account for up to 25% of the total weight. Cattle are being increasingly bred to have a lower fat content to meet demand.

Beef may contain **bacteria** (sometimes from the animal's intestine), some of which, such as **salmonella**, would be present on the surface and could cause **food poisoning**. Meat is a good medium for bacteria to grow on and should always be adequately cooked. A common source of infection is minced or ground beef such as in **hamburgers**. Beef can host some parasitic intestinal worms such as the cystic stage of *Taenia* and of *Echinococcus*. There is concern today over the disease known as **bovine spongioform encephalopathy** and its possible transmission to man.

NUTRITIONAL VALUE: variable according to the part of the animal: average: raw: protein 16.6%, fat 27.4%, calcium, iron, sodium.

ENERGY per 100g: average: raw: 313 kcal, 1310 kJ.

USES: a versatile meat, the best cuts are grilled or roasted, cheaper cuts are used in stews, casseroles, and for minced meat. See **olives, meat**.

beefburger An alternative name for **hamburger**.

beef olives See **olives, meat**.

beef tartare Fillet or rump **steak** finely chopped, formed into a flattened ball with an egg-yolk placed in the centre. It is served uncooked with lemon slices. See **food poisoning**, **bovine spongioform encephalopathy**.

beef tea An extract of beef produced by prolonged boiling.

Beef Wellington See **en croûte**.

beer An alcoholic beverage made from **malt**, usually that extracted from **barley**, and **hops** fermented with **yeast**. Ale generally refers to a light-coloured beer but there is some variation with locality. Beers differ according to strength, quality of **malt** and degree of roasting. The dark beers and stouts are made from well-roasted malt and pale beers from lightly-roasted malt.

Flavour is determined by the variety of hops and yeasts and the nature of the **water** used.

Traditionally draught beers are matured in oak **barrels** and sold from the cask. Today the barrels are mostly made of **aluminium** or stainless steel, the beer filtered to remove all yeasts and then pressurised with **carbon dioxide**. Natural beers matured in the wood have a limited life and require careful handling and skill to maintain and serve. Modern cask beers may be very similar to bottled and canned beers.

Strictly there are only 4 ingredients in beer, namely water, yeast, malt and hops, but today it may contain a number of **additives** to increase the 'head' and prolong life; some beers are made with other fermentable grains which are cheaper than malted barley. Low-alcohol beers have recently been introduced in the interests of safer driving. See **lager, root beer, spruce beer, stout**.

ALCOHOL CONTENT: 3—9%. Speciality high-gravity beers may have an alcohol content up to 14% and low-alcohol beers less than 1%.

ENERGY per 100ml: 30—60 kcal, 125—250 kJ.

beeswax (E901) A natural product of the honey-bee, *Apis mellifera*. Beeswax varies in colour from almost pure white to dark brown. It cannot be digested by any animal, with the sole exception of the wax-moth which infests bee-hives.

USES: purified beeswax is an accepted food additive for glazing food products and diluting colour. Its main use is for church candles and high quality wax polishes.

beestings Colostrum, the first albuminous fluid excreted by the mammary glands of mammals before true milk flows. It is only available from a few dairy farms.

NUTRITIONAL VALUE: Protein 1%, fat 2%, carbohydrate 5%.

USES: for making speciality cheeses and in some traditional farm recipes.

beetroot A **root** vegetable derived from the wild *Beta vulgaris*, with a deep crimson, sweet flesh. The red pigment is betanin, which is stable in an acid medium but becomes yellow as the pH changes towards alkaline.

NUTRITIONAL VALUE: protein about 2%, carbohydrate 10%, vitamin B complex, vitamin C and minerals.

ENERGY per 100g: cooked: 44 kcal, 189 kJ.

USES: cooked and eaten hot as a vegetable, sliced in vinegar for salads, in soups, particularly **borsch**.

beetroot red (E162) See **colour**.

beet sugar Sugar, extracted from the **sugar-beet** which is widely cultivated in Europe. Beet sugar is identical in all respects to cane sugar.

beignet Small spoonfuls of choux **pastry**, deep fried, drained of oil; sometimes rolled in sugar and served with jam, sometimes with grated **cheese** as a savoury.

benedictine A liqueur made originally, from a secret recipe, by the monks of the Benedictine monastery in Fécamp in Normandy.

bentonite (E558) Soap clay, also known as fuller's earth, a naturally occurring inert clay found only in western USA, which has the peculiar property of forming a thick suspension in water.

USES: for clarifying wines, as an **anti-caking** and emulsifying agent and for its absorbent properties.

benzaldehyde The chemical substance responsible for the smell of almonds and present in the kernels of apricots, peaches and plums.

benzoic acid (E210 and related compounds **E211–E219)** Permitted food **preservative**, found naturally, and also prepared synthetically. Used in fruit drinks and wines.

benzoyl peroxide A chemical bleaching agent used commercially for whitening **flour** by bleaching the yellow pigments of **carotene** and **xanthophyll**.

bercy A basic brown sauce containing white wine and chopped shallots.

bergamot mint A perennial **herb** of the mint family, *Mentha monarda* or *Mentha citrada*, with a smell of lemons, similar to **bergamotte orange**. Also known as *Mentha Odorata*.

bergamotte orange *Citrus aurantium bergamia*, a member of the citrus family grown for its distinctive smell and the oil extracted from the rind. A feature of Earl Grey tea and Eau de Cologne.

beriberi A deficiency disease of the nervous system due to a lack of **vitamin B1** (thiamine). It became prevalent when polished **rice** replaced natural rice as the main source of food in the East, as the vitamin is lost when the outer coat of the rice grain is removed. It is prevented by eating natural rice or by adding other sources of vitamin B1 to the diet. The vitamin is widely distributed in foods of animal and vegetable origin and adequate quantities are taken with a normal mixed diet. The disease is now very rare in the developed countries.

berry A fleshy fruit which contains several seeds, such as **blackberry, currants, gooseberry, raspberry** and **tomato**. In contrast, the seeds of the **strawberry** are on the outside and it is not botanically a berry. All contain **vitamin C**.

betanin (E162) See **colour**.

betel nut The nut of *Areca catechu*, a tropical

palm of Asia, which is sliced and wrapped in the leaf of the betel pepper *Piper betle* with **lime**, ground tobacco, red dye, sometimes a clove, and occasionally cocaine. The wad is known as Pan; it is astringent and the **alkaloids** act as a stimulant. The users place the wad inside the cheek and release the ingredients by chewing, the sputum becomes red and there is a high incidence of cancer of the mouth in addicts.

betteraves Beetroot pickled in hot **vinegar**, and flavoured with **spices** and **onion**.

beurre noisette Butter heated until it develops a brown colour.

bicarbonate of soda A mildly alkaline sodium compound of carbonic acid.
USES: as an ingredient in **baking powder**. Added to water when cooking green vegetables, it preserves the green colour but destroys the **vitamin C**. It can be added to the water when cooking **pulses** to soften the skin and reduce the amount of **inulin** which causes flatulence. Also used as a mild alkali to clean bottles, the inside of refrigerators and freezers.

biffin A variety of **apple** or an apple dried and pressed flat.

bigarade The name given in France to the bitter **seville orange** and a brown **sauce** flavoured with it.

bilberry *Vaccinum myrtillis*, also known as blaeberry, whortleberry, hindberry and huckleberry; a small shrub which produces dark-red or purple berries and grows wild on heaths, usually in association with heather.
NUTRITIONAL VALUE: negligible.
USES: in tarts and pies, in sauce, particularly to accompany duck and lamb.

bile A yellow viscous fluid manufactured by the liver and stored in the gall bladder. Its function is to emulsify **fats** and aid **digestion**. The yellow colour is due to

breakdown products of **haemoglobin**. **Cholesterol** may be deposited in the gall bladder, mixed with bile pigments, to form gallstones.

bill of fare Alternative name for **menu**.

biltong Meat from various sources cut into strips along the muscle fibres, salted and dried.

biological value A term used to express the amount of **protein** in food which can be utilised by the body. **Milk** and **egg** proteins can be almost 100% utilised, **meat** and **fish** have a high biological value, but some foods such as **grains**, and grain products, including **bread**, have only 50% of the protein available.

bird's nest soup Soup made from the nests of Asiatic swallows which they build in the roofs of high caves in the far East, using saliva. The saliva sets and is formed into white intermeshed strands by the birds. It is usually associated with Chinese fare.

bishop's weed See **ajowan**.

bitter One of the four tastes to which the tongue is sensitive; the others are **salt**, **sweet**, and **sour**. See **bittering agent**, **flavour**.

bittering agent A substance used to give a bitter flavour to drinks and food. The principal agents used are, **hops** for **beer**, **quinine** for **bitter lemon**, **angostura bitters**, **gentian**, **quassia**.

bitter lemon A **lemon** drink flavoured with **quinine** and aerated with **carbon dioxide**.

bitter orange See **seville orange**.

black beans Dried beans with a rich meaty flavour; they should be presoaked and boiled for at least 10 minutes to destroy the **lectin**, then simmered for 1–2 hours until soft. See **beans, pulses**.
NUTRITIONAL VALUE: uncooked: protein

20%, fat 1–2%, carbohydrate 45%, minerals.

ENERGY per 100g: uncooked: 262 kcal, 1096 kJ.

USES: in Caribbean recipes with herbs, spices, and tomatoes, with rice, in casseroles and soups. In Chinese cooking they are often fermented and cooked with ginger, garlic, chicken and soy sauce.

blackberry *Rubus fructosus*. A heavily-seeded hardy shrub. The fruits are borne on long, wandering, thorny stems, on bushes known as brambles. The berry is red, ripening to dark-purple and becoming soft; it does not keep well. It is pleasantly acid with a characteristic flavour. There are many wild and cultivated variants. A few of the latter are thornless.

NUTRITIONAL VALUE: protein 1–2%, fat 1%, vitamin A, vitamin B complex, vitamin C 24mg per 100g.

ENERGY per 100g: 57 kcal, 238 kJ.

USES: often cooked with apples, in pies, tarts, preserves, particularly jelly.

blackbread See **rye bread**.

black butter Butter heated until it is brown and used as a sauce with added seasoning.

blackcock *Lyrurus tetrix*. A game-bird similar to black **grouse**.

SEASON: 20th August to 10th December; from 1st September to 10th December in the New Forest, Devon and Somerset.

NUTRITIONAL VALUE, ENERGY VALUE and USES: as for grouse.

blackcurrant *Ribes nigrum*. A hardy shrub, producing small clusters of black berries which are acidic, with a strong characteristic flavour.

NUTRITIONAL VALUE: carbohydrate 6.6%, vitamin C up to 200mg per 100g.

ENERGY per 100g: 28 kcal, 117 kJ.

USES: stewed, in pies, tarts, mixed with other fruit, as a puree in desserts such as mousse, ice-cream, sorbet, in preserves. The juice is concentrated and used diluted

as a drink and is the main constituent of the alcoholic drink, **cassis**.

black eye beans Pale beans with a black spot and an earthy flavour, a variety of *Phaseolus*. Sold dried, they should be presoaked, boiled for 10 mins and simmered for 45–60 mins until soft.

NUTRITIONAL VALUE: uncooked: protein 22%, fat 1.5%, carbohydrate 45%, fibre 2.5%.

ENERGY per 100g: uncooked: 270 kcal, 1130 kJ. Cooked: 108 kcal, 452 kJ.

USES: they blend well with spinach, ham and garlic. Traditionally served in the deep south of the USA with pork and sweet potatoes. Also used for soups and casseroles.

black PN (E151) Permitted synthetic black food-colouring. See **colour**.

black pudding A large **sausage** made with minced pork fat, herbs, onions, pig's blood and oatmeal.

black spot leaf See **alesander**.

blade, shoulder A part of the foreleg of an animal, containing the scapula.

blanching Partial cooking by immersion in boiling water for a short time and then cooling quickly. The moist heat loosens skins of fruit such as peaches and tomatoes and makes them easy to remove. In vegetables it also destroys **enzymes** and some **micro-organisms** which lead to deterioration even at the low temperatures of a deep-freeze. There is some loss of vitamins, minerals and protein. Blanching can also remove some undesirable flavours and salt. It is not usual to blanch acid fruits prior to deep-freezing because the process softens the texture and changes the flavour to that of cooked fruit.

blancmange A dessert made from milk and set with cornflour or **gelatine**; often flavoured and coloured. Proprietary dry ingredients are readily available in packets.

blanquette Slices of **chicken** or **meat**, especially **veal**, cooked in water or **stock**. The cooking liquor is thickened with cream or egg-yolk to make a sauce.

bleach To make pale or whiten. Bleaching agents permitted under EEC regulations are based on sulphur in the form of **sulphur dioxide** gas, sulphurous acid or agents which release it. All are reducing agents and attract oxygen, interfere with **enzymes** which degrade food, prevent the growth of **bacteria**, **moulds** and **fungi** and are used as **food preservatives**. They disperse on cooking. Other agents are used commercially for bleaching **flour**. Domestic **chlorine**-based bleaches are only for use with utensils and never for food; they should be used strictly according to manufacturer's instructions. Some individuals are sensitive to bleaches and may develop allergic skin rashes or **asthma** attacks.

blend To mix two or more products together. The process may be carried out by hand, with a fork or spoon, or just by shaking. Nowadays electrically-powered equipment with high-speed rotating blades, is frequently used. See **blender**, **food processor**.

blender An electrically-powered device with high-speed rotating blades used to liquefy or homogenise a mixture of solid and/or liquid ingredients. Used to produce soups, purees. Also known as liquidiser.

blini A thin pancake made with **buckwheat** or **flour** using **yeast** as the raising agent. Traditionally served hot with **caviar**.

bloater A whole ungutted **herring** which has been partially dried, heavily salted and lightly smoked. A speciality of Great Yarmouth in Norfolk. It has a strong flavour and does not keep well, so that it is not always readily available.

USES: cooked and eaten whole or made into bloater paste.

blood Animal blood is a valuable source of food, containing **protein** and **minerals** and, depending on the state of the animal when it was collected, **fats** and **vitamins**. See **haemoglobin**.

USES: an essential ingredient in **black pudding** and related **sausages**. Chicken blood is used for thickening sauces especially in coq au vin, and is a Spanish delicacy cooked with onion and peppers.

Bloody Mary A cocktail based on **vodka**, **tomato** juice and seasoning.

blood pressure The pressure of blood in the arteries due to their resistance to flow. It is variable in health and normal for it to rise temporarily in response to anxiety, cold and exercise. A sustained rise above normal is associated with diseases of the heart and strokes; obesity and a high-intake of **salt**, are among the causes. Systolic pressure is the peak level following contraction of the heart and diastolic is the level to which it falls between beats. A sustained diastolic pressure above 100mm of mercury is undesirable.

blown A term used to describe the 'blown out' or bulging top or bottom of a tin containing food contaminated by gas-forming **bacteria**, which have survived the heat used in sterilisation or gained entry in transit. Sufficient pressure is produced, in time, to burst the container. Some of the contaminating bacteria may be highly dangerous, such as *Clostridium botulinum*. The contents of a blown tin must never be eaten. Canned meat, fish and vegetables are most vulnerable. Leaking, dented or damaged cans should be discarded as potentially contaminated. See **botulism**.

BMR See **basal metabolic rate**.

boar's head An historic English Christmas dish. The whole head is cooked, decorated, and ceremoniously brought in at dinner.

boboutie Meat balls, usually curried, of African origin.

boletus edulus The penny bun **fungus** or cep. A common fungus which grows in forests during late summer and autumn. It is generally accepted as being one of the best flavoured of all fungi. No fungus should ever be eaten unless its identity is certain.

NUTRITIONAL VALUE: protein 1.6%, vitamin B complex, minerals.

ENERGY per 100g: 13 kcal, 54 kJ.

USES: eaten cooked on their own, stuffed, to flavour casseroles, soups.

bolognaise sauce A sauce made with minced beef, flavoured with bacon, tomato, onion, herbs and seasoning to serve with pasta particularly **spaghetti**.

Bombay duck A small transparent fish known as **bombil** or **bummalo;** an Indian delicacy, usually salted and cured. See **curing**.

USES: served with curries.

bone The rigid connective tissue which forms the skeleton of all mammals, birds, reptiles and most fish. It is composed of a matrix of flexible **collagen** set with a mixture of calcium carbonate and calcium phosphate. The calcium can be dissolved out with an acid such as vinegar or during digestion in the stomach; it is not softened by cooking. See **rickets, osteoporosis**.

bonito The term used to describe a variety of pelagic **fish** in different seas. The Atlantic bonito is a form of large **mackerel**; others are related to the **tuna**.

bonne bouche Tit bit, small savoury dish.

borage *Borago officinalis*. An annual **herb**, native of the Mediterranean countries, which grows well during the summer in southern England. It has blue flowers with a cucumber-like flavour.

USES: the flowers can be finely chopped in salads or used whole as a decoration, a feature of the apéritif **Pimms**.

Bordeaux Red and white wines made in the district of Bordeaux. Red Bordeaux wines are known as clarets.

bordelais Cooked in red wine.

boric acid Once used as a food preservative, now banned.

borsch A traditional **beetroot** soup from Russia.

botargo A dish of Arabian origin made from the salted and dried **roe** of the female **tuna** or **mullet**. It was known to the ancient Egyptians and is still a favourite food in Mediterranean areas.

bottles Glass bottles for wines and spirits are traditionally made in standard sizes. The most widely used has a capacity of 750 ml; the 700 ml bottle is being phased out. Other sizes are:−

1 Litre.

Half bottle or 375ml.

Magnum Equals 2 standard bottles.

Double magnum Equals 4 standard bottles of **claret**.

Jeroboam Equals 4 standard bottles of **champagne** or 6 of **wine**.

Methusaleh Equals 8 standard bottles, usually of champagne.

Salamanzer Equals 12 standard bottles, usually of champagne.

Nebuchadnezzer Equals 20 standard bottles, usually of champagne.

bottling A method of preserving food, mainly **fruit**, in glass jars by heat-sterilising and sealing to exclude air. Home-bottling is safe for most fruits, including tomatoes, because of their acidity, but the procedure is not safe for **vegetables** unless special precautions are taken and a **pressure cooker** used. See **botulism, preservation of food**.

The term also refers to filling bottles with liquids such as **wine**.

botulism The most serious form of **food poisoning**, due to the toxin produced by a soil bacillus, *Clostridium botulinum*. This **anaerobe** forms highly resistant **spores** that require exposure to 120°C (248°F) for at least 10 mins for their destruction. They can survive in sealed food-tins that have been inadequately sterilised or in damaged tins which allow entry of the bacillus. The effects of botulism come on 3–36 hours after consumption of contaminated food; they include weakness, visual disturbance, breathing difficulty, paralysis and may be fatal. Home-**canning** or **bottling** of **meat**, **fish** and **vegetables** cannot be relied upon to be safe, although home-bottling of acidic fruits is acceptable. Fortunately botulism is now rare. Anyone with the disease or suspected of having it, must seek medical advice urgently. See **blown**.

bouchée A small savoury made with puff pastry.

bouillabaisse A thick **soup** or **stew** made with several types of **fish**, **vegetables** and **spices**. A speciality of the Marseilles region of France.

bouillon Simple stock or broth.

bouquet garni A small bunch of mixed **herbs**; commonly **parsley**, **thyme**, and **bay** leaf, but there are several variations.
USES: to flavour casseroles and soups.

bovine spongioform encephalopathy Also known as BSE and mad cow disease it is indistinguishable from scrapie which is endemic in sheep. A virus disease of **cattle**, **sheep** and other cloven-hoofed animals, it affects the brain and spinal cord, causing staggering and death; it became prevalent in the 1980s. The virus is resistant to heat used in high-temperature cooking, to strong chemicals and to radiation. The disease is transmitted by animal feed containing brain or nervous tissue from infected animals including sheep with scrapie. This source has now been banned.

There is some evidence that it may be transmitted from the mother to. the unborn **calf**.

The disease is notifiable and neither any part of the carcass nor any milk from the animal may be sold. Unfortunately the virus is present before the disease can usually be diagnosed. As far as is known, it has not been transmitted to man but there are very similar diseases in man (kuru and Creutzfeldt-Jacob disease) and other mammals; the lengthy incubation period of up to 15 years means that this time will have to lapse before a human link can be excluded. It is therefore unwise to eat brain or spinal cord and neither these nor any part of a diseased carcass may be used, even for pet food. **Mechanically recovered meat** should not be eaten and all **beef** should be from a reputable source, with a high standard of control over selection and slaughtering of cattle for human consumption. There are strict regulations controlling the disposal of diseased animals. The disease is expected to decline but at the time of writing it is still prevalent.

Bovril A proprietary concentrate of **beef** stock, beef **protein**, **yeast** extract and **spices**.
NUTRITIONAL VALUE: protein 25%, vitamin B complex, salt.
ENERGY per tsp: 20 kcal, 83 kJ.
USES: for flavouring meat dishes, gravy and soups, diluted with hot water as a drink, or as a spread on bread, toast, biscuits.

boysenberry A cultivar of a variety of **blackberry**.

brains Classified as **offal**. Although **calf** and **sheep** brains are considered a delicacy they should no longer be eaten. See **bovine spongioform encephalopathy**.

braising A slow-cooking process which preserves the maximum flavour of **meat**, fish and **vegetables**. They are cooked in a pan with a close-fitting lid in a small amount of liquid such as water, stock, wine, cider or beer. Meat should be sealed in hot **fat** first. The process can be carried out on top of the stove or in the oven.

bran The outer husk of **wheat** and other **cereals**, extracted during production, by milling, of purified **flours**. It is mostly cellulose and cannot be digested by humans. See **dietary fibre**, **flour** (**wholemeal**).

NUTRITIONAL VALUE: average: protein 12.5%, fat 4.5%, carbohydrate 25%, dietary fibre 20%, vitamin B complex, vitamin E. Proprietary bran preparations also contain **lactose** and other ingredients including **salt**. **Oat** bran contains fat 8%.

ENERGY per 100g: proprietary: average: 184 kcal, 770 kJ.

USES: as a source of dietary fibre to improve bowel function.

brandy A spirit distilled from **wine**. It contains **ethanol** with traces of higher alcohols and other substances known as **congeners**. Brandy is given a rating according to age; thus, 3 Star is 3 years old, VSOP (Very special old pale) 4– 10 years old, Napoleon 6–20 years old, and Extra reserve 50 or more years old. See **cognac**.

ALCOHOL CONTENT: 40%.

USES: as a drink, for flavouring desserts and for dishes which are set alight at time of serving, known as **flambé**.

brandy butter Butter, brandy and icing sugar beaten together to form a light, stiff sauce.

USES: traditionally as an accompaniment to Christmas pudding and mince pies.

brandy snaps Thin, crisp, ginger biscuits rolled into tubes immediately after baking; often filled with cream.

brawn A preparation of meat from a pig's head, with beef, onions and seasoning, which is boiled for 2–3 hours to tenderise the meat and extract the **gelatine**. The mixture is then put into a mould or basin to set.

Brazilian arrowroot See **tapioca**.

Brazil nut Also known as para nut, the seed of the tropical tree, *Berthollena excella*. Approximately 30 individual nuts are clustered together in each large fruit. The nuts are contained in a hard triangular-shaped case. They keep well but will go **rancid** once shelled, unless they are refrigerated or frozen.

NUTRITIONAL VALUE: protein 12%, fat 61.5%, carbohydrate (digestible) 4.1%, vitamin B complex, dietary fibre 9%.

ENERGY per 100g: 619 kcal, 2590 kJ.

USES: as dessert nuts, in sweetmeats, cakes and desserts.

bread The most universal staple food, made of **flour**, water and **salt**, and fermented with **yeast** to produce a sponge-like product. Only **wheat** flour contains the **protein**, **gluten**, capable of holding the **gas**, carbon dioxide, produced by the fermentation. The chemical processes involved are complex, and in principle, commence with the conversion of **starches** into **maltose**, by the **enzyme** diastase, present in flour, which then becomes hydrolysed to **glucose**, followed by the action of the enzyme zymase, present in yeast, which converts glucose into carbon dioxide and **alcohol**. Successful bread-making depends on using a flour with a high enough content of the precursors of gluten, which are gliadin and glutenin. The process takes time and is assisted by energetic stretching of the dough, a process known as **kneading**; in this way the dough develops greater elasticity and allows the volume to increase to more than double, with further increase occurring when the risen dough is placed in a hot oven for baking.

Strong flour made from imported hard wheat makes a better product for the home-baker, whilst commercial bakeries are able to use flour made from softer, home-grown wheats and achieve a similar result, using the **Chorley Wood process** of high-energy kneading. All bread flours are fortified with added **calcium** and have been treated with **flour improvers**.

A variety of breads are made and include:—

Brown. Bread made with brown flour, usually a mixture of white and wholemeal.

Granary. Coarse brown bread made with granary flour.

Malt. A sweet bread, usually containing sultanas and flavoured with malted wheat.

Pitta. A small risen loaf baked rapidly at a high temperature which becomes flattened with a central cavity to be filled with a variety of mixtures. Arabian in origin.

Pumpernickel. A coarse heavy, dark bread made with rye-flour and slowly baked in a flat tin. A traditional German bread.

Soda-bread. Bread risen with the use of baking powder in place of yeast.

White. Bread made with white flour and the most widely used in the UK.

Wholemeal. Bread made with flour milled from 100% of the wheat grain.

Unleavened. Bread made without a raising agent. See **chapatti**.

. NUTRITIONAL VALUE: white bread: average: protein 8.5%, fat 2%, carbohydrate 50%, vitamin B complex, calcium, iron and dietary fibre. Wholemeal bread: similar to white but with a higher content of vitamin B complex, vitamin E and dietary fibre.

ENERGY per 100g: average: white: 235 kcal, 1000 kJ. Wholemeal: 220 kcal, 900 kJ.

bread-fruit The large fruit of the tropical palm, *Artocarpus communis*.

NUTRITIONAL VALUE: Protein 1.5%, carbohydrate 25%, vitamin B complex, vitamin C 20mg per 100g.

USES: cooked in place of bread in some eastern countries because of its high carbohydrate content.

bread-and-butter-pudding A traditional English baked pudding made with slices of buttered bread interspersed with dried fruit and soaked in a mixture of milk and egg.

bread sauce A thick white sauce made with white bread-crumbs, onions, milk or cream, and flavoured with spices such as cloves and mace. Traditionally eaten with poultry.

bread staling Staling is a continuous process from the time the loaf is taken from the oven. First the starch gel becomes firm as it cools, at room temperature becoming firm enough for the bread to be cut. This is followed by a gradual contraction of the gel, resulting in a migration of water from the starch into the gluten; although the total water content may be unchanged, and the bread develops a dry texture. Some of this moisture softens the crust which becomes leathery. If the bread is wrapped there need be no loss of water from the surface. The process of staling can be reversed by heating the bread in an oven to 60°C (140°F) which is sufficient to allow the starch to recover the lost moisture from the gluten and give the bread a freshly-baked feel.

bread storing It is best stored at room temperature, wrapped to prevent loss of surface moisture. The low temperature of a refrigerator speeds up the staling process. Bread can however, be stored in a **deep freeze**, as the water becomes locked into the starch when it is frozen, so that when defrosted it is still fresh, although the crust will not be crisp.

bream Non-oily **fish** with firm flesh. There are many varieties, but Red Sea-bream, *Pagellus centrodontus* and Black Sea-bream, *Chrysophrys ayrata* are the two most important; they are good to eat fresh and are sometimes smoked. They prefer warmer waters of the Mediterranean but frequent coastal waters of the UK in the summer. Freshwater varieties such as *Abramis brama* are related to **carp** and are not usually eaten.

NUTRITIONAL VALUE: protein 16–18%, fat 0.5–1.0%, vitamin B complex and minerals.

ENERGY per 100g: average: 75 kcal, 314 kJ.

USES: grilled, baked or poached.

brew The preparation of a liquid for drinking by infusion as for **tea** or by fermentation as for **beer**.

brewer's grains The residue of brewing. It is high in **protein** and used mainly as animal feed.

Brie A soft full-cream **cheese** originally from Brie near Paris. Now much copied.

NUTRITIONAL VALUE: average: protein 22%, fat 24%, carbohydrate 0.5%.

ENERGY per 100g: 305 Kcal, 1276 kJ.

USES: as a table cheese, sometimes grilled.

brill A non-oily **flatfish**. See **dab**, **plaice**.

brilliant blue (E133) See **colour**, **synthetic**.

brine A strong solution of common **salt** used for **pickling** or preserving. The preservative action is due to the high osmotic pressure denying water for the growth of **moulds**, **fungi** and **bacteria**. See **osmosis**.

brioche Bread made with a yeasted dough, enriched with eggs and milk, either as rolls or as a loaf formed in a fluted mould.

brisket The breast of an animal.

brisling A Norwegian variety of **sprat**, rich in oil-soluble **vitamins A** and **D**. It is often canned.

British thermal unit The unit for the costing of gas used in Britain until 1992 when it was replaced by the Kilowatt hour. See appendix, heat units, tables of equivalents.

broad bean *Vicia faba*. The oldest of the beans cultivated for food in Europe and Asia. It is moderately hardy, matures early, and is extensively cultivated, commercially and in gardens. It freezes well but should be **blanched** first to destroy **enzymes** which cause deterioration.

NUTRITIONAL VALUE: fresh: protein 4%, carbohydrate 7%, vitamin B complex, vitamin C, dietary fibre.

ENERGY per 100g: cooked: 48 kcal, 201 kJ.

USES: shelled and boiled as a vegetable or may be cooked in the pod when very young; traditionally served with a white sauce or butter and parsley. Also used in soups and salads or as a purée. Sometimes used dried in Greece.

broccoli *Brassica oleracea botrytis cauliflora*. A hardy winter and early spring **cauliflower** consisting of many small heads of undeveloped flowers rather than one large head. Varieties of broccoli include purple-sprouting, which has small purple florets, and the dark green **calabrese** which has larger florets.

NUTRITIONAL VALUE: protein 2%, carbohydrate 1.5%, vitamin B complex, dietary fibre.

ENERGY per 100g: cooked: 16 kcal, 67 kJ.

USES: as a vegetable to accompany meat dishes, as fritters, or as a separate course with melted butter or a sauce such as **hollandaise**.

broche, à la or **en** Roasted on a **spit**.

brochette French term for **skewer** and the food cooked on it. See **kebab**.

broil To cook over hot coals on a grid or to grill.

broiler A young **chicken**, usually about 1–

1.5 kilos (2–3 lbs) in weight. Special strains are now bred to reach this weight in 12 weeks.

bromelin A **proteolytic enzyme** present in **pineapple**.

bronze An alloy of copper and tin, resistant to corrosion. Used by the Greeks and Romans for cooking vessels and cutting instruments. It is too costly for general use today.

broth Meat, **fish** and/or **vegetables** cooked in water and used with the liquid as a basis for **soups**.

brown colouring See **colour**.

brown discoloration Changes which occur on exposed cut surfaces of some fruit and vegetables with a low **vitamin C** content such as apples, bananas, peaches, parsnips. The process is due to the action of an **enzyme**, generally known as polyphenol oxidase and is harmless in the early stages but leads to deterioration if not checked: this may be done by cooking or the immersion of the food in an **antioxidant** solution such as lemon juice in which **ascorbic acid** is the active component (600mg ascorbic acid in 500ml water should protect 1.5kg of fruit). One **Campden tablet** could also be used. All are safe to be put in the cooking water. Dried fruit is often **sulphited** to preserve the natural colour. See **Maillard reaction**.

brown dutch beans A well-flavoured variety of **haricot beans**. Should be boiled for at least 10 minutes to destroy any **lectin** present and simmered for 1–2 hours until soft.

NUTRITIONAL VALUE: cooked: protein 6.5%, carbohydrate 16%, calcium, iron, dietary fibre.

ENERGY per 100g: cooked: 86 kcal, 360 kJ.

USES: traditionally used for making baked beans, also in stews, soups.

browning See **Maillard reaction**.

brucellosis Primarily a disease of cattle caused by the *bacterium Brucella abortus*, causing abortions. It is transmitted to man through unpasteurised **milk** and causes recurrent fever. *Brucella melitensis* causes a similar disease transmitted by goat's milk and is rare. See **pasteurisation**.

brussels sprout *Brassica oleracea bullata gemminifera*. A hardy member of the cabbage family producing multiple small tight leaf-heads, similar to miniature cabbages, along the length of the stem during the autumn and winter.

NUTRITIONAL VALUE: protein 3.5%, minerals, vitamin C up to 70mg per 100g, dietary fibre.

ENERGY per 100g: cooked: 18 kcal, 75 kJ.

USES: boiled or steamed as a vegetable.

BSE Abbreviation of **bovine spongioform encephalopathy**.

Bucellas A Portuguese white **wine** from the district of that name.

buckwheat Also known as beachwheat, saracen corn and kasha, the seed of *Fagopyrum esculentum*, a plant related to rhubarb. It is cooked like **rice** and has a distinctive flavour which is enhanced if it is lightly roasted first.

NUTRITIONAL VALUE: protein 11%, fat 2%, carbohydrate 70%, vitamin B complex, minerals.

ENERGY per 100g: 350 kcal, 1464 kJ.

USES: as a substitute for rice, milled into flour and mixed with, or used instead of, wheat flour in baking, to enhance casseroles and soups.

buffalo milk Rich milk, high in fat content from water buffalo. It is not usually available in Western countries.

NUTRITIONAL VALUE: protein 3.8%, fat 7%, carbohydrate 4.7%.

USES: for drinking, butter and cheese-making in India and other Eastern countries, for cheese-making in Egypt and Southern Italy. See **Mozzarella**.

buffer A chemical term used for a substance which resists change in pH when mixed with either an **acid** or **alkali**. The main buffers in food are **proteins**, such as **milk**. Milk subdues the high acidity of some fruits but will curdle unless it is stabilised by heating with a starch such as cornflour (see **flour**). Milk is useful as a first aid measure to help neutralise **poisons**.

buffet A meal set out with an assortment of cooked foods, salads and desserts; usually for self-service.

bulgar wheat Also known as burghal wheat and cracked wheat. The grain is boiled until it cracks open, then drained and dried. It is a staple food of the Middle East and is the oldest processed food known.

NUTRITIONAL VALUE: boiled or soaked and drained: protein 11%, fat 1%, carbohydrate 83%.

ENERGY per 100g: boiled or soaked: 366 kcal, 1531 kJ.

USES: in a variety of Middle Eastern dishes, salads, an essential ingredient of **tabbouleh**.

bulking agent A substance which increases the bulk of a food, during preparation or during digestion, without contributing significantly to the energy value. Examples include **polydextrose** and cellulose-based substances classed as food **additives** within the range E460–466.

bullace *Prunus interstitia*. The wild form of **damson**; a native of the UK.

bully beef Popular name given by troops in World War 1 to salted canned beef. Also known as **corned beef**.

bun A small sweetened **bread**, often containing dried **fruit** and sometimes **spices**.

burghal wheat See **bulgar wheat**.

Burgundy Red or white **wine** from the Burgundy district of France, mostly produced in the Cote d'Or.

burnet *Sanguisorba minor*. A hardy perennial **herb**; the leaves are sometimes used in soups and salads. Known as salad burnet.

burns See **accidents**.

butane See **gas**.

butter An emulsion separated from **milk** or **cream**, usually the latter, by churning. The complex colloidal system is converted to a solid emulsion with the separation of the liquid residue known as **buttermilk**. The characteristic flavour is due to **diacetyl** produced by the **lactose**-fermenting **bacterium** *Streptococcus lactis*. **Salt** and colouring are usually added but unsalted butter is available. See **ghee**.

NUTRITIONAL VALUE: fat 80%, mostly saturated, vitamin A, vitamin D. Reduced-fat versions are now available containing a higher proportion of water and as little as half the fat.

ENERGY per 100g: 740 kcal, 3096 kJ.

USES: spread on bread or toast, for frying, in pastries, cakes, desserts, sauces. Some reduced-fat alternatives are unsuitable for cooking; recipes for the specific product should be followed.

butter bean *Phaseolus lunatus*, also known as Lima bean, Madagascar bean. A tropical climbing bean with large white seeds and a good flavour. Should be presoaked, and cooked for 45–60 mins. Sold dried.

NUTRITIONAL VALUE: cooked: protein 7%, fat 2%, carbohydrate 17%, dietary fibre.

ENERGY per 100g: cooked: 110 kcal, 460 kJ.

USES: widely used cooked as a vegetable; enhanced by the addition of a sauce such as tomato, parsley.

butter cream A rich soft mixture of unsalted butter, egg and sugar.

butter icing A soft rich icing for cakes, made with icing sugar and butter.

buttermilk The fluid left after the **fat** from milk or cream has been separated out into **butter** by churning. Contains **diacetyl** giving it a butter-like flavour. It cannot be used as skimmed milk as it is sour. It is made commercially by adding a culture to skimmed milk.

NUTRITIONAL VALUE: fat 1–2%, with small but variable quantities of **protein** and **lactose**.

ENERGY per 100g: 40 kcal, 167 kJ.

USES: with bicarbonate of soda as a raising agent in scones, cakes, soda-bread, in butter substitutes and reduced fat spreads to give flavour.

butternut The fruit of *Juglans cinerea*, the American **walnut**. The shell is oval, thick and contains a sweet oily **kernel**.

NUTRITIONAL VALUE: protein 15%, fat 50% mostly unsaturated, carbohydrate 10%, vitamin B complex.

ENERGY per 100g: 510 kcal, 2134 kJ.

USES: as a dessert nut.

butylated hydroxitolene (E321) Permitted **antioxidant**; prepared synthetically.

byssus The threads, like filaments or hairs, with which **molluscs** attach themselves to rocks. They are poisonous and must be discarded.

C

cabbage *Brassica oleracea capitata*. A member of the brassica family, widely grown for its edible leaves and available throughout the year in temperate climates. Leaves vary from white to dark green according to variety.

NUTRITIONAL VALUE: protein 1%, vitamin A, vitamin B complex, vitamin C up to 35mg per 100g, minerals, dietary fibre.

ENERGY per 100g: raw: 22 kcal, 92 kJ. Boiled, 15 kcal, 56 kJ.

USES: a valuable and inexpensive vegetable, best boiled for a short time; the addition of **bicarbonate of soda** to the water preserves the green colour but destroys vitamin C. The white and pale green varieties may be shredded and eaten raw in salad, especially in **coleslaw**.

cabbage palm *Sabal palmetto*. A subtropical palm with an edible growing bud, cooked and eaten as cabbage or in salads. Grown in southern United States, Mexico and New Zealand.

caboc A double-cream cheese rolled in oatmeal; of Scottish origin.

cacao *Theobroma cacao*, a tropical tree of American origin, which produces seeds from which **cocoa** and **chocolate** are prepared. Contains caffeine and the related drug theobromine.

cacik A **cucumber** salad dressed with seasoned yoghurt and garlic.

cactus A fleshy plant of American origin which has the capacity to store water. At least one species, the **prickly pear**, has edible fruits and leaves. See **nopales**.

cadmium A poisonous substance which

plays no role in human or animal life and is present in industrial waste and tobacco smoke. It is toxic, and may be found in soil near old lead mines and heavy industry; also in sewerage effluents, where it may pollute river and sea water, and so be taken up by crops and marine life, creating a cause for concern.

Caerphilly cheese A mild white semi-hard, crumbly cheese, first made in Wales and now widely copied.

NUTRITIONAL VALUE: protein 25%, fat 35% mostly saturated, vitamin A, vitamin B complex, minerals.

ENERGY per 100g: 415 kcal, 1736 kJ.

USES: a table cheese; not suitable for cooking.

caffeine An **alkaloid** with stimulating properties, present in **coffee**, **tea**, **cocoa**, **chocolate** and **cola nut**. Caffeine raises blood pressure, increases alertness, and is a diuretic. Some find the effects troublesome and sufficient to prevent sleeping. It is not harmful in moderation but heavy consumption can cause tremor.

Coffee-beans contain 1% caffeine and tea-leaves 1.5–2.5%. However, so much more coffee is used in a single prepared drink, that the caffeine content is about 5 times more than that of a cup of tea. Cocoa beans have a similar content of caffeine to that in coffee beans but prepared cocoa powder contains only 0.1%. The safe quantity of tea and coffee that can be consumed depends on their strength but, in general, not more than 3 cups of coffee and 6–7 of tea should be taken daily. Caffeine in instant coffees provides a similar amount per cup to that prepared from ground coffee. Decaffeinated coffee (in both bean and instant form) and tea are available.

caffeol An **essential oil** responsible for the aroma of **coffee**. The quality of the coffee, strain and length of time roasted determine the amount released. The oil is also released

by grinding but is quickly lost unless the ground coffee is stored in an airtight container, preferably at a low temperature, as in a refrigerator or freezer.

cafétière A coffee pot. In the UK, refers to one with a filter-plunger.

calabrese A member of the *brassica* family grown for its edible, usually green, florets. See **broccoli**.

calamares Spanish name for **squid**.

calamus See **sweet flag**.

calciferol See **vitamin D**.

calcium A mineral which is the most important inorganic constituent of bones and teeth. The total in the average adult is in excess of 1.0kg. It is also an essential constituent of tissue and body fluids, where it plays an important role in nerve and muscle function and the beating of the heart. A daily intake of at least 0.5g is required to sustain an adequate level, which is provided by a mixed diet that includes milk, other dairy products, vegetables and cereal foods. Absorption is dependant on **vitamin D** and sunlight. Most **bread** and **flours** are fortified with added **calcium carbonate**.

Calcium deficiency is a contributing factor to the reduction of bone density in the elderly. See **osteoporosis**.

calcium acetate (E263) Food preservative, used in mixes such as commercially prepared **cheesecake**.

calcium acid phosphate A substance used as a source of acid in **baking powders**, which depend on heat to release carbon dioxide.

calcium alginate (E404) A food **additive** prepared from seaweeds.

USES: as a gelling agent, thickener and **emulsifier** in ice-creams and similar commercially-produced foods.

calcium benzoate (E213) A food **preservative** which prevents the growth of **fungi** and **moulds**.

calcium carbonate (E170) A mineral occurring naturally in the form of chalk, limestone, marble. It is responsible for most of the hardness of water, causing deposits in kettles, water-pipes and hot-water systems. See **water**.

USES: as a white colouring agent, an alkali, dusting powder on dry foods, as a calcium supplement and to reduce the acidity of wine.

calcium hydrogen sulphite (E227) A salt of sulphurous acid which releases **sulphur dioxide** and is used as a food **preservative**. It has a similar action to other salts of sulphurous acid such as sodium bisulphite. See **Campden tablets**, **bleach**.

USES: used in beer, wine and soft drinks.

calcium propionate (E282) A chemical substance which occurs naturally in some **cheeses**.

USES: as a food preservative in dairy and baked products, pizzas.

calcium silicate (552) A naturally occurring mineral.

USES: as **bulking agent**, dusting powder on chewing gum, and as an antacid in indigestion tablets.

calcium sorbate (E203) A synthetically prepared **preservative** and antifungal agent.

USES: in milk products, frozen pizza.

calcium sulphate (516) Pure gypsum; a naturally occurring mineral.

USES: as a firming and **bulking agent**.

calf The young of a **beef** animal and the source of **veal**; the calf is killed at about 3 weeks. The term also refers to the young of other animals such as elephant, seal.

calorie The unit of energy required to raise the temperature of one gram of water by one degree Celsius. The unit is too small for practical use and the larger unit of 1000 calories is used; it should be written kilocalorie but is usually referred to as kcal. The daily requirement for adults is in the order of 1500 to 3000kcal depending on size, age and activity of the individual. 1 kcal is equal to 4.184kJ (kilojoules). See **joule**.

calorimeter An instrument for measuring heat released by burning a substance in an atmosphere of oxygen (see **gas**). Although the body releases heat by a complex multi-stage chemical action based on **enzymes**, the amount released from food corresponds closely with that estimated by calorimeter. See **energy**.

Calvados A liqueur distilled from fermented apples, from the Calvados district of Normandy. See **congeners**, **spirits**.

ALCOHOL CONTENT: 40%.

calves' foot jelly The foot of a calf boiled in water to extract the **gelatine** which forms a jelly when cooled; once a recommended food for invalids. Also known as neat's foot jelly.

Camembert A soft full-fat cheese covered with a white **mould**, *Penicillium candidum*, originally made in the Camembert district of Normandy in France. It has a water content of 55%, ripens quickly and does not keep. The mould hydrolyses the **protein** to develop the particular flavour of the cheese, which has only a short period when it is at its best for eating. Traditionally camembert was made with unpasteurised cow's **milk**, and has been associated with outbreaks of food poisoning due to **Listeria monocytogenes** and **salmonella**. Now it is often made from pasteurised milk which is safer. It should be purchased in small quantities and stored in a cool place. See **penicillin**.

NUTRITIONAL VALUE: protein 20%, fat 20% mostly saturated, vitamin A, vitamin B complex, minerals.

ENERGY per 100g: 160 kcal, 669 kJ.

USES: a table cheese; not generally used for cooking, but can be grilled.

camomile or **chamomile**. A low-growing **herb**, *Anthermis nobilis*, related to the chrysanthemum.

USES: for flavouring and for making herbal tea.

campari A bitter-sweet aperitif, of Italian origin, flavoured with gentian, bitter orange, quinine.

NUTRITIONAL VALUE: alcohol content 25%.

USES: usually drunk diluted with soda water, bitter lemon or tonic water.

Campden tablets (E223) Tablets of compressed sodium bisulphite, usually weighing 0.44g and releasing **sulphur dioxide** when dissolved; this disappears on exposure to air and in cooking. Introduced during World War 2 as a cold **preservative** for fruit.

USES: for controlling fermentation and bacteria in home wine-making, sterilising bottles and equipment. As an **antioxidant** to prevent the brown discoloration on cut surfaces of fruit, particularly **apples**, **plums** and **peaches**. It will also bleach fruit colours such as the reds and purples but not the yellows.

campylobacter A **micro-organism** which is a common cause of **food poisoning**; it is often spread from pet animals and birds pecking at milk bottles. It causes acute illness with vomiting and **diarrhoea**. See **hygiene**.

Canada rice See **rice, wild**.

canapé A small **biscuit**, **pastry** or piece of **bread** covered or filled with a savoury mixture.

Canderel A proprietary low-calorie **artificial sweetener** made with aspartame and mixed with some sugar. It is unstable when heated.

USES: in place of sugar for sweetening prepared food or in drinks, but unsuitable for cooking.

candied peel The **peel** of **citron** and other **citrus fruits** boiled and cooled several times in **sugar syrup** so that it absorbs the sugar and crystallises.

USES: as a sweetmeat, in cakes, desserts and **mincemeat**, for flavouring and decoration.

candy A sweetmeat of boiled **sugar** which has crystallised.

cannabis Also known as hashish, marihuana, Indian hemp. An addictive drug extracted from the leaves or flowers of the hardy herb *Cannabis sativa* or *indica*. It has been found in honey from nectar gathered from wild hemp flowers.

cannelloni Hollow tubes of **pasta** large enough to take a filling.

USES: for filling with meat and/or vegetable mixtures and served with a cheese sauce.

canning The packaging of food in steel containers which are protected inside from rusting and chemicals in the food, by a coating of tin and then lacquer. The canning process was developed by a Frenchman in 1795 and patented in 1810, when tinplate was first used. With modern methods and machinery, the cans are filled, any residual air extracted, sealed, and sterilised by heat, under pressure. Fruits (including tomatoes), are rendered safe at a temperature of 95–100°C (200–212°F) but vegetables, fish and meats need a temperature of 120–175°C (248–347°F) for total safety. The duration of exposure to heat is related to the physical nature of the food and must destroy all **food poisoning micro-organisms** and their **spores**. Home-canning of any food is not advisable.

If a can shows any sign of denting, damage, leaking or being **'blown'** the contents must never be used. **Lead** solder used for sealing cans has in the past been the cause of fatal lead poisoning on expeditions using mainly canned food but solders nowadays are lead free. Manufacturers' sell-by dates should be observed. The contents of opened cans should be used immediately or transferred to a glass, plastic or china container, stored in a refrigerator and used within a few days. See **botulism**.

cape gooseberry Also known as golden berry. The fruit of *Physalis peruviana*, a native of South America, growing best in warm conditions. It is a cherry-sized, yellow berry.

NUTRITIONAL VALUE: vitamin C.

USES: eaten raw, in various desserts and for preserves.

caper The immature flower-buds of *Capparis spinosa*, a subtropical shrub which grows wild around the Mediterranean. See **nasturtium**.

USES: the buds are pickled and used for flavouring savoury dishes and sauces.

capercaillie *Tetrao urogallus*. A game-bird; a large species of **grouse**.

SEASON: October 1st to January 31st.

capon A neutered cockerel; the bird grows to a large size and has tender flesh. It is now illegal to neuter birds by using **hormones**, and as surgical castration is expensive, capons are rare.

capsanthin (E160c) The natural red/orange dye prepared from *Capsicum annum*, the sweet red pepper.

USES: for flavouring and as an orange colouring.

capsicum A member of the genus *Capsicum annum*. See **chilli**, **pepper** (**sweet**).

carafe A glass flask for **wine**, usually in a measured quantity and used for house wines.

caramel See **colour**.

caramel (E150) Prepared from **carbohydrates** and used as a brown colouring agent.

caraway seeds The aromatic seeds of the plant *Carum carvi* which grows in Europe and Asia.

USES: as a spice; a feature of German and Austrian dishes, such as **sauerkraut**, on bread, in seed-cake.

carbohydrates A group of chemical substances containing oxygen, hydrogen and carbon but lacking nitrogen (see **gas**). The group includes **sugars**, **starches** and **cellulose**. Sugars are immediately available but starches must be cooked to break down the cell walls which contain them. Humans are unable to digest cellulose as they lack the necessary **bacteria** in the digestive tract; nevertheless cellulose is of great importance as **dietary fibre**. The principal sources worldwide are:— **cassava**, **cereals**, **root** vegetables, **sugarcane**. See **diabetes**, **diet**, **potato**, **pulses**, **sugar**, **wheat**, **rice**.

ENERGY: All have 3.75 kcal, 16 kJ per g.

carbon A basic **element** from which all **organic** substances are formed. Food which is burned is reduced to carbon. See **charcoal**.

carbon black (E153) See **colour**.

carbon dioxide (CO_2) See **gas**.

carbon monoxide (CO) See **gas**.

carbonnade A rich dish of meat, usually beef, cooked in beer in the oven, with pieces of bread floating on top, which absorb fat and turn a golden brown.

carborundum *Silicon carbide*. An intensely hard **abrasive** used on iron or steel, such as on the tops of old fashioned stoves; it should not be used on stainless steel or other metals or surfaces. It is the basis of emery paper and grindstones.

carboxymethyl cellulose (E446) An **additive** prepared from wood **cellulose**.

USES: as a gelling agent, to add bulk and reduce energy value in foods such as cakes and biscuits, to enhance texture in mousses, sauces, processed cheese, ice-cream.

carcass The body of an animal prepared for jointing and cutting up to be sold by a butcher.

cardamom The highly aromatic dried fruits of *Eletaria cardamomum* and *Amonum cardamon*, tropical shrubs related to ginger. Usually sold as the dried seed-pods. Ground cardamom rapidly loses its flavour. The pods should be stored in sealed containers in the dark.

USES: to flavour pickles, sauces, curries, and sometimes cakes.

caries Decay of teeth due to **bacteria** which form mild **acids** and dissolve the enamel of the teeth. Growth of the responsible bacteria is encouraged by consumption of sweet, sticky foods, retention of food around the teeth, poor mouth hygiene and build up of plaque. See **dental enamel**, **fluorine**.

carmine (E120) See **colour**.

carmoisine (E122) See **colour**.

carnauba wax (903) A very hard natural wax extracted from the leaves of the tropical palm, *Copernicia prunifera*. The wax is used as a glazing and polishing agent for sugar confectionery.

carnivore An animal which feeds only on other living creatures.

carob Also known as Locust bean *Cerotonia siliqua*. A subtropical evergreen tree, Southern European in origin, bearing long pods containing sweet-tasting beans with a chocolate-like flavour.

NUTRITIONAL VALUE: protein 20%, fat 1.5%, high carbohydrate content, gums.

USES: the ground seed is used as a health food and a cheap substitute for chocolate. Gums extracted from the seeds are used commercially in ice-creams, various dessert mixes, salad cream and pie filling. Widely used for animal feed.

caromel See **caramel** (alternative spelling).

carotene A yellow/red chemical from which the body makes the oil-soluble **vitamin A**, also known as retinol. Carotene is present in many plants and fruits, in which it is often obscured by **chlorophyll**, also in dairy products, carrots, fish and meat. There are adequate sources of carotene and vitamin A in a normal mixed diet. Deficiency, which is rare in developed countries, causes thickening and dryness of the cornea and may lead to blindness. People who drink large quantities of carrot juice may turn yellow.

carp *Cyprinus carpio*. A freshwater non-oily **fish** which has been farmed since biblical times in Asia and the Middle East, throughout Europe since Roman times and now in Israel. It is omnivorous, long-lived, reaches a large size and was kept in 'stew ponds' in monasteries where it supplied valuable **protein** food. It is not often available in the UK.

NUTRITIONAL VALUE: protein 16–18%, fat 0.5–1%, vitamin B complex, minerals.

ENERGY per 100g: average: 75 kcal, 314 kJ.

USES: can be cooked by any method but best baked or poached.

carrageenan (E407) A natural jelly-like **polysaccharide** extracted from seaweeds. See **carragheen**.

carragheen *Chondrus crispus*. An edible purplish seaweed, collected at low water. It is boiled to extract the jelly-like material.

NUTRITIONAL VALUE: nil.

USES: widely used as a gelling agent or thickener in commercial preparations of ice-cream, desserts, cake decorations, cheeses, salad dressings, quick-setting jellies.

carrot *Daucus carota.* A hardy plant grown for its sweet, orange/yellow, edible **root**.

NUTRITIONAL VALUE: protein 7–10%, carbohydrate 5–6%. Rich in **carotene**.

ENERGY per 100g: average: raw: 24 kcal, 100 kJ. Cooked, 20 kcal, 90 kJ.

USES: as a vegetable, in stews, casseroles, cakes, sliced or grated raw in salads.

carte du jour The menu available on the day.

cartilage The flexible firm structure which forms the skeleton of young mammals and later becomes converted to bone. It remains throughout life as the skeleton in **fish** of the **shark** family, including rays and **skate**.

carya See **hickory**.

casein The **protein**, caseinogen, precipitated in **milk** when it curdles, together with other milk solids, **lactose** and salts. Dried skimmed-milk is almost entirely casein; it has the property of absorbing and neutralising acids and some poisons. See **curd**.

NUTRITIONAL VALUE: almost pure protein.

USES: used extensively in the form of dried skimmed-milk, in the commercial production of a wide range of processed foods, ice-cream, yoghurt, desserts, sweetmeats. Large amounts are fed to animals where there is a surplus from **cream** and butter- making. It has been used as a basis for water-resistant glues and plastics.

caseinogen The soluble milk protein which, when precipitated, forms **casein**.

cashew apple See **cashew nut**.

cashew nut The kidney-shaped nut of a semi-tropical tree, *Anacardium occidentale*. The flowers produce a large hanging fruit with an acidic flesh called the cashew apple. The single nut is attached to the lower end of the fruit; it is sweet and highly esteemed but expensive because of the low yield.

NUTRITIONAL VALUE: average: protein 17%, fat 46% mostly unsaturated, carbohydrate 28%, vitamin B complex.

ENERGY per 100g: average: 587 kcal, 2456 kJ.

USES: eaten alone, cooked in a variety of chicken and other meat dishes, curries, desserts.

cask A round vessel made of wooden staves, bound with iron, used for storing liquids. See **barrel**.

casserole A large dish or container made of metal, enamelware, heat-proof china or earthenware, with a lid. Also refers to the food cooked and served in it. See **stew**.

cassoulet A rich **stew** of mixed meats, such as pork and lamb, with white beans.

cassava Also known as manioc. A starchy substance prepared from the root of the tropical palm, *Manihot utillisima*, from which **tapioca** is made. It is a high yielding crop, well in excess of **cereals**. There are many varieties of similar palms. In the raw state, all contain a poisonous glucoside, **linamarin**, related to cyanide, which is destroyed during processing cassava for food.

NUTRITIONAL VALUE: almost pure carbohydrate, vitamin B complex, vitamin C, minerals.

ENERGY per 100g: 109 kcal, 456 kJ.

USES: a major source of human and animal food in tropical countries.

cassia A **spice** from the bark of the shrub *Cinnemona cassia*. It is similar to **cinnamon** but coarser and with a stronger flavour.

USES: as for cinnamon. Oil extracted from it is traditionally used to flavour Easter biscuits.

cassis An alcoholic drink made from **black-currants**.

ALCOHOL CONTENT: 15%.

castor-oil Oil extracted from the seeds of *Ricinus communis*. It is naturally bland, but if taken by mouth, is broken down by the enzyme, **lipase**, to form ricinoleic acid, a potent irritant. The seeds also contain ricin, one of the most potent known poisons.

USES: as a powerful laxative which should be used with caution and only under medical supervision; also, mixed with zinc oxide, as a bland lubricant for the eyes and the skin of babies.

catabolism The breaking down of complex organic substances by any living **organism** with the liberation of **energy**. See **metabolism**.

catalyst A substance which speeds up, or initiates, a chemical reaction without itself undergoing any change or becoming part of the product of the chemical change. Examples are **enzymes** and **nickel**, used in hardening unsaturated fats to convert them into hard **margarines**, in the presence of hydrogen.

catmint *Nepeta cataria*. A decorative hardy shrub with blue flowers attractive to cats and bees.

USES: commonly used in ancient times for flavouring.

cattle A general term for animals which graze on pastures, such as cows, bulls, oxen.

caudle A form of soup or gruel made with oatmeal and flavoured with spices and wine.

caul The amniotic membrane; a thin transparent sheet which encloses the foetus of mammals.

USES: to wrap meat to be cooked in the oven to prevent burning and as an edible skin for **faggots**. See **omentum**.

cauliflower *Brassica oleracea botrytis cauliflora*. A member of the brassica family grown for its large white flower-heads. Summer and winter varieties are available in temperate climates. See **broccoli**.

NUTRITIONAL VALUE: protein 2%, carbohydrate 1–2%, vitamin B complex, vitamin C up to 80mg per 100g, dietary fibre.

ENERGY per 100g: raw: 13 kcal, 55 kJ. Boiled: 9kcal, 38 kJ.

USES: as a vegetable, cooked by boiling, steaming, stir-frying, often served with a cheese sauce, raw in salads.

caviar The highly-prized black eggs of the **sturgeon**. Other fish-eggs, dyed black, are sold as caviar but lack the distinctive flavour. Generally available canned. See **lumpfish**.

NUTRITIONAL VALUE: protein 30%, fat 20%, vitamin A, vitamin D, minerals.

ENERGY per 100g: 340 kcal, 1422 kJ.

USES: a luxury savoury dish usually served as a **canapé** or on hot toast with butter and lemon. In Russia it is eaten with a spoon and often accompanied by **vodka**.

caveach Fish or meat fried in oil and pickled in vinegar.

cayenne A very hot, red condiment prepared from the hot red varieties of *Capsicum frutescens*, also known as **chilli** or **chili**, which are dried and ground.

USES: a highly potent flavouring used in **curry** dishes, **chilli con carne** and many highly spiced meat and vegetable dishes.

celery *Apium gaveolens*. A vegetable with a characteristic flavour, grown for its leaf-stalks, which need to be protected from light during growth, to prevent them from turning green and so producing a bitter flavour.

NUTRITIONAL VALUE: protein 0.9%, carbohydrate 1.3%, vitamin C up to 5–7mg per 100g, dietary fibre.

ENERGY per 100g: raw: 8 kcal, 33 kJ.

USES: eaten raw with cheese, in salads,

cooked as a vegetable, in soups, stews, casseroles.

celeriac *Apium graveolens rapaceum*. A form of **celery** grown for the swollen base of the stem which has the flavour of celery. It is reputed to be an aphrodisiac.

NUTRITIONAL VALUE: boiled: protein 1.6%, carbohydrate 2.0%, vitamin C, dietary fibre.

ENERGY per 100g: boiled: 14 kcal, 59 kJ.

USES: cooked as a vegetable, in soups, stews, casseroles; grated raw in salads.

cellulose A **carbohydrate** which forms the connective tissue of plants giving them strength; it cannot be digested by man although some breakdown occurs in the large bowel due to the action of **bacteria**. It becomes harder with age and is responsible for toughness in vegetables. All **herbivores** have bacteria in their digestive tracts to break down cellulose which becomes an important source of nutrition. It is important to humans as **dietary fibre**.

cellophane The tradename for the first transparent wrapping material prepared from wood pulp in 1925 and widely used today. It is safe for food, but very brittle, sometimes coated, and not recommended for use in a conventional or microwave oven.

celtuce *Asparagus lettuce*. A vegetable of Chinese origin, grown for its leaf-stalks.

NUTRITIONAL VALUE: protein 0.8—1%, vitamin B complex, carotene, vitamin C up to 5mg per 100g, minerals, dietary fibre.

USES: in salads.

centrifuge An appliance for separating heavy from light ingredients by centrifugal force using rotation at high speed.

USES: for the separation of cream from milk; small centrifuges, known as spinners, are used domestically for drying lettuce and salad crops after washing; also for the extraction of water from clothes in washing machines.

cep or **cèpe** See **boletus edulus**.

cephaloids A widely distributed group of **molluscs** which includes **octopus**, **squid** and **cuttlefish**. Mostly eaten in Southern Europe.

ceramic hob A form of electrically heated hob in which the heat source is covered by a heat resistant ceramic plate and separated from the cooking pot, the heat being transferred by infra-red rays. The first were based on a simple radiant element but more recently a form of halogen lamp has been introduced which heats up almost instantaneously. The principle benefit is ease of cleaning. See also **inductive hob**.

cereals Edible **grain** crops including **barley**, **bulgar wheat**, **maize**, **oats**, **rice**, **rye**, **sorghum**, and **wheat**; the most important food crops worldwide which, in some countries, form 90% of the daily diet. In the UK cereal products provide about a third of the **carbohydrate** and **protein** intake.

The term also refers to breakfast foods such as cornflakes, wheat flakes, bran flakes, puffed rice and many others.

NUTRITIONAL VALUE: variable; in the unrefined state they contain protein 4—14%, carbohydrate 25—60%, fat 1—2%, vitamin B complex, carotene, vitamin E, minerals, dietary fibre.

USES: in bread, gruels, biscuits, cakes, breakfast cereals and many cooked dishes; also used in brewing and whisky-making.

CFCs A group of gases composed of carbon, fluorine and chlorine which are particularly stable, have a low boiling point, liquefy easily under pressure and are commonly used in heat exchangers in domestic refrigerators and commercial refrigeration plants and as propellants in spray cans. Now of worldwide importance because they collect in the upper air, leading to a breakdown of **ozone**, and increase the amount of active **ultraviolet light** reaching the earth's surface. Steps have been taken to phase out CFCs and replace them with safer alternatives.

Chablis A French white **wine** from Chablis in Burgundy.

chafing-dish A small **frying-pan** used for cooking at the table over a portable source of heat.

chalk See **calcium carbonate**.

Chambertin A rich, full-flavoured red Burgundy, or the term used to describe any dish cooked in this **wine**.

chamomile See **camomile**.

Champagne A premium **wine** from the Champagne district of France. It is allowed to complete its primary **fermentation** in the bottle and then by a special technique, a second fermentation takes place to produce the sparkling wine of quality. It must be bottled in thick-walled bottles and the corks wired to withstand the high pressures generated in the second fermentation.
ALCOHOL CONTENT: 12–13%.

champignon French for **mushroom**.

chanterelle *Cantherellus cibarius;* also known as girolle. A large yellow or orange almost funnel-shaped **fungus**, highly esteemed as one of the most delicious of the edible fungi. Grows in woods during late summer and autumn. See **mushrooms**.
NUTRITIONAL VALUE: see **fungi**.
USES: grilled or fried and eaten on its own as a savoury with toast, in a variety of savoury dishes.

chantilly Slightly sweetened whipped cream flavoured with vanilla.

chapatti or **chapati** Thin unleavened bread eaten throughout northern India. It is made with finely ground wholemeal **flour**, water and salt mixed to a soft dough and cooked on a **griddle** or in a heavy frying-pan. Served with **curries**.

chaptalization The term used in **wine**-making for the addition of sugar to the **must** during fermentation in order to increase the **alcohol** content.

charcoal A smokeless fuel made by burning hardwoods with insufficient oxygen for full combustion, leaving almost pure **carbon** in a solid, light-weight state. Charcoal burns slowly with the production of carbon dioxide and carbon monoxide if the oxygen or air supply is restricted. Charcoal also has the property of absorbing smells and some poisons. See **gas**.
USES: as a fuel for barbecues, out of doors, where the poisonous gases produced rapidly escape. Used in granular form to absorb smells in cooker hoods.

charcuterie A **pork** butcher's and the raw and processed pork products sold in it.

chard See **swiss chard**.

charlotte A pudding made in a mould lined with slices of buttered bread, filled with fruit and cooked; usually served hot.

charlotte russe A classic French dessert made in a mould which is lined with sponge fingers and filled with a mixture of egg custard and whipped cream and set with gelatine.

chartreuse A French liqueur, green or yellow in colour and flavoured with aromatic herbs. The term also refers to a mould of jelly, blancmange, rice, containing pieces of fruit, vegetable, meat.

chasseur Implies a dish prepared with white wine, mushrooms and shallots, such as chicken chasseur, or a brown sauce containing these ingredients.

chateaubriand A large, thick, **fillet** steak grilled and usually served to be shared between two or more persons.

chaudfroid A variation of **velouté** or brown sauce to which is added **aspic** or **gelatine**.

USES: to coat pieces of chicken or other meat to be served cold.

chayotte *Sechium edele.* The only species of a tropical perennial climbing plant bearing large pear-shaped fruits, up to 1kg in weight, with a single seed. Also known as vegetable pear and pepinetto. The young shoots and expanded roots can also be eaten.

NUTRITIONAL VALUE: fruits: protein 1%, carbohydrate 7.5%, vitamin C. Roots: carbohydrate 20%.

ENERGY per 100g: fruits: 32 kcal, 134 kJ. Roots: 75 kcal, 313 kJ.

USES: eaten as a fruit or cooked as a vegetable. The roots are cooked as potatoes.

Cheddar cheese A hard cheese, said to be the most widely manufactured and consumed cheese in the world. It was first made in Cheddar in Somerset. It varies in strength according to age; the strong mature cheese being up to 8 months old. Traditionally it is manufactured in round blocks and wrapped in muslin to mature at a temperature of 0–5°C. It develops a surface **mould** which is removed with the muslin.

NUTRITIONAL VALUE: protein 25–33%, fat 30–35%, vitamin A, vitamin D, calcium, iron.

ENERGY per 100g: average: 406 kcal, 1699 kJ.

USES: as a table cheese and for cooking in a wide range of dishes.

cheese A solid mass of **milk** ingredients formed by the coagulation of caseinogen, by souring or **rennet**, and yielding **casein**, which is then separated from the **whey**. In Europe, milk from cows, sheep and goats is most commonly used. All cheeses, except **cottage cheese**, **curd cheese**, and **cream cheese**, are salted, sometimes compressed, and left to mature. Variations in the conditions under which these processes are carried out, and the addition of special micro-organisms and moulds to some cheeses, accounts for the very large number of different ones that are available worldwide (over 1000 named).

Most cheeses have a high **protein** and saturated **fat** content with **vitamin A**, vitamin B complex, **calcium** and **iron**.

There are no hard and fast rules which can be applied to the classification of cheeses because of the vast number of variations and specialities and the fact that textures change with maturity. The following are very broad categories into which most will fall:—

Hard cheeses. All have a low water content which gives them a hard texture, relatively good keeping qualities and suitability for cooking. They include **Cheddar**, **Emmental**, **Gruyère**, **Parmesan** (very hard).

Semi-hard cheeses. These have a higher water content (of up to about 40%) than the hard ones and are often slightly crumbly or have a soft but firm texture. Many of the blue cheeses fall into this category which includes **Caerphilly**, **Edam**, **Gorgonzola**, **Gouda**, **Roquefort**, **Stilton**.

Soft cheeses. These have a water content of up to 75%, mature quickly and do not keep well. They include **Brie**, **Camembert**, **Ricotta**, also **cottage**, **cream** and **curd cheeses**.

All cheeses should be wrapped, but not in **clingfilm** or **foil**, to exclude air, and stored, when necessary, in a cool place, which nowadays, is often in a refrigerator, although sometimes the low temperature can alter the character of the cheese.

Some cheeses, particularly soft ones, are made from unpasteurised milk and have been the cause of **food poisoning** from **listeria monocytogenes**; children, pregnant women and the elderly are the most vulnerable and should avoid such cheeses. See **processed cheese, pasteurisation, penicillin**.

cheesecake A dessert with a biscuit base.

Cooking is not required if prepared biscuit is used. When cool it is covered with a mixture of **cottage cheese** and/or **curd cheese**, **cream cheese**, sometimes **cream**, and flavouring such as **lemon** and a setting agent such as **gelatine**; usually turned out of its tin for serving cold. Some cheesecakes are made with **egg** and are baked; these may have a **pastry** base.

cherry A small hardy stone-fruit related to the plum. *Prunus avium* is the sweet and *Prunus cerasis* the sour (Morello) cherry. From these two native cherries many varieties have been cultivated; some red and others black. They are available canned and crystallized.

NUTRITIONAL VALUE: carbohydrate 11.9%, vitamin B complex, vitamin C.

ENERGY per 100g: 45 kcal, 188 kJ.

USES: sweet varieties are eaten as a dessert fruit and used in a variety of desserts. Morello cherries are the best for cooking and preserves. Crystallized cherries are used in cakes, puddings and for decoration. The wild cherry is fermented and distilled to make **kirsch**.

chervil *Chaerophylum bulbosus*. A hardy perennial plant, native of southern Europe, grown for its grey or blackish edible bulbous roots, similar in shape and form to a **carrot**. Usually lifted and stored to be eaten during the winter.

USES: as a winter **vegetable**.

chervil *Anthriscum cerofolium*. A hardy annual herb grown for its feathery, parsley-like leaves.

USES: as a garnish and in soups; it has a more delicate flavour than parsley.

chestnut A sweet, edible starchy **nut** from a deciduous tree *Castanea sativa*, grown throughout Europe. Chestnuts are valued for their characteristic flavour and can be bought or gathered fresh in the late autumn or early winter; canned or dried they are available all the year. They are not to be confused with **water chestnuts**.

NUTRITIONAL VALUE: raw: protein 3%, fat 3%, carbohydrate 37%, vitamin B complex, minerals; (as compared with most other nuts which are high in fat content and low in carbohydrate).

ENERGY per 100g: raw: 178 kcal, 745 kJ.

USES: must be cooked when used fresh; presoaked and cooked if dried. Traditionally roasted and eaten alone when fresh, but also used in other dishes such as soups, stuffings, casseroles, desserts, crystallized to form **marrons glacés**.

chewing gum A gum, sweetened and flavoured, originally made with an extract from **chicele** bark, but nowadays, much of it is made largely from synthetic substances which are related to synthetic rubbers.

Chianti A red or white **wine** from the district of Tuscany, Italy.

chicele Gum extracted from the bark of *Achras sapotucea*, also known as sapodilla and naseberry; used in **chewing gum**.

chicken The young of the domestic hen, before coming into lay, and the meat from it. Chickens are bred commercially to be ready for eating at 10–12 weeks. See **broiler, muscle**.

NUTRITIONAL VALUE: protein 20%, fat 5–10% (mostly saturated), vitamin B complex, minerals.

ENERGY per 100g: raw, 125–197 kcal, 523–824 kJ.

USES: now one of the most widely used sources of animal protein, replacing beef. It is versatile and lends itself to a wide range of cooking methods and dishes.

WARNING: all poultry should be regarded as infected with **salmonella** and must be fully cooked. Special hygiene precautions are required to prevent contamination of other foods. Much of the chicken sold today has been frozen, and must be completely defrosted and then fully cooked without delay. Special care is required when cooking in the oven or microwave cooker to ensure that the internal temperature reaches at least 90°C (180°F). Any portion not eaten straight away must be kept in a refrigerator at less than 5°C (41°F) and for not more than 3 days. Frozen chicken should be stored at − 18°C (−0.5°F) until required. See **food poisoning**.

chick pea *Cicer arietinum*, also known as Egyptian **pea** or **bean**. A subtropical plant with a large seed; cultivated for centuries, especially in India and around the Mediterranean where it is a valuable food crop, sharing the properties of other pulses. The dried seed is nut-like and requires long presoaking (up to 24hr) and cooking by **simmering** until it is soft.

NUTRITIONAL VALUE: cooked: protein 8.3%, fat 1.4%, carbohydrate 20.3%, vitamin B complex, minerals, dietary fibre.

ENERGY per 100g: cooked: 122 kcal, 510 kJ.

USES: an essential ingredient of the Middle Eastern dish **humus**, also used in a variety of meat and vegetarian dishes, casseroles, soups.

chicory *Cichorium intybus*. Sometimes known as endive. A plant which grows wild throughout much of Europe and has been used as a salad crop since Roman times or earlier. First developed in Belgium in the 1840s, the white chicons are produced by cutting off the natural green foliage and forcing the roots, in darkness, to produce the tight shoots which are allowed to grow to a length of 10−15 cms.

NUTRITIONAL VALUE: vitamin C if grown in the summer in the light, small amounts of protein, carbohydrate, minerals and dietary fibre.

ENERGY per 100g: negligible.

USES: raw in salads, when it has a slightly bitter flavour, cooked as a vegetable dish, sometimes wrapped with slices of ham and covered with a cheese sauce. The large taproot of the variety known as Magdeburg chicory is roasted and ground and added to **coffee** to give it a characteristic flavour which is popular in France.

chilli or **chili** Small pungent fruits of the *Capsicum frutescens*. Most of them ripen from green to red but there are variations in colour, flavour and hotness. Care should be taken when handling chillies as they can cause blisters on the lips and in the mouth. It is important to wash off any traces that get on the hands. See **cayenne**.

USES: chopped in **curries** and highly-spiced dishes, particularly Mexican, such as **chilli con carne**, in pickles, chutneys, sauces.

chilli con carne A hot, spicy beef stew, of Mexican origin containing red kidney beans, peppers, onions, tomatoes and flavoured with **chilli**.

Chinese artichoke *Stachys sieboldii*. Also known as Crosnes or Chorogi. A hardy plant with edible roots which resemble greatly enlarged insect larvae. They have a subtle, delicate flavour but are rarely available in the UK.

Chinese cabbage *Brassica pekinensis*, also known as Chinese leaves and pe-tsai. A vegetable with tightly packed heads of pale green leaves.

NUTRITIONAL VALUE: vitamin C, minerals, dietary fibre.

ENERGY per 100g: negligible.

USES: fresh in salads, chopped and lightly cooked as a vegetable.

Chinese eggs A Chinese speciality sometimes known as '100-year-old eggs'. They are duck eggs, preserved by covering with a mixture of lime, straw ash, caustic soda and salt and then left for a period of several months, during which the white and yolks coagulate and partly break down with discoloration. They are considered a delicacy.

Chinese food syndrome The development of unpleasant side effects associated with the consumption of an excess of **monosodium glutamate**. It is so named after a number of people became ill following a meal in a Chinese restaurant. Present restrictions on the use of monosodium glutamate make a recurrence unlikely.

Chinese gooseberry *Actinidea chinensis*. See **kiwi fruit**.

Chinese pepper *Zanthoxylum piperatum*. Also known as Japanese Pepper and Anise Pepper (distinct from **star anise**). A moderately hardy shrub grown for its black seeds, which are dried and used as a pepper-like spice. Unrelated to *Piper nignum*, the true **pepper**.

Chinese persimmon See **persimmon**.

chips Hard vegetables, cut into sticks or thin slices. Most commonly refers to potatoes, which are then fried.

chipolata A small **sausage**.

chitterling The prepared small intestine, usually of the **pig** or **lamb**. Classed as **offal**.

chive *Allium schoenoprasum*. A hardy member of the onion family grown for its tall, thin, hollow leaves with a delicate onion flavour; a more recent introduction has a garlic flavour. Available for most of the year but the plants die back for 2 or 3 months in the winter depending on climate.

USES: chopped as a garnish on, and to add flavour to, potatoes and root vegetables, soups, savoury dishes, salads.

chlorine A green, noxious, gaseous **element**, when in its pure state. In small quantities, it is essential to animal life, and is present in the stomach as **hydrochloric acid** and in tissue fluids as sodium chloride (common **salt**). The gas dissolves readily in water and is a powerful oxidising and bleaching agent which destroys most forms of life. It is the active principle in domestic **bleach** which must never be taken internally. It is used extensively in a very dilute form, and carefully controlled way, to sterilise tap-**water**, swimming pools and other liquids, when it is quite safe.

chlorophyll The natural colour in all green plants. A chemical substance essential to plant life, for the manufacture of plant foods in the presence of light; the process is called **photosynthesis** and involves the combination of carbon dioxide with water to form carbohydrates. Chlorophyll plays no active part in animal life, although it is the means whereby plants build up **energy** for subsequent use by all animals. It is destroyed by prolonged boiling and by acids. The colour loss, when cooking green vegetables, can be inhibited by the addition of a little bicarbonate of soda, but this destroys the **vitamin C**. Loss of chlorophyll in canned vegetables is compensated for by incorporating green dyes.

chlorophyll (E140) See **colour**.

chocolate The food prepared from the fermented and ground roasted seeds of the cacoa tree, *Theobroma cacoa*, with additional hard **fat** and **sugar**; this is plain eating chocolate. In the highest grades of chocolate the fat is usually all **cocoa butter**, extracted during the manufacture of cocoa. Hardened vegetable fats are used in less expensive products. Milk solids are added to make milk chocolate. The pleasant eating sensation is, in part, due to the melting in the mouth of cocoa butter and other fats used. If chocolate is not stored in a cool place, there is a tendency for the fats to migrate to the surface and cause bloom, a whitish appearance; this is quite harmless.

NUTRITIONAL VALUE: variable with manufacturer but average fat content is 30%, mostly saturated, carbohydrate 50–60%, small quantities of **caffeine** and **theobromine**.

ENERGY per 100g: average: 530 kcal, 2217 kJ.

cholera A serious infectious disease, due to a **micro-organism**, *Cholera vibrio*. It causes intense **diarrhoea**, vomiting, muscle cramps and is often fatal. Now rare where living standards are good, but residents and travellers are at risk in less developed countries and in the tropics. It is spread by water supplies, the sea, food, seafood and flies which are contaminated with human **faeces**. Immunisation is recommended when visiting some Eastern countries but is not, however, absolute protection and the usual precautions should still be taken: only sterilised water should be drunk, all unpeeled fruit, seafood such as **mussels** and **oysters** should be avoided and only hot, cooked food from a reliable source should be eaten. Medical advice should be sought at the onset of any symptoms. See **travel − risks of disease**.

cholesterol A sterol substance, present in the blood and tissues, which is a precursor of the steroid **hormones** and **bile**; it is essential for the normal functioning of cell membranes. An excess of blood cholesterol is related to the amount of saturated fats, from which it is manufactured in the body, consumed in food such as dairy products and meat.

Cholesterol is an important component of deposits in the walls of arteries, causing them to thicken, harden and become rough, a condition known as atheroma. The roughness attracts blood clots which, together with the atheroma, leads to partial or complete blockage resulting in conditions such as coronary heart disease, strokes, gangrene of the legs.

Approximately two thirds of the population in the UK have a blood cholesterol level which is higher than that recommended for health and the UK has one of the highest incidences of heart disease in the world. Thus, the need to reduce the level of circulating cholesterol is one of the most important reasons for changing eating habits. Total fat intake should provide less than 35% of energy, of which no more than one third should be in the form of saturated fats, the rest being unsaturated. See **diet**.

chorizo A highly-spiced **sausage** of Spanish origin, usually cooked by grilling.

Chorley Wood process A process, used commercially, for bread-making in which the manufacture is speeded up. High-energy kneading makes it possible to make a good quality loaf using a proportion of **flour** made from soft wheat, in place of the more expensive, imported, hard strong flour made from hard wheat. The process uses double the usual quantity of **yeast** with a small amount of **ascorbic** acid and up to 20% more water. There is a high conversion to **gluten**, by rearrangement of its molecular structure, to provide the optimum viscoelastic state for retention of the carbon dioxide produced during the rising stage. This results in the shortening of time taken in preparation for baking.

chop A section of meat taken from the loin or thorax containing either a rib and/or vertebra. Usually **pork, lamb** or **veal**. Care must be taken to remove any vestige of spinal cord. See **bovine spongioform encephalopathy**.

chop-sticks Implements used in China and Japan for eating instead of a fork or spoon.

chop-suey A Chinese dish of vegetables with a small proportion of meat, chicken, fish, stir-fried in oil.

chorogi See **Chinese artichoke**.

choucroute See **sauerkraut**.

choux pastry See **pastry**.

chow-chow A **pickle** of mixed **vegetables** flavoured with **mustard** which colours it yellow.

chowder A thick **soup**, often made with a milk base, and traditionally **fish** or **shellfish**, or both. It can also be made with **meat** and **vegetables**. The name is a corruption of the french 'chaudiere', a large, heavy cooking-pot or cauldron.

chow mein A Chinese dish of stir-fried noodles with any mixture of meat, chicken, fish, vegetables. It may be served hot, or cold as a salad.

chromium One of the **trace elements**, which in minute quantities, is essential for **enzymes** which control **glucose** metabolism and blood formation. Adequate quantities are available in a mixed diet; yeast, liver, meat, vegetables and grains all contain chromium.

chufa Also known as tiger nut and earth almond. The expanded tubers of *Cyperus esculentis*, a subtropical grass-like plant of southern Europe and India with nut-flavoured edible roots.
NUTRITIONAL VALUE: protein 5%, fat 25%, carbohydrate 45%.
ENERGY per 100g: 414 kcal, 1732 kJ.
USES: may be eaten as a nut but principally used for making a milk-like drink which is a Spanish speciality.

chutney A **condiment**, originally Indian and made from tropical fruits, vinegar, spices and sugar cooked together. Now made with a variety of home-grown fruits and vegetables.

cider The fermented juice of apples, usually containing 3–6% alcohol; it may be still or effervescent. The apple varieties are selected for their low acidity, high sugar content and the presence of some tanins to give character. Scrumpy is the name given to a strong farmhouse cider favoured by ardent cider drinkers. It contains small quantities of **cyanide**, produced from precursors present in the apple pips, sulphur dioxide and **methanol**. Large manufacturers normally clear cider with carbon dioxide, which reacts with cyanide and escapes. Any remaining cyanide is detoxicated in a healthy **liver**, so that scrumpy is unlikely to harm a modest drinker. Alcoholics, with damaged livers, are unable to detoxify cyanide, and thus, excessive quantities of scrumpy may result in serious degenerative disorders of the nervous system, including blindness, especially in smokers.

cinnamon Peeled bark of the tropical evergreen tree, *Cinnamomum zeylanicum*, of South-East Asia, which has aromatic properties; it is sold rolled up to form sticks or ground as a powder. See **cassia**.
USES: as a flavouring in a wide range of recipes for confectionery, biscuits and savoury dishes.

citric acid (E330) An acid occurring naturally in citrus fruits and also synthetically prepared. Widely used as an acidifying agent in foods and drinks, also to improve setting of jams and fruit jellies which rely on pectin.

citron The fruit of *Citrus medica*, a native of India. The fruit is characterised by the thick, rough skin. It is used mainly to make **candied peel**.

citrus fruits A large family of subtropical and tropical **fruits** characterised by a thick skin and a segmented pulp. The group includes **citron**, **grapefruit**, **lemon**, **lime**, **orange**, **tangerine**, **kumquat**. Many hybrids have been developed, some of which are seedless. The skins contain **essential oils** used for flavouring and the **pith** contains **pectin**. See **diphenyl**.

clam The name given to a range of marine bivalve shellfish which includes the scallop, *Pecten maximus* found in European coastal waters, and others, *Venus mercanaria*, *Maetra solidissima*, *Mya arenaria* and *Tivela stultorum* common in coastal waters of the USA; often quite large with a characteristic edible stalk.

NUTRITIONAL VALUE: average: protein 25%, fat 1%, iron.

ENERGY per 100g: average: 100 kcal, 418 kJ.

USES: can be cooked by a variety of methods; usually served in the shell; also in the form of clam **chowder**, popular in the USA.

claret Red wine from Bordeaux.

clarify To make clear. Butter is clarified by heating to boil off the water. Liquids are clarified by allowing the suspended matter to settle or by filtering. Wines which do not respond to settling, filtration or use of **bentonite** or egg white may require special enzymes, such as **pectinase**, if **pectin** is present, or **amylase**, if starch is present.

clary *Salvia sclarea*. A hardy, decorative annual garden **herb**, with leaves that are bitter and aromatic.

USES: for flavouring omelettes or savouries. Rarely used today.

clingfilm Transparent PVC film containing chemical **plasticisers** to make it soft and give it the property of clinging to itself and to hard surfaces such as glass, china, pottery. It is widely used for wrapping food in order to exclude **micro-organisms** and air and to retard moisture loss. The plasticisers have been found to migrate into food containing **fat** in relation to the concentration of the fat and the temperature at which the food is stored. Up to 60% of the plasticiser may migrate into **cheese** stored at room temperature for 5 days. Clingfilm should not, therefore, be used to wrap any food containing fat, which includes cheese, sandwiches and meat products, but is safe for fruit and vegetables. Some proprietary clingfilms may be used in a **microwave oven**, but manufacturer's instructions should be followed, as new types of film have been developed and are available.

clostridium botulinum and **perfringens**. Two of a group of **anaerobic spore-forming**, rod-like **bacteria**. See **botulism, food poisoning**.

cloves The flower-heads of a tropical tree, *Eugania aromatica* which contain an **essential oil**.

USES: they are used dried as a flavouring in **curries** and other savoury dishes and sauces, fruit dishes especially with apples. The oil has anaesthetic and antiseptic properties and is used, mixed with zinc oxide, as a temporary filling for decayed teeth.

cobalt An essential **trace element**, a constituent of vitamin B12. Adequate quantities are present in food and high doses are toxic.

cobnut A large variety of **hazelnut**, *Corylus avellana*.

NUTRITIONAL VALUE: average: protein 18%, fat 50% mostly unsaturated, carbohydrate 5%, dietary fibre 10%, vitamin B complex.

ENERGY per 100g: average: 540 kcal, 2259 kJ.

USES: eaten whole, chopped and sometimes roasted in desserts, savoury vegetarian dishes.

coca Refers to the leaves of the evergreen tropical shrub, *Erythroxylon coca*, a native of South America, which contain cocaine, the dangerously addictive **alkaloid**; this drug, in concentrated form, is known as **crack**. The leaves are chewed by the natives and are sometimes used in the East, for wrapping **betel nuts** for chewing.

Coca-cola A proprietary carbonated soft drink flavoured with an extract of the **cola nut** and spices, with sweetener and phosphoric acid. It was originally made from a secret recipe but is now much copied. See **cola drinks**.

cocaine See **coca**. One of the most dangerous of the addictive drugs.

cochineal (E120) See **colour**.

cockle *Cardium eduli*. One of several varieties of the family *Cardium*; an edible, heart-shaped, ribbed bivalve shellfish found in sand around shorelines and harvested at low tide. Should be cleansed in clean salt water before being cooked. Subject to water pollution and a potential cause of **food poisoning**.

NUTRITIONAL VALUE: protein 18–20%, fat 2%, vitamin B complex, calcium, iodine.

ENERGY per 100g: 94 kcal, 393 kJ.

USES: as a snack and in seafood dishes.

cocktail A mixture of alcoholic and other liquors taken as an **apéritif** before a meal. Also as a first course, such as prawns in a sauce or a mixture of fruits.

cocoa Prepared from the fermented seeds (cocoa-beans) of the tropical tree, *Theobroma cacoa*, a native of South America and now grown in Africa and elsewhere. The seeds are dried and crushed to remove about 50% of the **oil** known as **cocoa-butter**, leaving the powder which is cocoa; it has a chocolate-like flavour and contains the stimulants **caffeine** and **theobromine**.

NUTRITIONAL VALUE: protein 20%, fat variable 10–20%, iron, potassium.

ENERGY per 100g: 170–260 kcal, 711–1088 kJ.

USES: made into a drink with milk and sugar. Used as a flavouring in ice-cream, sugar-icing, sweetmeats, cakes and desserts.

cocoa-butter Also known as white chocolate. The hard **oil** extracted from the cocoa-bean during the manufacture of **cocoa**.

NUTRITIONAL VALUE: fat 60% saturated, 35% monounsaturated and 5% polyunsaturated.

USES: in the manufacture of **chocolate**, grease paints and cosmetics.

coconut The large nut of the tropical palm, *Cocos nucifera*, extensively cultivated in coastal areas of the tropics. The hard shell is lined by white flesh and, unless old, contains coconut-milk, a sweet refreshing liquid with a distinctive flavour. Coconut-fibre is made from the fibrous outer case of the nut. The sun-dried flesh is known as desiccated coconut or copra. See **coconut oil**.

NUTRITIONAL VALUE: fresh flesh, protein 4%, fat 35%, carbohydrate 10–11%. Dessicated: protein 5.6%, fat 62% (high on saturates), carbohydrate 6.4%. Coconut-milk contains protein 0.2%, carbohydrate 3%.

ENERGY per 100g: flesh, 375 kcal, 1569 kJ. Milk, negligible.

USES: fresh or dried in curries, biscuits, cakes, desserts and sweetmeats. The milk as a drink and for flavouring. See **arrack**, **jagerry**, **toddy**.

coconut oil Extracted from the white flesh of the **coconut**. It is solid at room temperature.

NUTRITIONAL VALUE: fat 80% saturated, 20% monounsaturated.

USES: widely used commercially in ice-cream, chocolate, cooking oils (usually referred to as vegetable oil in lists of ingredients), grease paints, cosmetics.

cocotte A small fireproof dish for an individual serving.

cod *Gadus callarias*. A deep-sea **fish**, found in temperate and cold waters. It has firm white flesh and can weigh up to 5kg. See **fish worms, roe**.

NUTRITIONAL VALUE: protein 16–18 %, fat 0.5–1 %, vitamin B complex.

ENERGY per 100g: average: 75 kcal, 314 kJ.

USES: widely used fried, grilled, baked or poached, in fish pies, fish fingers.

cod-liver oil Oil extracted from the liver of the **cod**. An important source of **vitamins A** and **D**. It was known to be beneficial long before vitamins were discovered.

cod-worm See **fish worms**.

coeliac disease A disease in which the small bowel is unable to absorb the protein, **gluten**, and becomes sensitive to it. The condition usually becomes apparent in early childhood with associated **diarrhoea** and a failure to thrive. **Diet** plays an important part in treatment and any food containing **wheat** and **cereal** products (except **rice** which contains no gluten), such as bread, cakes, biscuits, soups, sauces thickened with wheat flour must be avoided. Special gluten-free foods are available.

coffee A stimulating beverage made from the fermented, roasted and ground beans of the tropical shrubs *Coffea arabica* (Arabica) or *Coffea canephora* (Robusta). Coffee made from the former beans has the better flavour but as the shrub is lower yielding it is more expensive. Many coffees available are blends which sometimes include **chicory**. The aroma is due to an essential oil **caffeol**. Coffee beans contain about 1% **caffeine**. The roasted beans should be stored in an airtight container, or in a refrigerator or freezer, to prevent loss of flavour and aroma. Once ground, they rapidly lose these properties and it is best only to prepare enough for immediate use.

coffee, decaffeinated Coffee made from coffee beans from which the **caffeine** has been extracted by using solvents such as methylene or ethylene chloride, or by carbon dioxide under pressure. Decaffeinated instant coffees are also available. There is some change in flavour.

coffee, instant Coffee in the form of powder or granules which dissolve immediately in water; widely used today. It is made by extracting the water-soluble components of coffee beans and **freeze** or **spray-drying** the resultant liquid. Premium grades are made with a high proportion of arabica beans and are freeze-dried. All grades contain the same amount of **caffeine** as fresh coffee.

cognac A premium **brandy** distilled from wines grown in the district of Cognac.

cointreau A **liqueur** made with **oranges**.

cola drinks Carbonated drinks made from an extract of **cola nuts** and containing about 10mg of **caffeine** per 100ml. They are acidified with phosphoric acid and sweetened. Examples are **Coca-cola**, **Pepsi-cola** which are much copied.

cola nut *Cola acuminata*. A tall tropical evergreen tree grown for its seeds which are similar to horse chestnuts, have a high **caffeine** content and a bitter-sweet flavour. Used in the popular **cola drinks**.

coleslaw A **cabbage salad** made with chopped or sliced white and/or red cabbage, dressed with **mayonnaise** or other creamy salad dressing. There are many variations with additions such as carrot, celery, celeriac, sultanas, nuts.

coley *Pollachius pollachius*. A **fish** very similar to **cod**, with grey flesh which becomes white on cooking. It has less flavour than cod. Also known as coalfish, pollock and saithe. See **fish worms**.
   NUTRITIONAL VALUE: average: protein 18%, fat 1%, vitamin B complex, minerals.
   ENERGY per 100g: average: 81 kcal, 339 kJ.
   USES: suitable for most methods of cooking.

collagen The **protein** which is the main constituent of white fibrous tissue in tendons, ligaments, muscle sheaths and also found in skin, bone and cartilage; collectively known as **connective tissue**. Collagen has great strength, softens to some extent in cooking and is converted to **gelatine** after prolonged boiling. Processed collagen is used for **sausage skins**.

colloid A non-crystalline semi-solid substance such as **starch, gelatine**, which will not pass through a filter. A colloid forms a gel (jelly-like) in water.

colostrum Also known as **beestings**.

colour Many foods contain natural colours such as red fruits, green vegetables. Some are extracted and used as permitted **additives** for colouring other foods such as smoked haddock, kippers, commercially-prepared desserts, sauces and to replace colour lost in processing. Thus the term 'natural colouring' in the description of a food does not necessarily mean natural to that particular food.

Natural colours include:—

Anthocyanins. Extracted from the saps of flowers, fruits, stems and leaves of many plants. Reds (E163a,e,d,f), blue (E163b), purple (E163c).

Anthoxanthins. Yellow colouring found in potatoes.

Betanin or **beetroot red (E162)**. Dye extracted from beetroot.

Caramel (E150). Brown dye prepared by the action of heat or chemicals on carbohydrate.

Carbon black (E153). Black colouring obtained from burned plant material.

Carotenes (E160a). Orange-yellow dye extracted from carrots, tomatoes, rose-hips, oranges.

Chlorophyll (E140). Green colour present in all green plants. The main sources for the additive are nettles, grass and lucerne.

Cochineal or **carmine (E120)**. Red dye extracted from the dried female cochineal insect, *Dactilopius coccus*.

Lyopine (e160D). Red dye extracted from tomatoes.

Saffron. The dried anthers of the saffron crocus which impart a yellow colour to food when added during cooking.

For reasons of economy a number of synthetic dyes are permitted and used commercially, these include:—

Azo dyes. A group of strongly coloured nitrogenous compounds synthesised from benzine formed during the refining of petroleum. Originally benzene could be obtained as a very minor product during coal-tar distillation, and these dyes have sometimes been referred to as coal-tar dyes. All are synthetic and do not occur in nature. Some people are sensitive to these dyes and they can produce allergic reactions, particularly in those who are allergic to aspirin, suffer from eczema or who are asthmatic. Examples of azo dyes widely used are:—

Black PN (E151). Used in products such as blackcurrant cheesecake mix, brown sauce mix.

Carmoisine (E122). Used as a substitute for cochineal.

Tartrazine (E102). Yellow dye used commonly in commercially produced foods particularly confectionery and drinks. Hyperactivity in some children has been associated with this and other azo dyes, thus their use is now restricted.

Brown FK (154). Often used to give the brown colour to kippers and smoked mackerel.

Brown HT (155). Brown colouring sometimes used in chocolate cakes.

compote A dish of **fruit** poached in syrup.

condensed milk See **milk**.

condiment A spice, sauce, chutney or pickle used in small quantities to add to the piquancy of a dish such as pepper, mustard, salt, soy sauce. Some may have a high nutritional value but this is not significant in the small quantities normally used.

conduction The transmission of heat or

electricity. It is effected by a conductor and prevented by an insulator. The best conductors of heat and electricity are metals, but some materials which conduct heat are electrical insulators, these include glass, ceramics and rubber. All domestic **water** conducts electricity and most wood contains enough water to do so; therefore the latter should not be used as an insulator. Conductors may be in one piece, or parts joined together.

Special care is essential for safety with all electrical appliances, to ensure that insulators such as coverings or cables, sockets, switches are not worn or damaged.

confectioner's custard Also known as **crème patissiere**. A custard stiffened with flour or cornflour. Used in **flans, profiteroles, mille feuilles**.

confit An almond or sweetmeat coated in sugar.

confiture A sweetmeat or conserve made with fruit and sugar.

congeners Higher alcohols such as **fusel oil**, produced during fermentation of wines and malt liquors, and concentrated by distillation, in the preparation of spirits such as **brandy, whisky** to which they give character. Although in all but small quantities they are poisonous, taken in excess, such as in cheap spirits, they are responsible for hangovers. Careful control of the temperature of distillation reduces the amount present, and a further reduction takes place during the long period allowed for maturation of the more expensive brands. See **alcohol, vodka**.

conger eel *Conger conger*. A large marine **eel** with a firm, often tough, well-flavoured flesh. It is easier to skin after it is cooked.

NUTRITIONAL VALUE: see **eel**.

USES: the middle cut is used in a variety of fish dishes and the rest for stock for soups.

congo pea See **red gram**.

connective tissue Tissue which holds living matter together. In mammals and birds it includes bones and cartilage, ligaments, tendons, sheets of fascia and skin. These all contain **collagen** but meat has, in addition, another **protein** called **elastin**. Collagen can be softened by prolonged moist heat or by tenderising **enzymes** but elastin is resistant. Boiled for a long time connective tissue produces **gelatine**. Both collagen and elastin are responsible for the toughness of meat. Connective tissue is digested slowly and with difficulty. Fish have little connective tissue, thus their flesh is generally soft and tender. The connective tissue in plants is made up of **cellulose** and other non-digestible **carbohydrates** which become tough with age; lignin, the main substance in wood, may also be present but cannot be utilised in the body. The cellulose in young fruits and vegetables is softened by boiling but it is resistant when they are old. **Dietary fibre** is mainly cellulose.

consommé A clear meat **soup** which usually forms a **jelly** when cold. It can be served hot or cold.

constipation The infrequent passage of hard stools which may be painful, the reverse of **diarrhoea**. See **dietary fibre**.

cook-chill The system of commercial food preparation in which food is precooked, chilled to just above freezing-point and when required, reheated. Cook-chilled food has a safe shelf-life of only 2–3 days. It is of paramount importance that the food should not be allowed to warm up until it is needed, and that the reheating is thorough and penetrates the full thickness of the product, which should then be consumed without delay. Cook-chill is being increasingly used for commercial catering, in hospitals, and is available in supermarkets. The system carries a major risk of serious outbreaks of **food poisoning** if instructions are not rigidly adhered to. See **hygiene**.

cook-freeze Similar to **cook-chill** but the food is frozen to a temperature of −18°C (−0.5°F) for safe keeping and has a shelf-life of up to 3 months. The food must never be allowed to warm up during transfer from factory to the site of reheating for use. The risks of **food poisoning** are the same as for cook-chill.

cooking The treatment of food with heat. The great majority of natural foods need to be cooked to be made attractive and suitable to eat. The mixing and heating of food substances leads to many changes; **starches** present in plant cells in **cellulose** envelopes, are released by heat and converted to a **gel** by absorption of water, so that they can then be converted to **sugars** in the digestive tract and absorbed. Heat and moisture soften cellulose in hard **fruits** and **vegetables** and **collagen** in **meat**, to facilitate chewing, swallowing and digestion.

Foods should be selected at their optimum age to combine natural tenderness, flavour and maximum nutritional value. Cooking reduces, and can even destroy, the **vitamins** in food but a large proportion can be conserved in vegetables and fruit by using a minimum of water and cooking time. Avoiding an excess of water also prevents **minerals** from being entirely leached out. Cooking in the presence of oil conserves **essential oils** which impart flavour and allows them to blend with other ingredients. The heat of cooking destroys **food poisoning** micro-organisms such as **salmonella**, **parasites** and their eggs; also **enzymes** and micro-organisms which may not be dangerous but can lead to deterioration of the food. The temperature and cooking conditions such as dry heat (grilling, baking), moist heat (steam), immersion in water or oil, affect the flavour, colour and texture of the final product in characteristic ways.

The inside of solid food is heated by conduction and time must be allowed for this. Casseroles and foods which are part liquid, allow some heat to be transferred by convection currents set up in the liquid, so that the appearance of the outside of the food is not necessarily a guide to the state within. Most outbreaks of food poisoning are traced to inadequately cooked or reheated food containing dangerous micro-organisms which are still alive. See **frozen food**, **Maillard reaction**, **microwave oven**, **oven**, **thermometer**.

cooking, ethnic See **ethnic cooking, religious laws**.

copita A tulip-shaped sherry glass, used as a standard measure in licensed premises and holding 50ml.

copper Once the favoured material for cooking utensils, attractive to look at, an excellent conductor of heat, capable of being beaten into a variety of shapes and relatively resistant to corrosion by foods. Its high cost has led to replacement by the cheaper **aluminium** which has similar properties. Copper is essential to many plants and animals for its part in **enzyme** systems. There is an adequate intake in a mixed **diet**. Copper is toxic in excess, traditionally copper saucepans were coated with a protective layer of tin. See **trace elements**.

copra The dried and shredded flesh of the **coconut**.

coq au vin A traditional French dish of chicken, cooked in red wine, with bacon, small onions, mushrooms, herbs, and sometimes brandy. Originally a cock bird was used and some of the blood retained in the sauce.

cordon bleu An historic term; a rosette of dark blue ribbon conferred on female cooks of great skill since the days of Louis XV. Used nowadays to mean a cook, or cooking, of high quality.

coriander Also known as Japanese parsley. An annual herb, *Corriandrum sativum*, grown for its delicate green leaves and for its mature seeds. It grows well in warm, temperate climates.

USES: the fresh leaves are used as a garnish, in curries and in Eastern recipes. The seeds are ground and widely used in curries and a variety of spicy dishes. They are sometimes roasted before grinding, to enhance the flavour and are best used freshly ground.

cork The soft resilient bark of the cork-oak, *Quercus suber*, which remains unrivalled for making stoppers for wine bottles; also used as a heat insulator, for table mats and floor covering.

corked See **wine**.

corn In Europe means **wheat**, **oats** and **barley**, whereas in the USA and many other countries, the term means **maize**. Corn and wheat are among the most important food crops worldwide. Both were developed from wild grasses and were among the first food crops to be cultivated.

corned beef Salted **beef** preserved in sealed cans. Also known as bully beef. See **canning**, **blown**.

cornet A light, thin, aerated crisp biscuit formed into a conical shape to hold ice-cream.

cornflour See **flour**.

Cornish pasty A pastry case with a potato, onion and meat filling, baked in a moderately hot oven. Originally made in Cornwall for tin-miners to take to work.

corn oil Oil extracted from **maize** seed. It may have an unpleasant flavour and is not recommended for making salad dressings.

NUTRITIONAL VALUE: fat, saturated 15%, monounsaturated 35%, polyunsaturated 50%.

ENERGY per 100g: 900 kcal, 3766 kJ.

USES: for general cooking purposes, for blending with other vegetable oils, commercially for deep-fat frying.

corn-on-the-cob See **sweetcorn**.

corn salad See **lamb's lettuce**.

cornstarch Same as **cornflour**.

corn sugar The monosaccharide sugar known as **glucose** or dextrose obtained by breaking down the **starch** molecule in **cornflour**. Sold as a dry powder or syrup.

USES: mainly used in commercial production of confectionery.

corn syrup See **glucose syrup**.

cos lettuce A member of the *Lactuca* family of edible salad crops with long thin leaves forming a tight head. It is slightly coarser than round varieties but crisp and with a nutty flavour. See **lettuce**.

cosher or **kosher** Food prepared according to the laws of the Jews. Cosher means clean. See **religious laws**.

costmary See **alecost**.

cottage cheese A simple, mild, pure-white crumbly **cheese** with a neutral taste prepared from skimmed milk. It has a high water content and is low in **lactic acid**.

NUTRITIONAL VALUE: protein 11—16%, fat 2—4%, carbohydrate 2%.

ENERGY per 100g: average, 87 kcal, 364 kJ.

USES: widely eaten in Europe and the USA in salads, cheesecake recipes, pate and often used as a substitute for cream cheese in low-calorie diets.

cottage and **shepherd's pies** Dishes devised to use up meat and sometimes vegetables left over from a previous meal, traditionally the 'Sunday Roast'. The meat for cottage pie, beef, and for shepherd's pie, lamb or mutton, is minced, flavoured with onion, herbs, moistened with gravy, topped with mashed potato and heated in the oven. The pies can also be made with freshly cooked mince. When using pre-cooked meat, great care must be taken to heat it thoroughly to avoid the danger of **food poisoning**.

cottonseed oil Oil extracted from the seeds of several members of the *Gossypium* family in cotton-producing countries, particularly the USA and Egypt.

NUTRITIONAL VALUE: fat, unsaturated 25%, monounsaturated 20%, polyunsaturated 50%.

ENERGY per 100g: 900 kcal, 3766 kJ.

USES: mainly commercially in the manufacture of margarine, hydrogenated cooking fats, salad dressings, canned fish, deep-fat frying. It is a good general cooking oil and used as such in Egypt.

coulis A strained **purée** used as a sauce, such as tomato, raspberry, shrimp.

court-bouillon Liquid flavoured with a variable mixture of herbs, vegetables, seasoning, wine, lemon juice or vinegar; used mainly for poaching **fish** to enhance its flavour.

courgette *Cucurbita pepo*. A free-fruiting member of the **marrow** family grown to be harvested when the fruits are 4″–6″ long. Also known as zucchini.

NUTRITIONAL VALUE: Negligible.

ENERGY per 100g: 12 kcal, 50 kJ.

USES: eaten as a vegetable in a variety of ways, such as sliced and fried, steamed, boiled, baked, also split and stuffed.

couscous Also known as kouskous and couscouso. A form of granulated wheat flour of North African and Arabian origin,

prepared in various sizes of granules from small seeds upwards. It can be regarded as a form of **pasta** and is made from hard or durum wheat and cooked by boiling in water, the bulk of the cooked product being up to 3 times the dry volume.

crab Marine **crustacean**. Edible varieties include the common crab of Europe, *Cancer pagusus*, and *Callinectus sapidus* of North America. Only the white meat in the claws and the brown meat in the body are edible after cooking in boiling water; the feathery gills, known as 'dead man's fingers', are poisonous and must always be discarded. Dressing involves selecting the meat from within the shell and mixing it with the white meat, extracted by crushing the claws. They should only be taken from unpolluted waters.

NUTRITIONAL VALUE: protein 18–20%, fat 5%, vitamin B complex, calcium, iodine.

ENERGY per 100g: average: 121 kcal, 506 kJ.

USES: served cold 'dressed', in the shell, with salads, as a paste, in sauces.

crab apple *Malus pumilla*. A small, sour, bitter apple found in the wild. There are now a number of varieties in cultivation, grown for their decorative value and as pollinators for other apple-trees.

NUTRITIONAL VALUE: negligible.

ENERGY per 100g: negligible.

USES: mainly for crab-apple jelly.

crack See **coca**.

cracked wheat See **bulgar wheat**.

crackling The skin left on **pork** joints which becomes dry and crisp on **roasting**. Sometimes removed from the joint and cooked separately.

cran A measure used for herrings; about 40 gallons.

cranberry *Oxycoccus palustris* and *macrocarpus*. The red acidic berry of a small evergreen shrub which grows in marshland and peaty bogs. The American cultivated variety is larger and grown commercially.

NUTRITIONAL VALUE: vitamin C 10–12mg per 100g.

USES: traditionally eaten as a sauce with turkey at Christmas, but is also used in desserts.

crawfish See **langouste**.

crayfish *Astacus pallipes* and *Pallipes astacus*, small freshwater **crustaceans** found in rivers and lakes in Europe and North America. They look like very small lobsters but have less flavour. As with lobsters they are cooked live.

NUTRITIONAL VALUE: protein 20%, fat 3%, vitamin B complex and minerals.

ENERGY per 100g: 107 kcal, 448 kJ.

USES: best cooked in a **court bouillon** and eaten with salad.

cream The **fat** which rises to the surface of **milk**. It is obtained naturally or by the use of a separator or **centrifuge**. The residual liquid is skimmed milk. The bulk and stiffness of some cream can be increased by the process of whipping. The terms double, whipping and single are used according to the fat content. Single and clotted cream will not whip. Devonshire and Cornish creams are local specialities, partly clotted by heat and are normally thick. Modified, lower-fat cream substitutes are available as are those containing less saturated fat. See **crème chantilly, crème fraiche, soured cream**.

Cream as an adjective is used to describe a rich sweet **sherry** and a number of food products which may or may not contain cream such as **ice-cream**; also the process of amalgamating butter or margarine and sugar in cake-making known as 'to cream'.

NUTRITIONAL VALUE and ENERGY: average: protein 2%, carbohydrate 2.5%, fat: single: 18%. **Energy** per 100g:
195 kcal, 816 kJ.

whipping: 35%. **Energy** per 100g:
367 kcal, 1536 kJ.
double: 48%. **Energy** per 100g:
447 kcal, 1870 kJ.
clotted: 55%. **Energy** per 100g:
469 kcal, 1962 kJ.

USES: for pouring over desserts, whipped and piped as decoration on desserts, in ice-cream, in a variety of sweet and savoury dishes, in soups, sauces, in coffee and other drinks.

cream cheese Soft, moist **cheese**, made with full-cream milk and curdled by an acid, with added cream; usually sold in tubs or cartons. It does not keep well and should be refrigerated.

NUTRITIONAL VALUE: average: protein 9%, fat 35%, carbohydrate 3%.

ENERGY per 100g: average: 362 kcal, 1515 kJ.

USES: as a table cheese, sometimes mixed with garlic and herbs, in cheesecake and other prepared dishes.

creamer A powdered preparation of vegetable fats and glucose.

NUTRITIONAL VALUE: protein 2.5%, fat 32%, carbohydrate 57%.

ENERGY per tsp: 20 kcal, 84 kJ.

USES: as a milk or cream substitute with coffee and tea.

cream of tartar (E336) Potassium acid tartrate, also known as potassium hydrogen tartrate. The source of acid in many **baking powders**. It can also be used where a mild acid is required.

crème au beurre (butter icing) A soft, rich icing for cakes made with eggs, butter and sugar.

crème chantilly Whipped cream, slightly sweetened and flavoured with vanilla.

crème de menthe A peppermint-flavoured, green-coloured **liqueur**.

crème fraîche Originally any cream that was left to ferment and turn slightly sour naturally, at room temperature. Nowadays it tends to be commercially produced and is similar to **soured cream** but may have a higher fat-content.

crème patissière See **confectioner's custard**.

creole Describes dishes of Spanish-Mexican origin made with chicken or meat and rice, flavoured with hot peppers, tomatoes, spices.

crêpe A **pancake**.

crêpe suzette A thin **pancake** made from **batter**, flavoured with orange liqueur or **brandy**. After cooking it is spread with orange-flavoured **butter-cream**, rolled up, and at the moment of serving, a mixture of liqueur and brandy is heated, set alight and poured over the crêpe.

cress *Lepidium sativum*. A pungent plant cut shortly after germination, in the cotyledon stage. See **watercress**.
  NUTRITIONAL VALUE: protein 1–2%, small quantity of vitamin C.
  ENERGY per 100g: negligible.
  USES: in salads and as a garnish, often together with mustard, cut at the same stage in growth.

crocus See **colour − saffron**.

croissant A crescent shaped roll, of French origin, made with fat, flour and yeast.

crop The dilated upper, muscular end of the oesophagus of birds, where food undergoes the first stages of digestion, usually mixed with grit. It is not eaten.

croquette A savoury, which can be of minced meat, fish, potatoes, formed into a sausage-shape, rolled in egg and bread-crumbs and usually fried. See **panada**.

crosnes See **Chinese artichoke**.

croustades Shapes of fried **bread**, or **pastry** on which various mixtures are served.

croûte A thick piece of **bread** fried or toasted; used as a garnish or the basis of a savoury snack. See **en croûte**.

croûtons Very small cubes of **bread** fried or baked in the oven and used to garnish soups and salads. Sometimes flavoured with herbs or garlic.

crudités Raw vegetables cut up or grated and served with a savoury sauce as a starter or with **dips** as a snack.

crumpet A thick round pancake made with a batter of soft flour, water, yeast and salt cooked on a griddle. It has a characteristic honeycomb texture and is eaten toasted with butter.

crust The brown crisp outer layer formed on food cooked in the oven or under a grill. It has a distinctive flavour due to the formation of **melanoidin**. A feature of bread, pastry, biscuits and dishes finished with a layer of cheese, potato or breadcrumbs.

crustacean A large class of widely-distributed sea and freshwater arthropods with a hard shell, includes **crabs, crayfish, langouste, lobsters, prawns** and **shrimps**. See **fish**.

cryptosporidia A genus of parasites, at least one member of which infects the intestinal tract of cattle and causes scouring (diarrhoea) in calves. The parasite has become important, comparatively recently, due to intensive farming practices and seepage of effluents into water sources. It occasionally affects humans when it has passed through filter beds, being relatively resistant to chlorination, causing epidemics of **diarrhoea**. It can also infect salad crops by faecal contamination and has been found in meat and meat products such as sausages. Tap-water in countries with a high living standard is normally safe to drink, and where contamination of water supplies has occurred, the public have usually been warned to boil drinking water. There is no significant risk if all salad crops are thoroughly washed and meat and meat products fully cooked.

cucumber *Cucumis sativus*. A creeping annual plant which produces long green fruits with a characteristic flavour.

NUTRITIONAL VALUE: negligible.

ENERGY per 100g: negligible.

USES: eaten raw in salads, pickles, soups. A small variety, called gherkin, is usually pickled when young.

culinary (culinaire) Of the kitchen.

cumin or **cummin** A **spice** which is the seed of *Cuminium cyminium*, a herbaceous plant native to the Mediterranean region but originally from the Far East; related to **caraway** with which it is sometimes confused although the flavour and aroma of the seeds are quite dissimilar. Cumin is a widely used spice and particularly important in Indian and Middle Eastern cookery.

USES: in curries and many other spiced savoury dishes.

curaçao A liqueur flavoured with an extract from the peel of bitter oranges.

curcumin (E100) The deep yellow dye in **turmeric**, also known as Indian saffron.

USES: to colour processed cheese, curries, margarine. In commercially prepared dishes, such as savoury rice, it is used as a substitute for the more expensive **saffron**.

curd The solid which forms in **milk** when it goes sour. It is made of **casein** and **fat** and is the first stage in the making of **cheese**, when the milk is soured in a controlled way.

NUTRITIONAL VALUE: related to the grade of milk used and the amount of residual **whey**. Protein up to 15%, fat 2–20%.

USES: for the making of cheeses.

curd cheese Similar to **cottage cheese** but with a more creamy texture and a higher **fat** content, but not as high as that of **cream cheese**.

NUTRITIONAL VALUE: average: protein 15%, fat 12%, carbohydrate 2%.

ENERGY per 100g: average: 167 kcal, 699 kJ.

USES: as a table cheese, a spread mixed with garlic and herbs, in cheesecake, sweetened as a filling for cakes.

curdle To go solid or form insoluble granules. Milk becomes unstable before it starts to curdle and the process may be triggered by heat. See **curd**, **rennet**.

curing The chemical preservation of food, including **smoking**, introduced many centuries ago as a method of preservation of meat for winter use or on long sea voyages. The process is based on the incorporation of substances to inhibit the growth of **micro-organisms** which cause spoilage: salt, vinegar, nitrates, alcohol, sugar and exposure to smoke all have this property.

Traditionally, a mixture of salt and a nitrate or nitrite is rubbed into the meat over a period of weeks, during which time some drying takes place. This method is still used, but alternatively, the meat may be immersed in a solution of the chemicals and/or smoked. Today the process is usually speeded up by the injection of the chemicals into the substance of the meat.

Nitrites are harmful, except in small quantities, and are not permitted as food **additives** but because of the long history of their use in preservation and the benefits derived by the elimination of even the most virulent **food poisoning organisms**, it is accepted, on balance, that their continued use is justified. See **nitre**.

NUTRITIONAL CHANGES: slight.

USES: for all meats but particularly pig-meat and fish.

currant A variety of *Vitis vinifera*. A small sun-dried black grape. The high sugar content ensures good keeping properties in dry conditions.

NUTRITIONAL VALUE: protein 1.8%, carbohydrate 64.7%.

ENERGY per 100g: 250 kcal, 1046 kJ.

USES: in cakes, biscuits, puddings and sweetmeats.

currants See **blackcurrant, redcurrant, whitecurrant.**

curry The name given to meat, fish and vegetable dishes, of Indian origin, often containing turmeric and a wide range of other **spices** in different combinations. Some are hot to taste but this is not an essential feature and there are many regional variations. Curries are often served with rice and accompanied by side dishes such as banana, coconut, cucumber, chutney, pickle.

custard A sauce made with milk, eggs and sugar, usually flavoured with vanilla. See **custard powder**.

USES: as a pouring sauce, or when baked, as a dessert such as crème caramel, in tarts.

custard apple Also known as bullock's heart. The fruit of an Indian tree, *Annona reticulata*, with a juicy, sweet, aromatic and soft pulp. It can weigh up to 2kg. Closely related are sour and sweet sop, *Annona muriatica* and *Squamosa*, and also **papaw** which is grown in North America.

NUTRITIONAL VALUE: protein 1%, carbohydrate 20%, vitamin B complex, vitamin C.

ENERGY per 100g: 90 kcal, 377 kJ.

USES: as a fruit and to make a refreshing drink.

custard powder An inexpensive substitute for egg in custard, invented in the mid 19th century and first named Bird's Custard after the inventor. The original recipe is a trade secret but it is based on cornflour, colouring and vanilla flavouring. When heated to boiling point with milk and sugar it thickens to a creamy consistency. It tends to form a gel when cold.

USES: as a sauce with fruit and other desserts such as trifles.

cuttlefish *Sepia officianalis*. A relative of the **octopus** and **squid**. The flesh is firm and needs to be well cooked.

NUTRITIONAL VALUE: protein 18%, fat 1–2%, calcium, iodine.

ENERGY per 100g: 85 kcal, 356 kJ.

USES: best sliced into rings and cooked by frying.

cutlet A rib with meat on it, usually lamb, pork or veal, a vertical slice of whole fish including the bone, meat and/or savoury food, minced and formed into a shape resembling a meat cutlet.

cuvée A vat of carefully blended wines selected to provide a consistent high quality.

cyanide A highly poisonous salt of hydrocyanic acid, with a smell of bitter almonds, which can kill in a few minutes. Very small quantities are present in pips, kernels and fermented products but these can be detoxicated by a healthy liver. Cyanide accounts for the most serious effects of excessive consumption of scrumpy. See **cider**.

cyclamate Sodium cyclamate, a heat-stable artificial sweetener some 30 times as sweet as sugar. See **artificial sweeteners**.

cystic fibrosis A congenital disease associated with development of cystic spaces in lungs, kidneys and other organs. When the pancreas is affected there is impairment of pancreatic function with reduction in ability to digest food so that a special diet is required.

D

dab *Limanda limanda*. A **flatfish**, native of estuaries and coastal waters with a soft flesh and delicate flavour similar to flounder.

NUTRITIONAL VALUE: protein 17%, fat less than 1%, calcium, iron.

ENERGY per 100g: 77 kcal, 322 kJ.

USES: filleted or on the bone, best fried or grilled, but can be cooked by most methods.

dace *Leuciscus vulgaris*. A small freshwater fish related to carp but not of good eating quality.

dairy A place set aside for storing or processing **milk** and where **butter**, **cheese** and **cream** are prepared and/or sold. Used as an adjective to describe anything made or sold in a dairy or made with products of a dairy such as dairy ice-cream, yoghurt, buttermilk.

dal or **dhall** The Indian name for split pea which is a staple diet in India and a valuable source of **protein**. The term also refers to a dish, often a puree, made with split peas, **lentils**, **mung beans** or other **pulses**, flavoured with **spices**.

NUTRITIONAL VALUE: variable, depending on ingredients.

USES: as a dish on its own, as an accompaniment to curry dishes.

damson A variety of *Prunus instititia*, the fruit of which is a small dark-red plum which has a strong flavour and ripens in mid to late autumn; it is known as bullace when it grows in the wild.

NUTRITIONAL VALUE: negligible.

ENERGY per 100g: cooked: 32 kcal, 134 kJ.

USES: it is strongly flavoured and used cooked as a dessert, in jams and preserves.

dandelion *Tarazacum officinale*. A small wild plant of grassland with bitter leaves, bright yellow flowers and hollow stems. When forced by growing in darkness, the leaves lose their bitterness. The French name 'pissenlit' derives from its mild diuretic properties. Large-leafed varieties are available for cultivation.

NUTRITIONAL VALUE: vitamin B complex, vitamin C 25mg per 100g, minerals.

USES: blanched in salads; the root can be dried and ground as a coffee substitute.

Danish blue A full-fat, semi-hard, blue cheese of Danish origin. It was first made in the early 1900s as a cheaper alternative to the prestigious and expensive Roquefort. It is made with pasteurised cow's milk and spores of *Penicillium roquefortii* are added at the **curd** stage of manufacture. This produces an even blueing through the cheese during the maturation process. It has a strong, sharp flavour.

NUTRITIONAL VALUE: protein 20%, fat 29–30%, carbohydrate 1%.

ENERGY per 100g: 350 kcal, 1464 kJ.

USES: as a table cheese, in cooking.

dariole A small cylindrical mould for setting sweet or savoury mixtures which may be steamed or baked.

dasheen *Colocasia antiquorum*, also known as **yam**.

date *Phoenix dactylifera*. The sweet stone-fruit of the date-palm, grown in North Africa and similar climates in the Middle East where it has been a valuable food since earliest times. They are sometimes available fresh but more often dried (but very sticky) when they keep well in cool conditions.

NUTRITIONAL VALUE: average: fresh: protein 2%, carbohydrate 54%, vitamin B complex, calcium. Dried: protein 2%, carbohydrate 70%, vitamin B complex.

ENERGY per 100g: average: fresh: 100 kcal, 418 kJ. Dried: 250 kcal, 1046 kJ.

USES: fresh: as a dessert fruit; dried: as a snack, in cakes, puddings, sweetmeats.

daube Marinated **meat**, **poultry** or **game**, which is then stewed very slowly in water, **stock** or the **marinade**.

dauphine potatoes Boiled and sieved potatoes mixed with choux paste and deep fried in spoonfuls. See **pastry**.

dauphinois potatoes Thinly sliced potatoes layered in a shallow dish, covered with cream and baked in the oven.

deadly-nightshade *Atropa belladonna*. A hardy herb with small green and purple flowers and intensely poisonous black berries containing the drug atropine (used medicinally). It is found in the wild and in gardens. Children should be warned of its danger. Rather similar to **henbane**.

dead man's fingers The external gills of a **crab** which are poisonous and must never be eaten.

decalcify To remove **calcium**. Bone and egg-shells may be decalcified and made quite soft by immersion in a mild acid such as **vinegar**. Pickled herrings and eggs can be treated in this way.

decanter A glass flask for wine or spirits. **Lead** glass is used because of its brilliance for most cut glass and decanters, but lead can leach out of the glass if wines or spirits are left in a decanter.

decoct The process of extracting flavours by boiling.

deep freeze A cabinet for food storage which should be capable of keeping the contents at a temperature of −18°C (−0.5°F) for the purpose of suspending life of all **micro-organisms** and retarding the action of **enzymes** which lead to deterioration of food quality. Low temperatures will destroy food **parasites** but not micro-organisms, which will start to grow again as soon as the temperature is raised. Many modern domestic deep freezers use the outer wall of the cabinet for the heat exchanger and instructions for positioning must be adhered to. Chest freezers tend to be more economical in use than upright ones. See **blanching**.

deer Any member of the ungulate family *cervidae*, characterised by the presence of antlers in the males; the meat is known as **venison**. Herds of deer roam wild in uplands and moors throughout the UK, but they are now being farmed and venison is becoming more widely available at relatively low cost.

SEASON: for wild deer in the UK this varies according to the type and sex of the animal. There is no close season for farmed animals.

dégorger To remove strong taste by soaking in water; also to remove excess moisture prior to cooking from such items as aubergine, cucumber and courgette, by slicing and sprinkling with salt, leaving for about an hour under light pressure, rinsing in water and drying with absorbent paper.

dehydrate To remove water from foodstuffs such as peas, beans, lentils, apricots, grapes, coffee, milk for the purpose of **preservation** and ease of storage. Fruits are usually dried in the sun, whilst liquids are **roller**, **spray** or **freeze-dried**; the latter method preserves the most flavour. Protein, carbohydrate, fat and mineral content is not altered.

dehydration A state of fluid depletion in the

body which can be a serious consequence of persistent vomiting and **diarrhoea** if not treated. Medical attention should be sought urgently.

delicatessen A shop specialising in the sale of foods such as cooked meats, pâtés, pies, cheeses, prepared salads, speciality dishes.

demerara See **sugar**.

demersel Marine **fish** which feed at or near the seabed.

demi-glace A sauce made with bone stock flavoured with vegetables and reduced until it is a russet-brown colour. Used as a basis for other brown sauces such as **chasseur**, **bigarade**.

demijohn A bulbous wine flask usually covered in wickerwork.

demulsify To reverse an emulsion and return it to the original state.

dental enamel The ⸍outer ˳ hard-wearing surface of the exposed parts of the teeth protecting the main, but softer and sensitive, central structure made of **dentine**. Breaches of enamel open up the dentine to decay called **caries**. Enamel is strengthened by the presence of **fluorine** in water, and this is now generally added to water-supplies low in natural fluorides, and to toothpastes, resulting in a considerable reduction of dental decay. Dental enamel has only a limited power of regeneration to compensate for normal wear.

deodorise To remove smell.

depectinisation The removal of **pectin** from fruit by enzymes to make a clear free-flowing juice. See **pectinase**.

Derbyshire neck See **goitre**.

desiccate To dry out as a method of preservation.

desiccated coconut See **coconut**; a form of **copra**.

dessert The name given to the sweet course of a meal; also used to describe fresh fruits to be eaten raw, such as dessert apples, pears and grapes.

detergents Cleansing substances: **soaps**, solvents or chemicals, prepared as liquids or solids, which have the property of releasing oil and dirt from fabrics or surfaces. Many develop a foam, but this is not an essential function and non-foaming detergents are used in washing machines. They are not strictly classed as poisons, but utensils that are washed by hand and used for cooking or serving food, should be rinsed in clean water, as residual detergent may contaminate food.

Repeated use can remove the protective greases from the skin and cause dryness; some people become sensitive to detergents and develop dermatitis. Synthetic detergents are anionic and belong to the group of alkyl benzene sulphonates. Some, used for washing clothes, contain **proteolytic enzymes** extracted from cultures of **bacteria** to aid the removal of **organic** stains and dirt from fabrics. All detergents should be used sparingly and they are harmful to the environment if they leak, in any quantity, into rivers and water sources.

devilled A dish treated with a well-seasoned, spicy sauce, usually by **marinating**.

dewberry A close relative of the **blackberry**, having only a few individual fruit cells.

dewpoint The temperature to which air falls when it becomes saturated and moisture is deposited as dew. This can lead to food spoilage, as moistness encourages the growth of **moulds** and **bacteria**. Such growth is avoided by keeping stored food in as constant a temperature as possible and providing ventilation for fruit and vegetables.

dextrin A product of the partial breakdown

of **starch** by heat, acid, alkali or enzymes. It occurs during the cooking of bread or making of toast; it also occurs naturally in **rice**. It has the same nutritional value as starch. Used commercially as an adhesive or gum.

dextrose Another name for **glucose**.

diabetes A metabolic disorder characterised by a rise in the blood-glucose level, leading to **glucose** being excreted by the kidneys and appearing in the urine, a state known as glycosuria. The disease is associated with a number of long-term complications, such as disorders of the nervous system with loss of sensation in the feet, increased fat deposits in the lining of arteries leading to heart attacks, strokes and disorders of the retina of the eyes, which can affect vision.

Type 1 diabetes mainly affects children and is due to loss of production of **insulin** by the pancreas. It is treated by injections of insulin, combined with a controlled **carbohydrate** diet.

Type 2 affects an older age group and is due to insulin deficiency, although to a lesser extent than Type 1. It is treated by a controlled, reduced carbohydrate diet, often with calorie restrictions, as subjects with this kind of diabetes are commonly overweight. Sometimes drugs are used as well, which may either stimulate the production of insulin or increase the tissue sensitivity to it.

Thus diabetics need to know the carbohydrate values of food and drink. Stabilisation on treatment is aided by the diabetic using special impregnated strips of paper, which change colour, to allow the measurement of the level of blood or urine glucose. Management must be under medical supervision. There is no evidence that a high intake of refined sugars, which are rapidly absorbed, increases the risk of developing diabetes. See **sorbitol**, appendix for tables of food values.

diacetyl A chemical substance produced from acetoin by the action of *Streptococcus lactis* and other *lactobacilli* on lactose in milk, and responsible for the characteristic flavour of **butter**.

diallyl thiosulphinate The **essential oil** responsible for the smell of **garlic**.

dialysis The process of separating large and small molecules in fluids, using the principle that small molecules pass more easily through a semipermeable membrane. Semipermeable membranes occur widely in plant and animal kingdoms and are essential in biological processes of growth and nourishment. Such membranes may be made artificially and used for separation or purification purposes.

diarrhoea Frequent bowel action with abnormally soft or liquid stools, commonly caused by the ingestion of food contaminated with harmful micro-organisms such as **salmonella**, other **bacteria**, and certain viruses. It may also be due to foods, an excess of **dietary fibre**, some diseases of the bowel, some antibiotics and the misuse of laxatives. With severe diarrhoea there is a risk of water and salt loss, which is likely to be most serious in babies and the elderly, and medical advice may be necessary. If medical help is not immediately available, treat by replacing water and salt loss by drinks containing 1 teaspoonful of salt and 4 teaspoonfuls of sugar in 500ml of water or by salt and water in which rice has been boiled and contains carbohydrate. See **campylobacter, cholera, dysentery, food poisoning, typhoid**.

diastase A mixture of two forms of **amylase**. A naturally occurring **enzyme** found in **cereals**, capable of breaking down **starches** into **maltose**. It has an essential function in fermentation, for the action of **yeast**. Diastase is more active when the temperature is raised, as with **barley** for malt production.

diet A plan for eating. Food should provide a balanced intake of essential substances required for health, and include **vitamins**, **minerals**, **carbohydrates**, **proteins** and **fat** in quantities sufficient for energy output, to provide body heat, for growth where appropriate and to repair or replace tissues which wear out or have been damaged by disease or injury.

Vitamins and minerals are essential for the functioning of body systems, the action of nerves and muscles, for the digestive system and for the defence system to protect against disease.

In principle, the diet should be based on an average intake of carbohydrates providing 60–65% of energy requirements, total fats not in excess of 35% energy, with a third saturated, the rest monounsaturated and polyunsaturated; protein providing the remainder. **Salt** intake should not exceed 3g a day; a higher intake is associated with a risk of raised **blood pressure**. In practice intakes of both fat and salt in the UK are higher than is desirable. More than adequate quantities of vitamins and minerals are contained in a mixed diet, and one which includes vegetables, fruit and some whole grain products, also contains the necessary amount of **dietary fibre** to maintain a normal bowel function.

Food will differ from day to day and variations spread over a period of a week or so will balance out, the total quantity depending on age, sex and habits. There should be no dependence on a single food item. **Vegetarians** can obtain adequate quantities of protein provided they include **pulses**, whole grain and **dairy** products. Modern marketing provides products in a clean state, requiring the minimum preparation for cooking, and frozen products are ready prepared.

The Department of Health publishes a table of recommended dietary needs. Chronic excess energy intake leads to fat being stored causing **obesity**. Special diets are required for particular disorders such as **diabetes**, disorders of food absorption and inability of the body to use certain food substances. For these medical advice is essential.

Babies behave in a different manner from adults and are intolerant of salt; changes to adult foods must be introduced gradually, to avoid adverse reactions, until tolerance is established. Excess of any single food or supplement can lead to serious problems.

The public should be wary of manufacturers' claims for the benefits of food supplements such as vitamins, amino acids and minerals. There is no medical evidence to justify taking such food supplements under normal circumstances. The exceptions are some of the elderly, those who have a restricted diet because of disability, ignorance or poverty, children, pregnant and lactating women and some strict vegetarians. Where supplements are needed they should only be taken on medical advice. See **cholesterol**.

dietary fibre Plant-cell material. It consists of **cellulose** and other **polysaccharides**, including **pectin**, and gums together known as non-starch polysaccharides (NSPs). They provide the structural elements of plant foods and are present in **cereals**, **fruits**, **vegetables** and **nuts**. Dietary fibre is not broken down by the human digestive system until it reaches the large intestine, where it is metabolised by **bacteria** and converted into short-chain fatty acids and other substances which are absorbed into the bloodstream, and various gases (hydrogen, carbon dioxide and methane) which are expelled as **flatus**.

The major benefits of dietary fibre in the large bowel are to prevent constipation and help reduce the risk of diverticulitis and bowel cancer. It may also help in reducing the risk of coronary heart disease and in the management of diabetes. Current recommendations are that the adult diet should contain an average for the population of 18g dietary fibre per day (within the range 12–24g).

digestion The term covers the chemical breakdown of foods by digestive **enzymes** in the stomach and small intestine into their basic components, to the stage when they can be absorbed into the bloodstream and utilised in the body, but not the fermentation of **dietary fibre** in the large bowel. The process starts with chewing, which breaks foods into smaller particles; these are then mixed with mucin in **saliva** to aid swallowing. **Starches** are converted into **sugars**, **fats** into an **emulsion** and **fatty acids**, and **proteins** into **amino acids** in sequence through the stomach and small and large intestine. There is a chain of exposure to the enzymes of digestion made possible by control of the pH to provide the environment in which they best operate.

Disorders of digestion can occur at any stage and may be due to indigestible foods such as unripe fruits, old vegetables, inadequate cooking or faults in the enzyme systems from disease.

digitalis A powerful **alkaloid** present in the leaves of *Digitalis purpurea*, commonly known as the foxglove. Used in the treatment of heart conditions in very small doses. All parts of the foxglove should be regarded as intensely poisonous and never be eaten.

Dijon mustard A speciality French **mustard**.

dill *Peucedanum graveolens*. A hardy annual **herb**.
   USES: the leaves and seeds for flavouring soups, cucumbers, mayonnaise, sauces, fish, potatoes and other vegetables. The leaves are feathery and used for garnishing.

diphenyl (biphenyl (E230). A commonly-used **fungicide** for preventing **mould** growth on **citrus fruits**. Used as a spray on fruits during growth or as a dip after picking. All purchased fruit should be considered to have been so treated and preferably peeled before eating. Washing will not remove all the diphenyl but it is not harmful in small quantities.

dips Piquant mixtures of cream-like consistency made with various herbs, spices and cream or cream cheese into which individual pieces of fresh vegetables or savoury biscuits are dipped and eaten as a snack.

disaccharide A **sugar**, composed of two monosaccharides. Sucrose is made of **glucose** and **fructose**, **lactose** of one molecule of glucose and one of **galactose** and **maltase** of two molecules of glucose.

disaccharide intolerance An inability to digest disaccharides. The condition can be inherited or due to degenerative changes in the intestine. Treatment, under medical advice, includes the provision of a disaccharide-free diet. See **galactosaemia**.

disinfectants Also known as germicides, they are unrelated groups of chemicals which all have the property of preventing **bacteria** from multiplying. Stronger disinfectants will destroy bacteria and viruses, though spore-bearing bacteria are relatively resistant. Many disinfectants will damage or destroy all living tissue so must be used with great care, avoiding all contact with skin and mucous membranes. Weaker disinfectants that can be applied to skin are sometimes called antiseptics. Disinfectants and antiseptics must never be taken internally and always used in strict accordance with instructions and never in excess.
   EXAMPLES:—
   STRONG. Phenol (carbolic acid), formalin, cresol, 'Lysol' , 'Jeyes fluid', chlorine-forming agents, such as 'Chloros', 'Milton', domestic bleach.

NOTE. These agents must not be mixed with acids such as 'Harpic'; to do so produces dangerous quantities of chlorine gas. Formalin, as a solution in water, produces ethylene dioxide.

MEDIUM. 'Dettol', chlorine-forming agents for **water sterilisation**, such as chloramine.

ANTISEPTICS, 'Betadine', chlorhexidine, hexachlorophane, 'Savlon', alcohol and alcoholic iodine solution, potassium permanganate, hydrogen peroxide, which may be applied directly to the skin but not mucous membranes.

disk-mill A device for grinding between two rotating discs with serrated surfaces. Used for small coffee-grinders, pepper and salt-mills.

disodium citrate (E331b) Food additive used as an **antioxidant**, buffering and emulsifying agent; mainly in processed cheese. See **buffer, emulsifiers**.

disodium hydrogen orthophosphate (E339b) Food additive used as a **buffer**, gelling agent and stabiliser in cooked meats, sausages, butter and margarine. See **emulsifiers**.

distil The process of extraction by evaporation and condensation by using a still. Used for the purification of water, any volatile liquid, desalination of sea-water and for selective extraction from a mixture of substances with differing boiling points, such as alcohol in the preparation of **spirits**. High degrees of purity are obtained by careful control of the temperature of the still and by second distillation.

diuretic A substance which causes a diuresis, which is an increase in volume of urine. Individual sensitivity to these substances varies, thus coffee, tea and beer may have a diuretic effect. The increased urine volume is inconvenient but not necessarily harmful unless excessive. Diuretic drugs are widely used medicinally to lower **blood pressure**

and eliminate body fluids which accumulate in excess due to cardiac failure and other conditions. See **caffeine**.

DNA Deoxyribonucleic acid. The genetic material present in the cell nucleus of almost all living matter. The complex molecule contains the information which determines the cell characteristics and those of the whole organism. See **genetic engineering**.

dogfish See **rock-salmon**.

Dolcelatte A mild, blue-veined, full-fat soft **cheese** from Italy.

NUTRITIONAL VALUE: average: protein 17.3%, fat 35%.

ENERGY per 100g: average: 380 kcal, 1590 kJ.

USES: as a table cheese.

dolmas See **vine leaves**.

double saucepan One saucepan which is made to fit inside another with a space for water between the two. Used for controlled cooking where it is important that the temperature of the food being cooked in the inner saucepan does not rise above the simmering point of water.

dough A mixture of water or **milk** and **flour**, the basis of **bread, buns** and **scones, pastry**.

doughcakes The term includes a range of cakes based on yeasted bread dough enriched with a variety of other ingredients such as eggs, dried fruit, fat, spices, sugar. **Baking powder** may be used instead of **yeast**.

doughnut A bun of sweetened dough, traditionally containing jam in the centre, cooked by deep-fat frying and then rolled in caster sugar.

Dover sole *Solea solea*. A **flatfish**; the best are caught off the coast of Dover. It is acknowledged by the French that they are better than the ones caught off Calais. It is very thin-skinned, and superior in texture and flavour to the more common and cheaper **lemon sole**.

NUTRITIONAL VALUE: protein 18%, fat 1–2%, calcium, iodine. See **fish**.

ENERGY per 100g: 85 kcal, 356 kJ.

USES: usually grilled or fried on the bone which is then sometimes removed before serving.

dragée Sugar-coated confectionery in the form of hard, smooth, ovoid shapes made by multiple coating around a core such as dried fruit, nut.

dram A liquid measure of 1/8th of an ounce which is equal to 3ml. The term is used in the UK for a measure of **whisky** of about 25ml.

drambuie A Scottish **liqueur** made with **whisky** and **honey** and flavoured with **herbs**, using a long held secret recipe, which dates back to the time of Bonnie Prince Charlie.

drawing The preparation of birds for cooking. The removal of all viscera, gizzard, crop, intestines, lungs, liver and reproductive organs. Drawing contaminates the bird's cavity with **bacteria** released from the bowel and drawn birds should be frozen, or refrigerated at 5°C (41°F) or below, and cooked within 3 days. See **food poisoning**, **hygiene**, **salmonella**.

drawn butter Melted butter, or butter whipped with water or vinegar until it is thick. In America it means clarified butter. See **clarify**.

dredge To sprinkle with flour or fine sugar using a dredger, which is a container with a perforated top; the size of the holes is related to the material used.

dress To clean, trim, remove the contents of the thorax and abdomen, and **truss** birds, in preparation for cooking. Dressed **crab** is a specialist procedure. Also, to cover

with **sauce**; such as white sauce with vegetables or **mayonnaise** or **vinaigrette** with salads, cold meat or fish. See **drawing**.

dried fruit Fruits such as apricots, currants, raisins, sultanas, which have been dried either by exposing them to sun or by more controlled conditions in special, ventilated, cool ovens. See **sulphur dioxide**, **sulphited**.

dried meat The earliest way of preserving **meat**. The meat is cut into strips and dried in the sun or over a fire. Some is salted first, different localities having their own special methods of preparation. See **drying**.

dripping The **fat**, mainly saturated, which separates from **beef**, **lamb** or **pork**, together with some of the meat juices, when cooked in the oven.

drumstick The lower part of the leg (tibia) of a fowl or turkey.

drupe Any sort of stone-fruit.

dry The term used to describe wines which have a low sugar content, dry **sherry** is known as **fino**.

dry ice Solidified carbon dioxide, made by allowing the compressed **gas** to expand rapidly; the drop in temperature causes it to solidify, forming a hard white block with a temperature of −79°C (−110°F). It is used for refrigeration where power is not available and can cause burns if it comes into contact, even very briefly, with the skin.

drying The oldest form of food preservation not using chemicals. It is based on the principle that, in the absence of water, function of all living matter is suspended and in some instances it can also be killed. Many seeds, **spores** and **yeasts** will survive, some for many years, in the dry state and can subsequently be brought to life again with water. Dried foods such as **apricots**,

beans, cereals, peas, raisins, are important food items. Meats, fish and milk can be preserved in this way. Salt may be added to hasten the drying of meats, and chemicals as additional preservatives. See **freeze–dry, roller–dry, spray–dry, preservation, sulphur dioxide.**

Dublin bay prawn See **langoustine.**

duchesse potatoes Mashed boiled potatoes beaten with milk, egg and butter, piped into decorative shapes and lightly browned in the oven.

duck A widely-distributed waterfowl related to the goose and swan, found wild in most countries of the world and belonging to the family *Anatidae*. Many varieties are selected to suit local conditions and are bred or domesticated for food and for their eggs. Ducks have more natural **fat** than hens, and their flesh a more distinctive flavour. Ducks are unsuitable for modern factory **egg** production; their eggs are therefore expensive 'to produce and not often available. They differ from hens' eggs in taste and the nature of the white which has a different balance of soluble **proteins** and does not whip as well. Eggs must be fully boiled or cooked to be safe to eat. See **drawing, hygiene, salmonella.**

NUTRITIONAL VALUE: high in saturated fat, much of which can be extracted during cooking.

ENERGY per 100g: roast 314 kcal, 1314 kJ.

USES: roasted, in casseroles, pâtés.

dulcin A synthetic sweetener, also known as Sucrol and Valzin, 250 times as sweet as sugar but not considered safe for human consumption and no longer available.

dulse *Rhodymenia palmata,* an edible seaweed, purple and red with a strong, somewhat spicy flavour. It can be tough.

NUTRITIONAL VALUE: negligible; some calcium and iodine.

ENERGY per 100g: negligible.

USES: boiled and used as vegetable.

dumpling A mixture of flour, salt, water and suet made into balls and boiled, to be eaten with stewed meat; the dough is also used to cover apples to make apple dumplings.

duodenum The first part of the small intestine which receives food from the stomach and where the pH is reversed from **acid** to **alkali** to allow the pancreatic **enzymes** to function. It is also the part where bile enters the intestine.

durian *Durio zibethinum.* A tall, tropical, evergreen tree bearing large hard-skinned, multiseeded fruits. The flesh is soft, aromatic and sweet when ripe but once opened, it deteriorates very rapidly producing an offensive smell and for this reason it is rarely on sale and hoteliers and restaurateurs will not permit it on their premises.

durum See **flour.**

dysentery Infection of the large bowel, causing **diarrhoea**, in some cases, with blood-stained stools. Bacillary dysentery is caused by **bacteria** of the *Shigella* group, the commonest being *Shigella sonnei* responsible for Sonne dysentery. Amoebic dysentery is caused by a protozoan, *Entamoeba histolytica*. Dysentery is contracted by swallowing water or food contaminated with **micro–organisms** from other humans; man is the only reservoir of infection. The disease is notifiable. Medical advice must be taken. See **hygiene.**

E

E The letter followed by a number identifies a food **additive** approved for use in countries of the European Economic Community. If the number only is listed the additive is awaiting approval. See appendix for sources of information.

earth almond See **chufa**.

eau de vie Same as **brandy**. **Alcohol** produced by distilling **wine**.

eccles cake A sweet pastry containing currants and spices; originally from the north of England.

echinoccocus See **hydatid cyst, tapeworm**.

éclair A small light cake made with choux pastry (see **pastry**), filled with cream and covered with chocolate.

Edam A Dutch medium-fat, semi-hard cheese made with semi-skimmed milk and prepared in balls, allowed to mature for a few weeks and coated in red wax. It is firm with a mild flavour.

NUTRITIONAL VALUE: protein 28%, fat 25% (reduced fat types are available)
ENERGY per 100g: 352 kcal, 1472 kJ.
USES: a table or cooking cheese.

eddo See **yam**.

EEC European Economic Community. The states of Europe which have collectively, under the Treaty of Rome, agreed to standardise matters of trade, commerce, consumer products, standards for the environment.

eel *Anguilla anguilla*. The common eel. Lives most of its life in rivers, lakes and ponds where it grows to maturity and is usually caught. The mature eel, crossing wet grass if necessary to reach rivers and the sea, swims across the Atlantic to the Saragossa Sea to spawn. The young eels, called **elvers**, return to the rivers of Europe, in the UK, particularly the River Severn where they are caught in large numbers and eaten as a delicacy. Mature eels are edible but tough and require long cooking.

NUTRITIONAL VALUE: protein 17%, fat up to 12%, vitamin B complex, minerals.
ENERGY per 100g: 180 kcal, 753 kJ.
USES: boiled, grilled or baked, smoked. Boiled and allowed to cool in the stock, they are a delicacy known as jellied eels.

eel, conger See **conger eel**.

effervescent The state of a liquid in which carbon dioxide (see **gas**) has been dissolved under pressure and escapes from the surface as in canned and bottled soft drinks, and beers. Transient effervescence can be produced by an immediate chemical reaction between an **acid** and a salt of carbonic acid, such as sodium or potassium bicarbonate. In **beer** and **champagne**, the carbon dioxide is traditionally produced by the action of **yeast** on **sugars**. Many drinks today, including most beers, are pressurised with carbon dioxide at the time of bottling or canning.

egg-plant See **aubergine**.

egg The germ from which life of most insects, birds, reptiles, fish and mammals originates. In the culinary sense, only those eggs which contain a natural food store are used as food by man. These include eggs from cod, herring and sturgeon (see **roe**) and eggs of the hen, duck, and **quail**.

Only birds' eggs have a hard shell of **calcium carbonate**. The hen is the usual source of eggs for consumption today and they are produced by modern factory methods to keep the cost down, and to provide a supply all the year round; they are not fertilised. Farm or free-range eggs cost more to produce and may be fertilised; they are entirely suitable for consumption. In the past, duck and goose eggs were commonly eaten but they are now expensive and rarely available.

The egg contains yellow yolk, with the germ or embryo and a store of **fat**; it also contains **cholesterol**. The yolk is surrounded by the white, a mixture of soluble **proteins** of which 79% is **albumen**, 3% **globulin** and the rest **mucins**. There are slight differences in the ratio of proteins between whites of eggs of different species, which affects their whisking properties. Eggs contain **iron** and **sulphur** which combine to form ferric sulphide and cause the black areas occasionally seen in cooked eggs and which occur in stale eggs. **Bacteria** in contaminated eggs release sulphur and hydrogen which combine to form hydrogen sulphide, an unpleasant poisonous gas, giving rise to the characteristic smell of bad eggs.

When the whites of eggs are whisked, the hydrogen bonds which hold the molecules together are reformed in an arrangement which entraps air, producing the characteristic foam used in making foods such as meringues, soufflés and mousses. Egg proteins coagulate (set) at a temperature above 70°C (158°F) producing an opaque jelly best seen in boiled and poached eggs. The proteins in the yolk also set but this is modified by their high fat content.

Hen and duck eggs are capable of transmitting disease due to **salmonella** and remain a significant source of **food poisoning**: thus any drinks or uncooked food containing raw egg always carries a

risk and should be avoided by the elderly, the infirm, young children and pregnant women as should under or lightly cooked eggs. Commercial egg products, such as **mayonnaise** must be made with **pasteurised** egg. Egg-shells are porous but normally prevent **micro-organisms** entering the cavity; these can however penetrate if the eggs are washed or have any defect in the shell such as a crack, in which case they should be discarded. Contaminated eggs are dangerous before visible changes have taken place and long before they smell.

Eggs are graded in the UK as follows :—
 Size 1 over 70 g.
 Size 2 65–70 g.
 Size 3 60–65 g.
 Size 4 55–60 g.
 Size 5 50–55 g.
 Size 6 45–50 g.
 Size 7 under 45 g.

Duck eggs. See **duck**.

Gull eggs. Collected for food by coastal communities living near high cliffs.

Quail eggs are not widely available but can be obtained from some large supermarkets and specialist shops.

The taking of birds' eggs from the wild may be subject to restrictions and involve heavy penalties.

NUTRITIONAL VALUE: All varieties of eggs have approximately the same values:—
 Whole egg: Protein 12%, fat 11%. of which about 30% is saturated.
 White: Protein 9%, fat negligible.
 Yolk: Protein 16%, fat 31%, vitamin B complex, vitamin D, calcium and iron.
 ENERGY per 100g: whole egg: 150 kcal, 628 kJ.

USES: a versatile food with many varied uses in cooking, such as boiled, poached, scrambled on its own, fried with bacon (part of the traditional British breakfast), in omelettes. An important ingredient in many cakes, desserts, savoury dishes. Egg-white was traditionally used to clarify wine.

egg buying and **storing** Only eggs with perfectly clean shells which have not been washed and are not cracked should be purchased. They should be stored in a cool place, preferably in a refrigerator at a temperature just above freezing but never frozen. Perfect eggs should remain safe to eat for several weeks but will lose their freshness. In the past, it was common practice to preserve eggs for the winter when they were scarce. Preservation is achieved by sealing the porous egg-shell, either by immersion in a 4−5% solution of sodium silicate, known as water-glass or by coating the shells with a soft waxy or greasy substance. In this state eggs free of any contamination will keep in a cool environment for several months. There is usually a slight loss of quality but they are acceptable for most purposes. See **albumin index, yoke index**.

eggs, dried Drying of eggs, which became widespread during World War 2, and which, with improvements in drying methods, using whole eggs or whites and yolks separately, is now the preferred method of storage commercially; most dried egg has been pasteurised. Dried eggs are reconstituted by mixing with water and only sufficient for the immediate purpose should be prepared and then cooked immediately.

elastin Connective tissue with elastic properties which surrounds individual muscle fibres and is also present in the skin. In the ageing process elastin is gradually replaced by **collagen** which does not stretch and is tougher. Both soften to some extent in cooking. Together with collagen, elastin accounts for the toughness of **meat**.

elder *Sambuca nigra*. A hardy, deciduous, flowering tree often found growing wild. The flowers are creamy white, borne in many-headed florets with a characteristic smell and the berries are small and dark-red with a strong acidic flavour.

USES: flowers: to give flavour and bouquet to home-made wines and gooseberries. The florets are separated from the stalks and used as an infusion in the wine or with the gooseberries after they have been cooked and are still hot or during cooking; also used to make elderflower wine and cordial. Berries: stewed with other fruit such as apples; made into wine.

element One of the essential parts of matter, such as oxygen, hydrogen, carbon, metals, which, in varying chemical combinations, make up water, alcohol, carbohydrates, fats, proteins and other substances essential to all living matter. See **trace elements**.

elver An immature migratory **eel**, *Anguilla anguilla*, about 6−8cm long; enters European rivers in the spring and is considered a delicacy.
NUTRITIONAL VALUE: protein approx 16%, fat 12%.
ENERGY per 100g: 180 kcal, 753 kJ.
USES: boiled or fried in oil and flavoured sometimes with garlic.

Emmental A hard Swiss full-cream cheese originally made in the Bernese Oberland but now widely made in Switzerland. The cheeses are wheel-shaped and characterised by large holes. The process of manufacture is lengthy and the cheese matures over a period of 4−6 months. It then has a mild, nutty flavour.
NUTRITIONAL VALUE: protein 27%, fat 37%.
USES: as a table cheese, and for cooking.

emulsifiers and stabilisers. Substances which, when added to a mixture of oil and water, assist in the formation of an **emulsion**. Some emulsions are naturally unstable and emulsifiers increase stability and thus increase shelf-life and lower costs. They are classed as food additives in the range E322−495. See **lecithin, mustard**.

emulsion A mixture of **fat** or **oil** and water; one of the ingredients is dispersed in very fine (microscopic) droplets which remain suspended in the other. An emulsion may be fluid such as **milk**, or solid such as **butter, margarine**. When oil is in droplets surrounded by water (the water being in the continuous phase), it is known as an oil in water emulsion and when water is in droplets and oil in continuous phase it is known as a water in oil emulsion. Margarine is an example of the former and has a dull surface, butter of the latter and has a shiny surface. Many emulsions are unstable and the components tend to separate; **milk** is an exception. See **emulsifiers** and stabilisers.

enamel A hard, glass-like coating baked at high temperature on metal, usually coloured; applied to saucepans and cooking utensils generally. It tends to chip if knocked and it is damaged by **abrasives**. It becomes rough with use and is stained by fruits and vegetables. It should be cleaned with a non-abrasive cleaner.

enamel, dental See **dental enamel**.

en croûte Fish or meat enclosed in a pastry case such as beef 'en croûte' (beef wellington), salmon coulibiac.

endive, also known as **chicory**. The variety *Chicorium endivia* has broad leaves with curled edges and is used raw in salads.

endosperm The outer seed-coat.

energy The capacity to do work. Food provides energy equivalent to heat generated when the dry food is burnt in an atmosphere of oxygen. The energy in food is released in the body by a complex series of chemical changes, controlled by **enzyme** systems. **Protein, fat** and **carbohydrate** can all ultimately be broken down into **glucose** for energy. However not all food material is available for conversion; **cellulose** and some complex sugars cannot be digested in the small intestine but are fermented by **bacteria** in the large intestine; some are converted into **fatty acids** and the energy released. Chemical changes in the body are highly efficient and food in excess of energy requirements is stored as fat. Energy value is rated in **calories** or **joules**. Until recently food energy was quoted only in calories but today joules are increasingly used. The units are too small for most purposes and the standard is equal to 1000 units and written kcal or kJ. 0.239 kcal = 1.0 kJ, 1.0 kJ = 4.184 kcal. See **calorimeter**.

VALUES per gram:—
PROTEIN: 4 kcal or 16.7 kJ.
FAT: 9 kcal or 37.7 kJ.
CARBOHYDRATE: 3.75 kcal or 15.7 kJ.
ALCOHOL: 7 kcal or 29 kJ Energy requirements for individuals depend on age, sex, activity and state of health, rising when there is injury or infection. See Tables in Appendix.

entrée A dish served between the main courses of a meal.

entrecôte A beef **steak**, taken from between the ribs.

entremets A small subsidiary dish served during a meal between other courses, such as asparagus, globe artichokes, sorbet.

enzyme An organic catalyst, produced by all cells throughout the animal and botanical kingdom. Enzymes have the property of bringing about a chemical reaction without themselves being incorporated in the initial or final products of the reaction. Many biological enzymes have been identified as being involved in vital processes, many of their names ending in 'ase'. Typical examples are the conversion of **carbohydrates** to sugars by **amylase, fats** to **fatty acids** and **glycerol** by **lipase**.

Awareness of the action of enzymes, and how they best function is of considerable value in understanding the nature of cooking. Enzymes produced by **bacteria** have an important function by fermenting

dietary fibre in the large bowel. Their action is affected by temperature and pH and most are destroyed by heat in cooking. Some are essential for the preparation of food, as in the complex processes of fermentation in **bread** and **wine**-making. Others cause deterioration of foods, leading to breakdown and development of unpleasant flavours and discoloration.

Frozen food may deteriorate even when the temperature is −18°C (−0.5°F). Vegetables are therefore 'blanched', by immersion in boiling water for a short time, to destroy those enzymes which would cause loss of quality during storage. See also **bromelin, myrosinase, pepsin, papain, trypsin, zymase**.

épicier A grocer.

epicure Someone who delights in food or has fastidious or refined tastes.

epigramme A small selected piece of meat, usually lamb, gently simmered until tender then dipped in egg and breadcrumbs and fried.

ergosterol See **vitamin D**.

ergot A poisonous **alkaloid** produced by a black fungus, *Claviceps purpurea*, a disease of **rye**, which can also affect other **cereal** crops under damp conditions. Ergotism was formally a serious problem in Europe, where rye was an important food crop, causing abortions in pregnant women and gangrene of the limbs but it is rare today. As a drug ergot derivatives have important medical uses.

erucic acid See **rape-seed oil**.

erythrosine (E127) Synthetic coal-tar dye; a permitted red food-colouring, used in disclosing tablets to reveal plaque on teeth.

escalope A boneless, thinly cut piece of meat, usually veal, often beaten to make it tender. It is generally dipped in egg and coated in breadcrumbs and fried.

escargot Usually means *Helix pomata*, the large edible **snail**, also known as Roman Snail; it is the most favoured variety and widely eaten in France where it is best fed on vine leaves. Commonly served with garlic butter. Other snails are also edible.

escherichia coli A **bacillus** normally present in large numbers in the large bowel in man and all animals. Its presence in water and other foods indicates faecal contamination and can be identified by laboratory tests. A few strains of *Escherichia coli* can cause gastro-enteritis in babies and occasionally in the elderly.

essence In cooking, refers to flavours extracted and concentrated by a process using solvents, distillation or evaporation of water. Some essences can be prepared synthetically, such as vanillin. Synthetic equivalents do not have the fine flavour of the natural product. See **extracts, essential oils, vanilla**.

essential amino acids See **amino acids**.

essential oils Volatile oils present in plants, giving each its characteristic smell, and therefore, flavour. Many food substances owe their special flavour to the presence of essential oils. Typical examples are **citrus fruits, herbs, spices, vegetables**. They are not directly soluble in water; thus the practice of 'sweating' onions and other vegetables in butter or oil on a low heat is designed to extract these flavours in cooking. The oils are available prepared as **essences**, by extraction using distillation and/or solvents for use with foods.

esters The chemical name for compounds of an acid with an alcohol. Fats and oils are the commonest forms of ester and are compounds of various **fatty acids** with **glycerol**.

ethanol (ethyl alcohol) The **alcohol** produced by fermentation of **carbohydrates** by **yeast**; it occurs in all fermented drinks and distilled spirits. Alcohol at a concentration over 14% is a preservative and at 70% in water will destroy some, but not all, **micro-organisms**. Ethanol has an energy value of 7 kcal per g or 29.2 kJ. **Wines** and **spirits** are used in cooking, both for the flavour they introduce and for their ability to extract flavours which are only soluble in alcohol, alone or with water. Wines are used for **marinading** and tenderising meat. Ethanol must not be confused with **methanol (methyl alcohol)**. See **alcohol safe limits**.

ethnic cookery Pertaining to the country of origin. The introduction of foods and cooking practices by people of other nationalities coming to live in the UK, has provided new opportunities and influenced eating habits. See **religious laws**.

ethyl alcohol See **ethanol**.

ethylene glycol A poisonous **higher alcohol** which must never be used in food or drink. Some unscrupulous wine-makers have used it in wine, to enhance the drinking appeal, and have seriously damaged the local wine-making industry when discovered. It is used as an antifreeze in car radiators and solar-heating systems.

evaporate To pass into an invisible state, as in loss of water in the drying of food and clothes, and loss of alcohol from exposed vessels. Evaporation can take place at low temperatures but is speeded up by a rise in temperature or a reduction in air-pressure. Evaporation is used in cooking to concentrate stocks, purees, and in jam-making, often with a wide, open pan to increase the area from which water can be lost. In commercial processes, evaporation is speeded by reducing the air-pressure in a closed container and so lowering the boiling point, thus preserving flavours which are affected by heat and conserving energy. See **freeze-drying**.

evaporated milk See **milk**.

evening primrose *Oenothera biennis*. A semi-hardy biennial with yellow flowers. Oil extracted from the seeds contains several essential **fatty acids** related to **linoleic acid** which are important for some biological functions. Evening Primrose oil has gained a reputation for relieving premenstrual tension and other medical conditions.

eviscerate The process of removing internal organs of animals. During the process the carcass may become contaminated with micro-organisms present in the intestines. See **food poisoning, hanging, paunch**.

ewe's milk Rich milk from sheep specially bred for milk production.
NUTRITIONAL VALUE: average: protein 5.8%, fat 6.7%, carbohydrate 4.75%.
ENERGY per 100ml: 101 kcal, 423 kJ.
USES: mainly for cheese-making. See **Ricotta, Roquefort**.

exchange resins Chemical substances which have the ability to absorb other chemical substances under certain conditions and then release them under other conditions.
USES: in **water-softeners, water-purifiers** and some dishwashers.

extraction rate Refers to the proportion of the original **grain** that is used after **milling**. Wholemeal flour is 100% extracted, wheatmeal 85%, white flour usually 70% but can be as low as 60%. The **bran** and **wheatgerm** represent the parts of the whole grain that are extracted and used for other purposes.

extracts The essential nature of a substance concentrated by evaporation of the water by boiling or other means. Typical examples are meat, yeast and fish extracts. They play a very important role in flavouring many dishes, such as soups, stews, sauces.

F

faeces The solid or semi-solid matter or stool excreted by the large bowel. The quality and quantity of faeces reflect the state of health and the character of the **diet**, especially the quantity of **dietary fibre**. Faeces consists mainly of very large numbers of **bacteria** which are normal inhabitants of the large bowel, together with undigested food remnants (**connective tissue**, some **cellulose, fats**), and water accompanied by a mixture of gases known as **flatus**. Consumption of an average mixed diet should be followed by the passage once or twice a day, of faeces which are comfortably soft, together with a socially acceptable amount of flatus. See **constipation, diarrhoea**.

faggot A ball-shaped mixture of minced pig **offal**, breadcrumbs and herbs bound with egg which may be wrapped in **caul**, and cooked in the oven or fried.

farina The **starch** made from any kind of **cereal**; also includes flour made from potatoes and chestnuts. In the UK refers to potato-starch. See **potato flour**.

fat Fat and **oil** are complex mixtures of **fatty acids** and **glycerol** composed of carbon, oxygen and hydrogen collectively known as **lipids**. Fat is the solid and oil the liquid state at room temperature; they are interchangeable and they share many of the same properties and uses. There are variations in similar products of the same name due to differences in the source, method of extraction and degree of purification which affects the ratio in the fats of individual fatty acids. The critical user may develop a personal preference, for instance with **olive oil**. Cooking oils may be mixtures of vegetable oils, some being designed as suitable for deep-fat frying.

Properties. Fats are insoluble in water but soluble in solvents such as benzene. They are capable of emulsifying with water and in this form are the basis of **butter, margarine, salad dressings, ice-cream**. They are able to dissolve and transport oil-soluble **vitamins** and **essential oils**. When used in cooking, high temperatures cause chemical changes in the food which are characteristic of fried food and the oils themselves impart distinctive flavours. See **fat, effects of heat, safety in use** below.

Classification. Fats are classified according to the degree of saturation, which is a chemical term referring to the binding of the carbon chain and the amount of hydrogen in the molecule and has an important bearing on their physical properties and behaviour in the body. In saturated fats the carbon chain is connected by only a single bond and the molecule cannot absorb any more hydrogen. In unsaturated fats the carbon chain contains, one (monounsaturated) or more than one (polyunsaturated), double or triple bond and the molecule is capable of absorbing additional hydrogen. At room temperature saturated fats are solid whilst monounsaturated and polyunsaturated fats are liquid.

Sources. Saturated fats are present mainly in meat, dairy products and poultry, while unsaturated fats are dominant in oils of vegetable origin and fish-oils. There are three exceptions: **coconut-oil, coco-butter** and **palm-oil**

which are mainly saturated, and solid at room temperatures.

Stability. Saturated fats are more stable than unsaturated fats, but both will become **rancid** in the presence of air and moisture, due to naturally occurring **enzymes** or **micro-organisms**. Both keep relatively well when refrigerated or frozen and covered to exclude air. Those rich in **linoleic acid** are known as drying oils, because of their ability to form a hard skin on the surface in the presence of air and are the basis of paints. All unsaturated oils have this property to some extent, particularly grapeseed, soya, sunflower and fish-oils, which makes it difficult to clean deposits from appliances, equipment or walls if not removed immediately. To delay or prevent deterioration, and thus prolong shelf-life, of food products such as cakes, biscuits and processed foods, **preservatives** are generally incorporated as food **additives**; these are mainly **antioxidants** based on **tocopherol** (E306–309).

Hardening of fats. Unsaturated fats may be converted to saturated fats by a process known as hydrogenation, in which hydrogen is attached to the free carbon atoms in the fat molecule; in this way the abundant unsaturated fats of vegetable origin can be used where hard fats are required such as in the manufacture of **margarine**, cooking fats. Soft margarines which are high in unsaturated fats contain 14–15% saturated fats to prevent them from becoming liquid at room temperature.

Health considerations. Three fatty acids, arachidonic acid, linolenic acid and linoleic acid are essential for health but only linoleic acid cannot be manufactured in the body from other fats; however, sufficient amounts are present in a diet which includes vegetable oils. There is strong evidence, from population studies, that the incidence of arterial disease, heart disease and strokes is directly related to the level of **choles-**terol in the blood and this is the higher, the greater the consumption of saturated fat, from which it is converted in the body. Unsaturated fats do not convert to cholesterol, and a diet high in the type of these fats found in fish-oils, olive-oil and most other vegetable oils is associated with a lower incidence of coronary heart disease, and possibly some cancers. See **diet** for recommended amounts of fat.

ENERGY: all fats and oils have the same value of 900 kcal, 3767 kJ per 100g.

USES: different fats are associated with specific uses. In general saturated or hard fats are used as **shortenings** for **pastry**, cakes, biscuits and also in **bread**. Unsaturated fats or oils are used for frying (although butter is preferred by many people for its flavour), salad dressings, to prevent food adhering to containers used in baking. See **melanoidin**.

fat – effects of heat and safety in use Fats and oils can reach temperatures of up to 330°C (626°F), but there are variations in similar products which affect their behaviour, and critical temperatures fall with repeated use. The figures given can only be regarded as guidelines.

Smoke-point. The point at which the emission of smoke from heated fat or oil is first be detected. This can occur at temperatures above 165°C (329°F) for animal fats and vegetable cooking oils and 230°C (446°F) for specially-prepared cooking fats or oils.

Flash-point. The point at which volatile products from the fats or oils are liberated and are capable of being ignited by a naked flame. This varies from 230°C (446°F) to 330°C (626°F).

Ignition-point. The point at which heated fats or oils may ignite spontaneously, which is reached at any temperature above flash-point.

Recommendations:
1. Cooking fats and oils should be chosen

for their high smoke-point in the interests of safety; generally vegetable oils are the safest to use but **olive-oil** has a relatively low smoke-point (as has **butter**) and should not be used for deep-fat frying.

2. Frying should be carried out before the smoke-point is reached and at a maximum temperature of 210°C (410°F).

3 Frying is safer carried out in a deep, rather than a shallow, pan unless only a very small amount of fat or oil is used.

4. Cooking fat or oil used for deep-fat frying, which is not in constant use, should be cooled and kept in an airtight container in a cool place.

5. For average domestic purposes, the amount of fat or oil lost in deep-fat frying should be replaced each time with fresh fat or oil and after heating 2–3 times, approximately one fifth of the initial quantity should be discarded and replaced. See **acrolein**.

fat hen *Chenopodium album*, also known as goosefoot. A hardy annual weed related to spinach and Good King Henry.

NUTRITIONAL VALUE: protein up to 5%, vitamin C up to 50mg per 100g.

USES: cooked and used in a similar way to spinach.

fat, hydrogenated See **fats – hardening of**.

fat substitutes Research to find a low energy (less than 7 kcal per g) substitute to replace fat in cooking, which is safe and usable, is unlikely to be successful in the foreseeable future. Such a substance would be neither digested by the **enzyme** system nor absorbed by the body and it would therefore be unable to act in the transport of oil-soluble **vitamins**, thus leading to deficiencies; also the lubricant properties of undigested fat substitute would result in uncontrollable leakage from the bowel. If the substitute were emulsified into small enough droplets to allow absorption, these could be carried in the bloodstream to lodge in tissues, and cause lasting and serious tissue reaction. For these reasons even highly purified mineral oil, such as liquid paraffin, is harmful, except in medicinal doses and must never be used in cooking.

Various ingredients can, however, be safely used as alternatives to fat in products such as ice-cream, salad dressings and spreads, which give a similar sensation in the mouth to fat and have a lower energy value. These include the use of natural gums and polymers of carbohydrate (polysaccharides) which add bulk and viscosity to the product, allowing an increase in water content, and in the case of ice-cream and mousses, extra air. Whey is used in reduced energy butter substitutes.

fatty acids Organic acids composed of hydrogen, carbon and oxygen which, when combined with an alcohol, form fats. Most fats contain free fatty acid which has not combined with an alcohol, particularly the more complex ones. Fatty acids are closely related to **hormones** and the steroids. Undesirable fatty acids are responsible for the flavours and odours that develop in **rancid** fat and fat-containing foods.

feast A festival or special occasion celebrated with plenty of good food.

feathers Also known as **byssus**.

fécule French term for **starch** including cornflour, arrowroot and potato-flour.

fennel *Foeniculum vulgare*. A half-hardy perennial, umbelliferous plant, related to **dill**, with thick ribbed stalks and fine feathery leaves. The leaves and seeds contain an essential oil with a hint of aniseed (**anise**) flavour. The variety *Foeniculum dulce*, known as Florence fennel, is more delicate and grown for its bulbous stalks. It can be grown in the South of England.

NUTRITIONAL VALUE: negligible.

ENERGY per 100g: negligible.

USES: the bulbous variety is used raw, sliced in salads or cooked whole as a vegetable; the feathery leaves are used as flavouring, particularly with fish and for garnishing. The seeds are used for flavouring in savoury dishes, sprinkled over vegetables such as cabbage.

fenugreek *Trigonella fuenum-graecum*. A tender annual **herb** grown for its seeds, leaves and stalks.

NUTRITIONAL VALUE: negligible.

USES: the seeds are widely used as a spice in Indian cooking, and can also be sprouted as a salad crop. The leaves, which are sometimes available in specialist shops, can be cooked as a vegetable but have a bitter flavour.

fermentation The breaking down of organic substances, particularly **carbohydrates**, by **enzymes** in **yeasts** and by **bacteria**, yielding **alcohols**, **fatty acids** and other compounds including carbon dioxide and other gases. Alcoholic fermentation is the production of **ethanol** (ethyl alcohol) by the action of yeasts on **sugars**, in the presence of moisture, and the essential process in the making of **bread**, **beer**, **wines** and the liquor from which **spirits** are distilled.

Wild yeasts are widely dispersed in nature on fruits, all growing matter and in the air; thus spontaneous fermentation will take place in any fermentable liquid or moist substance. Natural yeasts are often contaminated by **moulds** and are unreliable for use.

Fermentation is best started with pure, commercially-prepared, yeasts after any natural yeasts and moulds have been killed or suppressed. Some sugars, including **lactose** and **sorbitol**, cannot be fermented by bread and wine yeasts and so can be used as sweeteners for wine. Yeasts will continue

to work as long as there is fermentable material present and the alcohol content of the liquid is less than about 14%. Some strains of yeast can work above this level and are used for champagne and high-alcohol wines. Fermentation processes also take place in the large bowel during the digestion of **dietary fibre.**

feverfew *Chrysanthemum parthenium*. A hardy perennial **herb** credited with the property of reducing fevers and used as a prepared herbal remedy.

fibre See **dietary fibre**.

fig One of a large group of deciduous and evergreen trees which includes the **mulberry**. Some are grown as house plants. *Ficis carica* is the edible fig which has been cultivated since biblical times. It requires some warmth, but can be cultivated in the South of England; the fruit takes two seasons to ripen. It is sweet and has a large number of soft seeds and has mild laxative properties. Fresh figs do not keep well but are sometimes available in the UK. Most are sun dried, when they keep well due to their high sugar content. Dried figs are subject to infection with a **mould**, producing a toxin belonging to a group known as aflotoxins (also found on some nuts), which are capable of causing serious liver damage. All suspect dried figs should be destroyed.

NUTRITIONAL VALUE: fresh: protein 1.3%, carbohydrate 11 %, vitamin A, vitamin B complex, vitamin C. Dried: protein 4%, carbohydrate 60%.

ENERGY per 100g: fresh: 50 kcal, 209 kJ. Dried: 210 kcal, 879 kJ.

USES: as a dessert fruit, fresh and dried.

filbert The largest variety of **hazelnut** which is produced by a tall shrub, *Corylus maxima*. The nut keeps well in the shell but tends to deteriorate after a month or two when shelled, unless stored in a freezer.

NUTRITIONAL VALUE: average: protein

18%, fat 50%, mostly unsaturated, carbo-hydrate 5%, vitamin B complex.

ENERGY per 100g: average: 540 kcal, 2259 kJ.

USES: as a dessert nut and in a variety of vegetarian dishes, sweets and sweetmeats.

fillet Fish or a piece of meat from which the bone has been removed. Fillet steak is usually taken from the undercut of sirloin of beef.

fillo pastry See **pastry**.

filter See **strainer, water-filter**.

fines herbes The French term for a mixture of fresh **herbs** especially **chervil, chives, parsley** and **tarragon**, but may be just chopped parsley. Dried herbs can be used when fresh are not available. The herbs used are generally more delicately flavoured than those in **bouquets garnis**.

USES: for flavouring a variety of meat and savoury dishes, soups, casseroles, omelettes.

fino A variety of dry **sherry**.

finnan A **haddock** split open, with the head removed, lightly salted and cool smoked. Originally prepared in Findon near Aberdeen.

NUTRITIONAL VALUE: protein 20%, fat 1–2%.

ENERGY per 100g: 93 kcal, 389 kJ.

USES: usually cooked by poaching and served as for other fish. The main ingre-dient in **kedgeree**. Sometimes served with a poached egg as a breakfast dish.

fish An animal that has an internal skeleton, lives in water and breathes through gills. One of the most important food sources worldwide, providing **protein, vitamins** and **minerals**; oily fish all have a high content of polyunsaturated **fats**. Fish, unlike meat, does not keep well, and if not consumed within a few hours of catching must be stored on ice, refrigerated or canned. However, fresh fish stores well frozen for 6–9 months kept at −18°C.

The majority of fish inhabit the sea, but freshwater varieties include **carp, trout, perch**. Some, such as **salmon**, common **eels**, during their life-cycle, inhabit seawater and freshwater. Pelagic fish are those which live near the surface of the sea, such as **herring, mackerel** and related species; they feed mainly on other smaller fish, and have a fat content in their flesh varying from 5–20% of their weight. Demersel fish such as **cod**, all **flatfish, halibut**, live near the seabed and their fat is stored in the liver with only 2% or less in their flesh. Fish living in cold northern waters have longer-chain polyunsaturated fats, which remain liquid at lower tempera-tures, than those from tropical waters.

All fish should be fully cooked, hot smoked, or pickled in strong vinegar to destroy any parasites that may be present. Particular care is needed when cooking whole fish or thick sections by grilling or microwave. **Smoking** methods vary and most smoked fish should be cooked, although mackerel and salmon are usually safe. Raw fish should not be eaten except in Japan where the standard of quality control is exceptionally high. See **fish worms, food poisoning, red-tide**.

NUTRITIONAL VALUE: protein in all fish is constant at around 15–18%. Fat content varies with the species, environment, time of year and age. It is usually lowest at the tail end and highest near the head. Vari-eties of salmon, for example will have a range of 5–20%. The flesh of oily fish and livers of others contain high concentrations of oil-soluble vitamins A and D. The livers of **cod** and **halibut** are the highest known natural sources of these vitamins. All fish are rich in **calcium** and **iodine**. See **crus-taceans, molluscs**.

fish kettle An oval or rectangular, lidded, metal vessel, used for poaching fish. It has an inner, movable, perforated base on which the fish is placed and lifted out when cooked.

fish-oils The long-chain polyunsaturated oils of fish are unstable and readily oxidised, and therefore fish deteriorate much more quickly than meats. Commercial products made with fish oils are protected by **antioxidants**, most of which are related to **tocopherol**. There is evidence that fish-oils offer some protection against diseases of blood vessels. Thus, nations which have a high content of fish in their diet, have a low incidence of arterial diseases, such as coronary thrombosis, stroke. See **cod-liver oil**, **halibut-liver oil**.

fish selection A good fishmonger will sell only fish in good condition, either very fresh or frozen and the premises will be clean with no smell of fish. Whole fish should have bright eyes, feel firm, the scales not loose, have a sheen on the skin and the gills bright pink or red. It should have no smell and the stomach and the intestines should be intact. **Crab** and **lobster** should feel dense and heavy. If crabs have been cooked, always ask to have them opened and avoid any in which the contents are watery. See **shellfish**.

fish worms Parasitic worms can be found in the flesh of some fish, particularly **cod**, **haddock**, **hake**, **herring**, **mackerel**. The two common worms are, Anisakiasis, *Anisailis simplex*, also known as Herring or Mackerel worm, and Codworm, *Phocanema decipiens:* the former adult worms can reach a length of 20mm and the latter, usually found curled up in the flesh, may reach 40mm in length.

They both have a similar life-cycle. The contaminated fish must be eaten by a warm-blooded mammal, such as a seal or dolphin, in which the mature worm lays its eggs which pass out in the faeces. The eggs are eaten by small fish and shrimps which, in turn, are eaten by larger fish, where they hatch in the gut; the worms then migrate into the flesh where they mature. Humans can act as the intermediate host in the parasite's life-cycle, if raw, or incompletely cooked, contaminated fish is eaten. The worms are capable of causing ulceration of the gut and the symptoms can mimic appendicitis; they can also invade muscles and cause ulceration of the skin. See **fish**.

fitches The black, spicy, aromatic seeds of *Nigella sativa*, also known as Love-in-a-mist, are used in Indian recipes. Quoted in Isaiah Ch28, v25−29 and Ezekial Ch4, v9 in a recipe for bread.

fizzy See **effervescent**.

flageolet *Phaseolus vulgaris*. A small, delicate variety of **haricot bean**. When dried it is a pale-green colour.

NUTRITIONAL VALUE: Fresh: protein 2%, carbohydrate 2.7%, vitamin A, vitamin B complex, vitamin C up to 5mg per 100g, calcium and iron. Dried: cooked, protein 6.5%, carbohydrate 16%, calcium, iron, dietary fibre.

ENERGY per 100g: fresh, boiled: 20 kcal, 84 kJ. Dried, cooked: 100 kcal, 418 kJ.

USES: fresh, cooked in the pod as a vegetable, in salads. Dried, cooked as a vegetable, in casseroles, salads, vegetarian dishes.

flaky pastry See **pastry**.

flamber To give flavour to meat, poultry and sweets such as pancakes, christmas pudding, by pouring flaming brandy, sherry or liqueur over the food, usually at the table, and presenting it while still alight.

flan An open sweet or savoury tart with a **pastry** or **sponge** base.

flap-jack Originally a form of **pancake**, mentioned by Shakespeare. Also it is a flat biscuit made of rolled oats, fat and sugar-syrup.

flash-point See **fat − effects of heat** and **safety in use**.

flat-bread Also known as crispbread; a Scandinavian type of bread, made from rye and other flours, in the form of thin dry biscuits.

NUTRITIONAL VALUE: protein 8−10%, fat low, carbohydrate up to 75% vitamin B complex, minerals.

ENERGY per 100g: average: 340 kcal, 1423 kJ.

USES: as a substitute for bread, with cheese, pâté.

flatfish The group of seabed feeding fish which, during early development, undergo a change of shape from round to flat, and a migration of one eye so that both eyes lie on the upper surface. They are generally sluggish, but are among the best of the non-oily fish to eat. Examples include **brill, flounder, mullet, plaice, sole, turbot**. All have the same nutritional value with about 18% protein and only 0.5−1% fat.

flatus Gases naturally produced by **bacteria** fermenting **dietary fibre** and non-digestible polysaccharides such as **inulin** in the large bowel. It is a mixture of gases which includes carbon dioxide, methane, hydrogen, nitrogen.

flavour The flavour of food is a consequence of both smell and **taste**. The nose is highly sensitive and can identify a very wide range of smells characteristic of most foods. A good sense of smell is essential to the appreciation of food. Food taken when the nose is blocked cannot be smelled and those who, by injury or disease, lose some of their sense of smell are denied the appreciation of all but the four basic tastes. There are variations in individual appreciation of taste; foods appreciated by some are unpleasant to others. For example **saccharine** has a bitter taste to some, whereas others find it acceptable as a **sugar substitute**.

flesh Strictly, the muscles of mammals and birds, but in the culinary sense, often refers to fish and the soft part of some fruits and vegetables.

fleuron Small crescent pieces of puff pastry used to garnish fish.

flies A large group of two-winged insects, in contrast to bees and wasps, which have four wings. *Musca domestica*, the common housefly, is a potential carrier of disease because it may feed on both faecally-contaminated material and food-stuffs, hence transmitting **food poisoning bacteria** and other **micro-organisms**. Blue-bottle flies, *Calliphera vomitoria*, favour meat and have similar potentials, but the maggots which hatch from eggs they lay on the meat are harmless, although clearly unacceptable. To avoid contamination food should be covered and kept cool, preferably in a refrigerator.

flitch A whole side of bacon.

Florence fennel See **fennel**.

florentine The term used for a dish served with spinach and a mornay sauce; usually eggs or fish.

florentine biscuit Dried fruit and nuts on a chocolate base.

flounder *Platichthys plesus* and varieties. Small edible demersal **flatfish** which frequent estuaries around European coasts; similar to **dab**.

NUTRITIONAL VALUE: average: protein 15%, fat up to 3%, mostly unsaturated.

ENERGY per 100g: average: 85 kcal, 357 kJ.

USES: best grilled whole but may be baked or fried.

flour The finely milled product of **cereal** crops which may contain all or any ratio of the whole grain. The proportion of the whole grain present in the flour is called the extraction rate.

Wheat flours

Brown. Usually means a mixture of **wholemeal** and **white** flours but can mean any flour which is brown naturally or artificially coloured.

Durum. Flour milled from the durum strain of wheat *(Tritium durum)*; it has the highest **protein** content of any flour at 14% and is used for **pasta**.

Granary. A proprietary flour containing some **bran**, **wheatgerm** and whole grains, flavoured with malted wheat.

Malted. A flour containing **malt**, usually made from malted wheat, which is used rather than malted barley, as it gives a stronger flavour. Used for bread, biscuits, cakes.

Plain. Flour milled from the softer winter-sown European wheats with lower protein content than strong flour; it is the general-purpose flour preferred for biscuits, pastry and as a thickener for gravy, sauces. It has a protein content of about 9%.

Roller-milled. Flour produced by the usual method of high-speed milling, during which the flour becomes heated, leading to some loss of flavour. It is the cheapest to produce and provides most of the flour milled in the UK.

Self-raising. Flour containing raising agents usually mixed by the millers. It is used mainly for cake-making. See **baking powder**.

Stoneground. Flour, usually wholemeal, ground at a slow speed and remaining cool; it is generally coarser than roller-milled flour and has a finer flavour.

Strong. Flour milled from hard wheat with a high protein content, up to 13%; best for bread-making.

Wheatmeal. Name given to an 85% extracted **flour**, introduced during the Second World War and known then as National Flour. It contains more of the **wheatgerm**, **bran**, **vitamins** and **fibre** than white flour (70–75% extraction) but less than wholemeal and is paler in colour.

NUTRITIONAL VALUE: protein 10–12%, fat 2%, carbohydrate 70%, dietary fibre 6–7%, vitamin B complex, calcium.

ENERGY per 100g: average: 324 kcal, 1356 kJ.

White. Purified and freed of most of the fibre and germ; usually about 70% extraction.

NUTRITIONAL VALUE: protein 9–10%, fat 1.5%, carbohydrate 80%, dietary fibre less than 5%, vitamin B complex, minerals.

ENERGY per 100g: 340 kcal, 1423 kJ.

Wholemeal. Milled to contain all parts of the original grain, including all the wheatgerm and bran.

NUTRITIONAL VALUE: protein 10%, fat 2%, carbohydrate 75%, dietary fibre 10% (the highest content of all flours), vitamin B complex, minerals.

ENERGY per 100g: 306 kcal, 1280 kJ. Bread flours are usually fortified with calcium carbonate.

Other types of flour

Cornflour. A fine flour made from **maize** and which is almost pure starch. It produces an almost clear gel when dissolved in water, or other clear liquid, and brought to the boil. It may separate out if frozen.

NUTRITIONAL VALUE: carbohydrate 100%.

USES: as a thickening agent in desserts, soups, sauces. It is the basis of commercially prepared custard powder, desserts, sauces.

Rice-flour. A specialised flour used mainly as a dusting powder to prevent sticking, both when handling products and cooking. Also used in such products as rice bread. Milled from white rice it has 87% carbohydrate, 6.7% protein and a lower mineral and vitamin content than white wheat-flour.

Rye-flour. Milled from **rye** *(Secale cereale)*. It has a stronger flavour than wheat-flour and a slightly lower protein content of 8%. The gluten differs from wheat gluten and it will not make a good risen loaf with yeast. It has a similar vitamin and mineral content and is a valuable source of nutrients. More commonly used for a heavy bread in Europe and dry biscuits (Ryvita type). Usually mixed with a proportion of wheat-flour for baking.

Special flours. These can be made from any starchy material such as potato, millet, buck wheat, pea, soya bean and even dried root vegetables.

flour improvers Chemical substances, used commercially, to improve the appearance and baking quality of flour, a process known as **ageing**. In the past, it was found that freshly-milled flour improved after several weeks in store: the high cost of storage and knowledge of the process involved, led to the addition of very small quantities of oxidising agents, which enhanced the formation of **gluten** and removed the yellow colouring, due to **caratinoids** and **xanthophyll**. This gave rise to a whiter and more acceptable product. Flour for cakes, biscuits and pastry should have a low gluten content and for this reason these flours are treated only with a bleaching agent such as **chlorine**. The agents in common use for bread-flours include chlorine, sulphur dioxide, benzoyl peroxide, potassium bromate, ammonium persulphate and ascorbic acid.

fluorine An element found naturally in the form of fluorides, such as fluorspar; may be white or coloured. Fluorine strengthens **dental enamel** and retards **caries**. Fluorides in very small quantities are added to water supplies naturally deficient in fluorine. Excess fluorides can be harmful but toothpastes containing fluorides have a purely beneficial local action on the teeth and are quite safe.

foie gras See **pâté de foie gras**.

foil See **aluminium foil**.

food poisoning An inexact term, generally applied to acute illness resulting from the consumption of unwholesome food. It can be caused by eating substances which may be thought to be edible but are always poisonous, such as some toadstools, deadly nightshade; by inadvertently eating poisonous parts of certain fish and shellfish species, by eating potatoes that have turned green, or foods which contain poisons normally destroyed by adequate cooking such as **red beans** and **yams**; by foods or water which would usually be considered safe but have been contaminated by toxic agents such as **pesticides**, **heavy metals**, or by certain **bacteria** or their **toxins** and some **moulds**.

Shellfish can become 'poisonous' in polluted water and when eaten cause diseases such as viral **diarrhoea**, **salmonella**, **cholera**, **typhoid** and **hepatitis**. Similarly **red tide** can yield neurotoxins which find their way into shellfish. It is one reason why oysters should not be eaten during the warmer months of the year. Food, specially certain types of scomboid fish related to the mackerel, such as tuna, can become toxic if stored badly, due to the breaking down of tissue proteins and production of histamines, giving rise to flushing and diarrhoea when eaten.

The term bacterial food poisoning is restricted, in the UK, to acute illness due to consumption of foods containing certain pathogenic **bacteria** or their toxins. Large numbers of bacteria are involved, which multiply to dangerous levels because of incorrect storage of the food. This must be distinguished from the transmission of specific infections such as **bacillary dysentery**, **hepatitis**, **cholera** and **typhoid fever** which are normally transmitted from person to person by food or drinking-water contaminated by excreta of patients, or carriers of the diseases. **Brucellosis** is transmitted by the milk from cows infected with **brucella**. These infections are called 'food-borne diseases', since the food or water acts as a passive transmitter of the organisms.

In bacterial food poisoning the food plays a part, by acting as a nutrient for the multiplication of the organisms, before it is eaten. The prevention of bacterial food poisoning (and of food-borne diseases) requires protection of drinking-water, good animal husbandry, pasteurisation of milk, and hygienic food-handling. All except the last are beyond the control of the cook. Scrupulous personal **hygiene** is essential in all food-handling and can limit the transmission of food-borne diseases. Food poisoning due to bacterial multiplication in food can occur during any stage of food production, and it is therefore important to understand:

1) how bacteria may reach food and 2) under what circumstances they multiply in it. It is very common for food to become contaminated with small numbers of food poisoning organisms, and whilst steps should be taken to minimise this, it may not necessarily be harmful; however, it is essential to prevent multiplication of these microbes to dangerous levels.

How food poisoning bacteria reach food and multiply in it.

1. Some bacteria such as **salmonella** and **campylobacter** are commonly present in the bodies of animals and birds; hence meat, poultry or eggs may be contaminated at source, whilst fish may become contaminated rapidly after being caught. Wild birds are a potential source of campylobacter infection through pecking milk-bottle tops. **Bacillus cereus** is found in dusts and particularly on cereals and vegetables. *Clostridium botulinum* is widespread in the environment and can contaminate raw foods whilst *Clostridium perfringens* lives in the intestines of animals and can readily find its way into meat during slaughter. *Staphylococci* are often present on healthy skin but usually get into food

from septic lesions on the food-preparer's hands.

2. Food poisoning bacteria can only multiply in foods at temperatures between 5°C (41°F) and 60°C (140°F), and do so best at around body temperature.(It is therefore essential that foods which will permit bacterial multiplication are not kept for more than an hour or so in this temperature range).

3. *Clostridium botulinum* can multiply and produce toxins, when air is excluded, at temperatures as low as 5°C (41°F), which is lower than other bacteria; thus contaminated food kept, even in a refrigerator, for 7 days or more above this temperature could become dangerous. Fortunately poisoning from this bacterium is rare today.

4. Unpasteurised milk and dairy products made from it, also pâtés, may be contaminated with *Listeria mysotogenes*, a bacterium which can also multiply at low temperatures.

In general, for bacterial food poisoning to occur, the responsible bacteria, such as salmonella, must multiply in food before it is eaten, in order to produce the large numbers necessary for infection, or to form food poisoning toxins such as those produced by Staphylococci, Bacillus cereus, Clostridium perfrigens.

Principles of prevention of food poisoning and food-borne disease.

1. A high standard of hygiene must be observed to avoid the risk of contamination from sources mentioned above, whether animal, human or environmental.

2. All clothing worn by food-handlers should be clean and changed regularly.

3. Pets should be kept out of food-production areas.

4. Those with skin infections should not work at any stage of food-handling.

5. Those who have been victims of diarrhoea and whose work involves contact with food after it has been

cooked, or if it is to be eaten cold, should obtain medical clearance before returning to work.

6. Food liable to contamination such as meat, fish, poultry, which is not to be cooked immediately, should be stored in a refrigerator at 5°C (41°F) or less.

7. Frozen meat, poultry, game and fish should be completely defrosted and then cooked without further delay.

8. Vulnerable foods should be cooked adequately in order to destroy any food poisoning organisms already contaminating them. Care should be taken to ensure that the interiors of joints of meat (particularly those over 3kg), poultry and game are thoroughly cooked and a meat-thermometer should be used to eliminate guesswork.

9. Care should be taken not to contaminate cooked meat or other food with organisms from raw meat. For example, raw meat should be stored on the lowest shelf in the refrigerator to avoid any juices dripping down.

10. Cooked food, if not to be eaten hot, should be cooled rapidly (within one and a half hours), and refrigerated at less than 5°C (41°F) until required.

11. Foods in which *Clostridium botulinum* will grow, need special care. Modern commercially-produced canned food is safe, provided the cans are undamaged and the contents used immediately they are opened or removed from the can and refrigerated. It is not possible to guarantee the safety of non-acidic home-preserved foods such as vegetables or meats, and these should not be canned or bottled in a non-commercial situation.

Special care must be taken with food prepared by the **cook–chill** system, and this should be transported, stored and reheated with strict adherence to manufacturers' instructions. See also **aflotoxins, botulism, canning, crabs, dysentery,** **eggs, escherecia coli, fungus, giardia lamblia, ice, microwave ovens, mycotoxins, ohmic sterilisation, parasites, preservation, tuberculosis.**

food processor A multipurpose electrically-powered appliance for processing food-stuffs; usually with attachments for slicing, chopping, beating, whisking and sometimes liquidising and grinding.

food reaction A food reaction may be due to **allergy,** a disorder of digestion, **food poisoning,** a psychological reaction such as when there is an association of ideas and the belief that a foodstuff is going to cause trouble, even though it is acceptable and safe for others.

Foods may cause nausea, vomiting, diarrhoea or abdominal pain due to inability to digest the particular food, by reason of inadequate preparation and cooking, excesses of certain foods, or a defect in the digestive or metabolic systems. Examples are residual poisons in inadequately cooked **red beans,** uncooked **cereal** products, excess **pulses** and rare diseases such as **galactosaemia.** Babies react to sudden changes in diet and all changes should be introduced slowly over a period, until tolerance is established. Medical advice should always be taken for severe or persistent reactions.

fondant A soft sweetmeat that melts in the mouth.

fondue A sauce made of cheese, traditionally in Switzerland, with **Gruyère,** and wine, kept hot at the table and eaten from a communal dish with cubes of bread dipped into it with a fork.

Fondue bourguignonne is a meat dish, in which cubes of meat, usually beef, are cooked, by the individual at the table, in hot oil and served with a variety of piquant sauces.

fool A purée of fruit, fresh or cooked, sweetened and folded into whipped cream. Custard or fromage frais may be used as inexpensive low-fat alternatives.

forcemeat See **stuffing**.

formic acid (E236, E238) The acid of nettles and ant-stings. It is not poisonous in small quantities and is used as a food preservative and in descaling preparations for kettles and coffee machines.

fowl A domestic hen or cockerel of indeterminate age. The term also refers to turkey, goose (domestic and wild), guinea fowl, some wild water birds. See **broiler, chicken, pullet**.

fraise French for **strawberry**; also used to mean made with strawberry.

framboise French for **raspberry**, also used to mean made with raspberry.

frangipane Filling for pastry tartlets or flans made with butter, eggs and ground almonds and flavoured ˙ with almond essence, kirsch or orange-flower water.

frankfurter A smoked sausage containing pork and/or beef, originally from Germany, but now associated with American **hot dogs** They should be cooked by poaching when fresh but are available canned ready to use.

frappé Iced.

freeze To convert a liquid or gas to a solid state by a reduction of temperature. Water freezes at 0°C (32°F), but if substances such as sugar, salt, minerals, alcohol are dissolved in it the freezing point is lowered (by as much as 25°C (77°F) in the case of calcium chloride).

When food is frozen, in the domestic situation for storage purposes, the process should be carried out as rapidly as possible, at a temperature of −18°C (−0.5°F), to prevent the formation of large ice crystals, which may damage the cell structure of the food and so alter its character. Commer-cially, much lower temperatures are used. In some foods there is inevitable change in the structure, due to the extraction of water from the cells, such as in strawberries, eggs, liquids thickened with cornflour. See **deep-freeze, ice-cream, sorbet**.

freeze-dry To dry from the frozen state by evaporation, at a reduced pressure, thus preserving flavours; a process known as lypholisation. It is used for products such as instant coffee powders and granules, instant tea.

French bean The whole bean, including the pod, of *Phaseolus vulgaris;* also known as haricot vert. See **haricot beans**.

NUTRITIONAL VALUE: protein 1.2%, carbohydrate 1−2%, vitamin C, minerals.

ENERGY per 100g: boiled: 10 kcal, 42 kJ.

USES: boiled or steamed whole as a vegetable and eaten hot, or cold in salads.

French dressing or vinaigrette. An unstable emulsion of 3−4 parts olive-oil and 1 part wine-vinegar or lemon juice and seasoning.

fricadelle Minced meat, shaped into small balls and fried. Served plain or with a sauce.

frit Fried.

fritter Food such as fruit, pieces of chicken, dipped in **batter** and fried.

frog A wide range of amphibians found world-wide. *Rana esculenta* is the edible frog, introduced into England in the mid 19th century. Regarded as a delicacy, only the legs are eaten and are similar to chicken; they are more widely eaten on the continent of Europe than in the UK. High **protein** and low **fat** content.

fromage frais A simple, bland, low-fat, very soft cheese, sold in cartons.

NUTRITIONAL VALUE: protein 9%, fat up to 8% (obtainable virtually fat-free), carbohydrate 4%.

ENERGY per 100g: 36−108 kcal, 151−452 kJ.

USES: in a variety of desserts, as a

substitute for cream on fruit and desserts, in cheesecake, fruit fools, savoury dishes, sauces.

frosting See **icing**.

froth The foamy head which appears on fermenting liquors, particularly **beer** and a feature of British beer. Also formed by the action of **yeast** during the bread-making process.

frozen food Food for freezing should be fresh, carefully selected for quality, and in the case of **vegetables** and **fruits**, cleaned and prepared as for cooking. **Fish** and **poultry** are generally frozen whole, in large pieces or jointed, whilst **meat** may be in joints, chops, steaks, cut up for stewing or minced. Most vegetables should be blanched, by brief immersion in boiling water, to destroy **enzymes** which cause deterioration in storage. Certain fruit, such as apples, pears, peaches, can be immersed in a reducing agent, such as lemon juice or ascorbic acid, prior to freezing, to prevent discoloration. Cooked food for freezing should be cooled rapidly (within one and a half hours) and frozen immediately.

All food for freezing should be wrapped or packed in containers to exclude air and prevent water loss, then frozen as quickly as possible and kept at a temperature of −18°C (−0.5°F) until required. Freezing does not destroy bacteria, but only stops them multiplying. Most foods will retain their freshness for several months and under correct conditions of storage, are safe to eat for up to a year. The temperature should not be allowed to rise during storage.

Frozen food can become a serious source of **food poisoning** if there is delay in freezing, the temperature is allowed to rise at some stage in transit or storage, and if thawing, particularly of meat and poultry, is not complete before cooking; any of these circumstances allow bacteria to multiply and produce toxins. It is not necessary to defrost frozen vegetables and fruit before cooking. All poultry should be considered contaminated by **salmonella** and all frozen food treated with the same precautions as fresh food. Refreezing of defrosted food is unsafe and carries the risk that **micro-organisms** may have proliferated.

fructose Also known as laevulose. A mono-saccharide **sugar** and an isomer of **glucose**, rotating polarised light to the left, whereas glucose rotates light to the right. It occurs naturally in fruits and nectar but may be combined with glucose, as sucrose. Fructose is the sweetest-tasting of all sugars and does not crystallise. See **honey**, **invert sugar**.

fruit The part of a plant which bears the seed or seeds. This includes all the berry and stone-fruits and seedless hybrids such as **banana**. Some fruits such as **cucumber**, **marrow**, **tomato** are eaten as **vegetables** and **rhubarb**, which is a vegetable, is eaten as a fruit. Fruits generally have a relatively high content of **vitamin C**, some up to 100mg per 100g, and a sugar-content varying from 2–3% up to 60% (in the date). Their fat content is low, except the **avocado pear** which has up to 25% fat, mostly unsaturated.

fruits de mer A collective term (French) for seafood.

fry To cook in a pan in **oil** or **fat**. Deep-frying is to cook by immersing the food in a saucepan of oil. Stir-frying is the Chinese method of cooking in a **wok** using high heat, very little oil and keeping the food on the move; it is quick and preserves **vitamins** and flavour better than other methods. Food which is fried is cooked at a higher temperature than by boiling or steaming, because oil reaches a higher temperature than water. It undergoes changes in colour and flavour, the latter also being influenced by the type of fat used.

Frying in the home is quick, simple and applicable to a range of basic and ready-prepared products, such as bacon, eggs, chicken pieces, fish, potatoes, sausages, hamburgers. Fried food forms a major part of the **diet** of many, to the exclusion of more healthy foods; its high fat-content raising the total fat intake above the recommended level. Oil used in deep-frying should, as soon as it is cool enough, be placed in an air-tight container and kept in a cool place to prevent deterioration. See **Maillard reaction**.

frying and fire risk Frying requires a high temperature and there is always a potential fire risk. When **fat** smokes it means that the temperature at which it may spontaneously catch fire is being approached. See **fat – effects of heat and safety in use**.

If the pan does catch fire:–
1. Panic should be avoided.
2. Water should NOT be poured onto the flames.
3. The source of heat should be turned off.
4. The flaming pan should be smothered with a fire blanket or a wet towel.
5. The fire brigade should be called if the fire gets out of control.
6. The pan should never be carried to the nearest door walking forwards. Going backwards will ensure that any draft will blow the flames away from you. This should only be done if the fire is small or nearly out.
7. Only use a fire extinguisher containing powder or carbon dioxide. See **accidents**.

frying-pan A shallow circular cooking vessel with a handle. Frying pans should be made of thick metal, usually aluminium, copper or iron, to conduct the heat and prevent local burning. Some are specially treated to reduce sticking. In some areas frying pans are known as skillets.

fudge A soft sweetmeat made with highly concentrated **sugar-syrup** which has been heated with milk and butter and allowed to cool, forming very fine crystals which keep it soft; it may be flavoured with chocolate, vanilla, coffee.

Fuller's earth See **bentonite**.

ful medames Small brown beans with thick skins and an earthy flavour; grown in the Middle East and used in a variety of dishes and soups.

fumado A smoked fish, particularly **pilchard**.

fumaric acid (E297) A naturally-occurring acid used for acidifying and flavouring. It is prepared by fermentation.

fumé Smoked (French).

fungicide A chemical substance which destroys **moulds** and **fungi**. Any substance which destroys **micro-organisms** has this property. Fungicides are widely used in food preservation, many incorporated in the food. Biphenyl (E320) is extensively used, applied in a wax emulsion to citrus and other fruits. The approved list is found within the range E200–297. See Appendix.

fungus A widely dispersed group of primitive plants that do not use **chlorophyll**; it includes the common edible **mushroom**, other edible fungi, poisonous toadstools and **moulds**. Fungi occur in grassland, gardens and in woodland and grow on fallen trees and wherever there is moisture. They cause breakdown of organic matter ranging from dry-rot of timber, paper, to human disease and deterioration of foods. They are an important part of the ecological system. Some are of medical importance, whilst others are used in the making of specialist **cheeses**. Many are safe to eat and some highly prized, such as the **truffle** and the yellow **chanterelle**.

Those who collect fungi for eating must be certain of their identity; a few are highly poisonous, with the effects coming on minutes or hours after ingestion. The majority of fungi sold today in the UK are cultivated. The larger open mushrooms have a finer flavour than the small buttons. Used extensively to add interest and flavour to many dishes and ·in soups. **Microprotein** (Quorn) is prepared from a fungus now grown artificially for its high **protein** content and used as a **meat** substitute. See **boletus edulus, food poisoning, penicillin.**

fusel oil A mixture of complex alcohols, with an oily consistency. It is formed during the fermentation process, by the action of **yeast** on **amino acids**, and is poisonous except in very small quantities. It has a higher boiling-point than **ethyl alcohol** and is concentrated during distillation of liquors, particularly when the temperature used is too high. See **congeners.**

G

galactose A sugar found in plants such as beetroot and also present in malt; but mainly occurs, combined with **glucose** to form **lactose**, in **milk**. During digestion lactose is broken down into galactose and glucose, when it is absorbed into the bloodstream. Galactose forms naturally in the making of yoghurt. It is not normally important except for those who lack the ability to metabolise galactose; a disorder known as **galactosaemia.**

galactosaemia An inherited disorder characterised by the inability to metabolise **galactose**. The disorder in children is associated with stunted growth, mental retardation, and sometimes vomiting and jaundice. Those with the condition, must avoid all lactose and galactose-containing foods, which include milk, milk products and beetroot. See **disaccharide intolerance.**

galangal *Alpina officinarum* and *Alpina galanga*, tropical plants and natives of South-East Asia and China; related to **ginger**. Also known as laos in Indonesia and Malaysia.

USES: the expanded roots are used as a spice, for their peppery and ginger flavour, in curries and other dishes.

galantine Refers to **poultry** cooked and set in its own **jelly**. When meat such as **veal** or **game** is prepared in the same way the dish is always called Galantine of ... naming the principal ingredient.

gallates Substances based on gallic acid, an **astringent** and **antioxidant** found in plants. Used in the form of propyl gallate (E310), octyl gallate (E311), and dodecyl gallate (E312).

USES: as antioxidants for preserving fats and products made with fats, in margarine and snacks. Should not be used for babies, those with asthma or those sensitive to aspirin.

gall-bladder A reservoir of **bile**.

game A wild mammal, bird, or fish killed in sport by hunting, shooting, or fishing. Game animals have a lower fat content than their farmed counterparts. Game-birds and mammals tend to be tough, and so it is usual to allow them to 'hang' for a week or more to give time for natural tenderising processes to take place. This also introduces new flavours characteristic of game. Game killed in sport can only be taken during **season** to conserve breeding stocks. See **autolysis, hanging**.

game chips Thin slices of fried potato, more popularly known as **potato crisps**.

gammon The hindleg of a pig, but taken from the carcass after the whole side has been cured. See **ham**.

garam masala A variable mixture of aromatic spices used as a garnish on cooked food, particularly curries or added towards the end of the cooking period. There are many variations but it contains spices such as black **cardamoms, cinnamon, black peppercorns, cumin seeds, nutmeg, cloves**. It is best freshly ground and made in small quantities.

garlic *Allium sativum*. A hardy member of the lily and onion family with a strong smell due to an essential oil, diallyl thiosulphinate, which loses some of its strength in cooking. It grows well in temperate climates. It may have important medical properties.
USES: much used for adding flavour and character to a wide range of cold and cooked foods.

garnish To improve the appearance of food by decoration with substances such as fresh green herbs, lemon or cucumber slices, chopped nuts, candied peel.

gas A gas is defined as matter that has no definite shape and fills any space it enters. Air is a gas made up of 78% nitrogen and 21% oxygen with traces of carbon dioxide and other rare gases. It is of concern that modern industrial processes are responsible for pollution of the air by a range of gases harmful to the environment such as nitrous oxides, sulphur dioxide, causing damage to food crops through acid rain.

The common gases are:–

Butane. See **propane**.

Carbon dioxide (CO_2). A gas, which is colourless and heavier than air, produced when matter burns, by the action of yeasts on **carbohydrates** in the process known as **fermentation**, and by raising agents such as **baking powder**. It is essential in converting dough into **bread**, in the making of **beer, cider** and **wines** and is responsible for the fizz in soda water, beer, champagne and other sparkling drinks. Carbon dioxide will not burn or support animal life and is harmful if inhaled in more than small quantities. It is, however, essential to most plants which use it as food.

Carbon monoxide (CO). A colourless, odourless and imperceptible gas produced when matter burns without sufficient **oxygen** to form **carbon dioxide**. It is highly poisonous and has a great affinity for **haemoglobin**, thus rapidly replacing oxygen in the blood to form carboxyhaemoglobin changing the colour of the blood slightly to cherry-red. This subtle change is important because it indicates that the oxygen-carrying property of blood is destroyed causing asphyxiation. Hospital treatment must be given at once if CO poisoning is suspected.

Hydrogen. A highly combustible gas and the lightest. It is not found free in nature but in varying combinations with other elements. With oxygen it produces **water**; with carbon alcohols, **carbohydrates** and **fats**; with nitrogen, **amino acids** and **proteins**; with chlorine, **hydrochloric acid**.

Methane. A gas produced by the decomposition of vegetable matter which when mixed with other gases in the large bowel from the fermentation of **dietary**

fibre, becomes a component of **flatus**. It is the principal constituent of piped natural gas for domestic heating and cooking. Although odourless in the pure state, it is given a smell to help in the detection of gas leaks.

Nitrogen. A gaseous element which forms 79% of the atmosphere. An essential constituent of proteins, amino acids. It cannot itself be utilised by the body but humans and animals obtain it through protein-containing food. Simple nitrogen-containing chemicals are among the most important of the fertilisers in agriculture and are used to increase food production. See **nitre**.

Propane and **butane**. These are slightly more complex chemical substances than carbon dioxide and methane. They are used for heating and cooking, usually compressed in cylinders for use where piped gas is not available in domestic or commercial institutions. Obtained during distillation of mineral oils.

Oxygen. A gas which constitutes 21% of the gases composing the air. It is essential for all living animals and most, but not all, **bacteria** and plants. It is produced in green plants by the process known as photosynthesis, in which carbon dioxide and water are converted by **chlorophyll**, in the presence of sunlight, into starches, sugars and oxygen. It will not itself burn but many substances will burn in its presence and many will combine with oxygen, a process known as **oxidation**. This is responsible for deterioration of food and means that air must be excluded from food preserved in cans and bottles. An increasing range of foods are now sold in vacuum-packs to prolong their life and conserve freshness. See **antioxidants**, **haemoglobin**, **ozone**.

Warning! Methane, propane and butane are all heavier than air so escaped gas tends to flow downward and accumulate at floor level, eventually causing a risk of ignition by a flame or electrical spark from a switch or thermostat, static electricity from friction of clothes in a dry atmosphere, or even a nail in a shoe on a hard floor. They are highly explosive and capable of causing major damage to property, loss of life and fires. Ventilation of rooms where any gas appliances are used is vital to prevent the accumulation of noxious gases; there are strict laws controlling the safety of such appliances.

gastrin A **hormone** secreted by the stomach which stimulates the production of gastric juices.

gastrointestinal tract The collective term for the whole length of the tract between the mouth and anus.

gastropods A group of molluscs which includes snails, slugs and all shellfish except bivalves such as oysters, clams, scallops, cockles. The majority are edible.

gâteau A rich sponge or pastry based cake filled with **cream** or **butter cream**, sometimes fruit, and decorated.

gaufre See **waffle**.

gazpacho An uncooked **soup** of Spanish origin made with fresh vegetables such as cucumber, tomatoes, sweet peppers, onions, and served chilled.

gel A semisolid colloidal suspension with jelly-like consistency. See **colloid**.

gelatine A water-soluble **protein**, of low nutritional value, extracted from bones, skin, or other mammalian connective tissue and fish swim-bladder, by prolonged boiling. When dissolved in hot water and cooled it forms a **jelly**. It is digested by natural proteolytic enzymes found in some fresh fruits such as pineapple paw-paw and kiwi fruit; thus jellies made with these fruits will not set unless they are first heated to destroy the enzyme. See **agar**, **alginates**, **collagen**.

genetic engineering The replacement of a selected part of the **DNA** in the cell nucleus, known as a gene, which determines cell characteristics, by a gene from another source or even another form of life. In this way genes with undesirable properties may be replaced by others with normal or enhanced properties. Genetic engineering is used to improve food production of animals and plants, increasing disease-resistance, yield and quality. It is also used in the pharmaceutical industry for the production of drugs such as insulin. It has a great potential to benefit mankind but there are strict precautions to prevent its misuse.

Genoese cake A simple sponge cake but made with the addition of butter or other fat.

gentian The yellow alpine gentian, *Gentiana lutea*.
USES: as a bittering agent in aperitifs, liqueurs and medicinally.

German silver See **silver, german**.

germicide See **disinfectant**.

germination The first stage in growth of a seed when it swells in the presence of moisture and starts to sprout.
USES: sprouting barley-seeds are used in the production of malt. In the cotyledon stage **mustard**, **cress**, **alfalfa**, **mungo beans**, are used as salad crops and contain vitamin C.

geropiga Juice of **grapes** evaporated to a syrup used to sweeten **port**. A similar product known as arrope is used to sweeten and give colour to sherry.

ghee Clarified unsalted **butter**. Made by boiling butter slowly to remove water and filtering through muslin. Much used in Indian cookery.

gherkin A variety of cucumber, *Cucumis sativa*, a native of tropical America, producing large numbers of very small fruits.

USES: pickled as a snack, garnish or in sauces.

giardia lamblia A protozoal **parasite** which causes intestinal infection, giardiasis, with chronic **diarrhoea** and other symptoms. It is acquired by drinking faecally-contaminated water, or by hand to mouth transfer from the faeces of an infected person. Some strains have proved to be relatively resistant to **chlorine** and have caused epidemics of diarrhoea. Water companies usually advise customers to boil drinking water when contamination is suspected, until the supply is cleared.

gibelotte A savoury stew of rabbit, bacon and onions.

giblets The neck, crop, heart and liver from **poultry**, **duck** and **game** birds; used to make stock.

gill A little-used liquid measure, generally equal to a quarter of a pint or 142ml.

gin A spirit distilled from grain or malt flavoured with juniper berries and other herbs. It is low in **higher alcohol** and **fusel oil** content. See **congeners**.
ALCOHOL CONTENT: 30–40%.

gingelli See **sesame**.

ginger *Zingiber officinale*. The expanded part of the root of a tropical plant which has a hot flavour. It is sold as fresh or dried roots, in powder form, crystallised, preserved in syrup. Fresh ginger should be peeled and grated or finely chopped to bring out the flavour.
USES: as a spice in Indian cooking, in biscuits, cakes, sauces, crystallised as a sweetmeat and to make ginger beer and ginger wine.

ginger beer A refreshing carbonated drink made by fermenting a mixture of water, sugar, lemon juice and ginger with yeast. The sugar content is normally kept low to keep the alcohol content down.
ALCOHOL CONTENT: usually less than 2%

when made commercially, but if home-made it can be much higher.

gingerbread A cake or biscuit made with treacle and flavoured with ginger. Originally it was highly spiced and sweetened with honey.

ginger wine A wine made by fermenting sugar and water flavoured with **ginger** and other **spices**.

ginkgo *Ginko biloba*. Also known as the Maidenhair tree. A native of China, now cultivated in Southern Europe for its edible nuts, contained in a soft yellow plum-like fruit whose flesh has an unpleasant taste. The nuts, however, are pleasant and can be eaten raw or roasted.

ginseng A herbal product extracted from the root of *Panax quinquefolia*, a native of China and grown in South East Asia and Russia. It has a reputation in China for its health-giving properties but there is no scientific proof of this. It is claimed to have a wide range of beneficial properties due to the presence of **alkaloids**, the ginsenosides, including the reduction of stress, improvement in sexual function and prevention of hangovers. An athlete in the 1988 Olympic Games taking ginseng was found to have the banned drug, ephedrine, in his urine, although at the time this drug was not known to be present in ginseng. He was not penalised but any others who now take ginseng probably would be penalised as having taken a banned drug.

girdle See **griddle**.

girolle See **chanterelle**.

gizzard The second stomach of a bird.

glace Ice (French).

glass A brittle transparent substance made of oxides of silica obtained from sands. Glass becomes increasingly fluid as it is heated, making it possible to be shaped by blowing or moulding. Most glass, and the glaze on china, is resistant to acid but dissolves slowly in alkalis present in dish-washing powders, so that repeated use causes dulling of the surface. Dishwasher-proof glass and glazes are now available. Crystal glass, which includes most cut glass, contains **lead** which can be absorbed by drinks stored in decanters.

Glassware must be cooled slowly during manufacture, a process known as annealing. It will then be stronger and stand moderate changes of temperature without fracture, but this is not so with cheap glass which is under stress. Heat-resistant glassware for cooking can be used in a conventional oven and in a microwave oven, but some coloured glass contains metallic oxides and may crack in the latter; some glass can also be used on a gas or electric hob.

Glass is a poor conductor of heat and it is generally wise to warm it carefully and avoid exposure to sudden increase of heat; similarly cooling should be gradual. Even some heat-resistant glassware may crack if exposed to sudden extremes of temperature. Thin glass is less likely to shatter than thick.

glasswort See **samphire**.

glaze To give a glassy look to food, by coating with sugar syrup, jelly or fat. Also refers to the glassy surface of china and earthenware which makes it impervious to moisture.

gliadin See **gluten**.

globe artichoke See **artichoke, globe**.

globulin One of the clear **proteins** found in **milk**, **eggs**, blood and in tissue fluids; it coagulates at a temperature of 70°C (158°F) and becomes opaque.

glucose Another name for dextrose, a monosaccharide **sugar**, less sweet than fructose and sucrose. It crystallises easily, is the main constituent of **honey** and causes its hardness. See **glucose syrup, invert sugar**.

glucose syrup A syrup made by hydro-lysing maize with weak acid. It is a variable mix of sugars, mainly glucose with some fructose. It is much used commercially as a sweetener and, in the making of confectionery; it is valuable as it prevents crystallisation. Also known as corn syrup.

glucoside See **glycoside**.

glutamic acid The **amino acid** which, in the form of **monosodium glutamate** is the food additive 620.

USES: to enhance the flavour of meat dishes, soups, casseroles; used extensively in Chinese cookery.

gluten A protein with viscoelastic properties capable of holding the bubbles of gas formed during the fermentation of **bread-dough**. Gluten is formed from two precursors, gliadin and glutenin, which are present to their greatest extent in hard **wheats**; the content is low in other **cereals**, none of which will make a risen loaf. Conversion to gluten takes place during the rising process of bread-making. Sensitivity to gluten is the cause of the condition, **coeliac disease**. See **ascorbic acid, Chorley Wood process**.

glutenin A **protein** present in **wheat** which, together with gliadin, constitutes **gluten**.

glycerides Chemical name for combinations of **glycerol** with **fatty acids**. The term includes **fats**.

glycerine See **glycerol**.

glycerol (E422) A syrupy non-poisonous liquid, with a sweet taste. It is a **higher alcohol**, which is formed in the body by the hydrolysis of fats and is present in some plants, but generally prepared synthetically. It must not be confused with

ethylene glycol which is the antifreeze used in radiators, is poisonous and highly dangerous if taken by mouth.

USES: as a non-sugar sweetener for diabetics, in liqueurs, confectionery, icings for cakes (to prevent them from becoming hard).

glyceryl monostearate (E471) A recognised food additive, used as an emulsifier and stabiliser to enhance the character of cakes, cream toppings, mousses. It is formed naturally during digestion.

glycogen The form in which carbohydrates are stored in the liver and muscles, when not required for immediate use. Up to 350g are available to meet demands for energy. It is rapidly broken down to **glucose**. The only natural source is in seafood such as oysters, clams, whelks which are eaten alive.

glycoproteins Compounds of protein and carbohydrate present in **mucin**, characterised by their lubricating properties and essential for comfortable chewing of food, swallowing, passage of faeces, lubrication of joints and movement of tendons. The jelly substance known as vitreous in the eye is also a glycoprotein.

glycoside and **glucoside** A group of compounds of sugar and other molecules which are found in plants. Some are used for their medicinal properties such as digoxin in foxgloves; all are strong poisons and include those in red beans and yams. Most are destroyed by heat.

glycosuria The presence of **glucose** in urine, usually due to a raised blood glucose level in **diabetes**, but rarely also to a mild kidney abnormality (renal glycosuria).

glycyrrhizin A sugar found in the liquorice root, *Glycyrrhiza glabra*, and up to 100 times as sweet as sugar but having a liquorice flavour.

USES: for medicinal products as a

flavouring agent and in preparing some brands of tobacco.

gnocchi Small savoury dumplings made of **pasta** and ridged with a fork; can also be made with potato, semolina, flour.

goat A small ruminant, closely related to sheep, domesticated by man from earliest times for meat and milk. It is capable of subsisting under sparse conditions unsuitable for cattle. Special types have been bred for the production of milk used for cheese-making and consumption by those intolerant of cow's milk.

goat's beard See **salsify**.

goat's milk Usually obtained from small herds of goats specially bred for milk production. It is similar to cow's milk with a slightly higher fat and protein content. Goat's milk has been associated with the condition known as **brucellosis** but this is rare. Goat's milk like cow's milk should be pasteurised for safety.

NUTRITIONAL VALUE: average: protein 3.6%, fat 4.1%, carbohydrate 5%.

ENERGY per 100ml: average: 70 kcal, 293 kJ.

USES: to replace cow's milk for those who are sensitive to cow's milk proteins and for cheese-making.

gofio Flour ground from roasted wheat, barley or maize and used for a gruel by boiling with water. It may also be fried in flat cakes and used as an alternative to bread.

goitre Enlargement of the thyroid gland causing fullness in the front of the neck, which may be caused by a lack of **iodine** in the diet. It used to be common in defined areas of central England, whence the term Derbyshire neck. Improved diet and the introduction of iodine in salt has largely prevented the condition in many countries. There are several other non-dietary causes of goitre; all require medical advice.

gold (E175) Permitted metallic gold food-colouring for surface use.

golden syrup A thick sugar-syrup made as a by-product of the last stage of refining white sugar. It has a little of the flavour of brown sugars and contains some **invert sugar**.

ENERGY per 100g: 400 kcal, 1674 kJ.

USES: as a sweetener in various desserts and in treacle tart.

Good King Henry *Chenopodium bonus-henricus*, also known as Allgood. A hardy low-growing perennial **herb** with dark green arrow-shaped leaves. No longer much used; a low-yielding plant.

USES: as an alternative to **spinach**, with similar nutritional value.

goose The largest of the native **poultry** birds.

NUTRITIONAL VALUE: average: protein approx 18%, fat 16%, mostly saturated.

ENERGY per 100g: average: 216 kcal, 904 kJ.

USES: as other poultry but much less widely available. Until the introduction of **turkey** from North America with its lower fat content, it was traditional fare for festive occasions. See **pâté de foie gras**.

gooseberry The fruit of *Ribes glossularia*, a hardy shrub commonly cultivated but growing wild in parts of the UK. The fruit is acid, becoming sweet as it ripens. Most varieties remain green but some turn red when they are fully ripe.

NUTRITIONAL VALUE: low carbohydrate content except when fully ripe, vitamin C up to 30mg per 100g.

ENERGY per 100g: cooked, unsweetened: 14 kcal, 59 kJ.

USES. some cultivated varieties can be eaten fresh as a dessert fruit when they are fully ripe. Mainly used for cooking as stewed fruit, tarts, pies, gooseberry fool, jam and jelly. Green gooseberries turn red when made into jam. The ripe fruit can be used to produce a wine similar in character to Rhine wine.

Gorgonzola An Italian full-fat blue-vein cheese, which has been inoculated with *penicillium glaucum*. It matures quickly and is best eaten within 4–6 weeks. It should be stored wrapped and in a refrigerator.

NUTRITIONAL VALUE: average: protein 19%, fat 33%, mostly saturated, vitamin B complex, vitamin D, calcium, iron.

ENERGY per 100g: average: 370 kcal, 1548 kJ.

USES: mainly eaten as a table cheese.

Gouda A full-fat, semi-hard cheese of Dutch origin and now much copied. The young cheese is mild in flavour but when matured becomes stronger and more piquant.

NUTRITIONAL VALUE: average: protein: 28%, fat 32%.

ENERGY per 100gm: 390 kcal, 1632 kJ.

USES: as a table cheese and as a basis for processed cheese.

goujons Small strips of fish, such as plaice, sole, rock salmon, coated in egg and breadcrumbs and fried; often served as a first course with a piquant sauce.

goulash A highly-seasoned stew of meat, onion and other vegetables, including red sweet peppers and **paprika**. Of Hungarian origin.

gourds Members of the family of *Curcubitaceae*. The group includes cucumber, marrow, melon, pumpkin, squash and water melon. Some are grown purely for their decorative value.

gourmet An expert in good eating.

graham flour American term for wholemeal flour.

grain The seeds of plants of the grass family. See **cereals**.

graining The formation of fine crystals when white sugar-syrup is heated above 115°C (239°F) and allowed to cool, as in candy or **fudge**. Graining can be retarded by adding cream of tartar, which converts some of the sucrose to glucose and fructose, or by adding liquid glucose. See **glucose syrup**.

grains of paradise *Aframonum melegueta.* A native of West Africa related to **cardamom**.

USES: as a spice with a peppery flavour. Not often available.

gram An Indian term for pulses and particularly refers to small peas.

gram The International unit of weight of the metric system. One gram equals 0.035oz (1oz = 28g).

grape The fruit of a **vine**, *Vitis vinifera*, widely cultivated for over 6000 years in temperate and warm climates. There are many varieties, white, red or dark purple which are grown for special purposes. See **wine**.

NUTRITIONAL VALUE: variable, but all grapes are relatively high in sugar content when fully ripe; average 16%, vitamin C up to 4mg per 100g.

ENERGY per 100g: average: 63 kcal, 264 kJ.

USES: selected varieties are used as dessert fruit, for wine-making; sweet varieties are sun-dried for raisins, sultanas and currants where the high sugar content acts as a preservative; they then keep well in dry conditions.

grapefruit The fruit of *Citrus paradisi*, one of the largest of the citrus fruits. Yellow-skinned when ripe, with an acid, slightly bitter flavour and a low sugar-content. Pink flesh varieties are grown and have a finer flavour.

NUTRITIONAL VALUE: protein 0.6%, carbohydrate 5.3%, vitamin C 40mg per 100g.

ENERGY per 100g: average: 24 kcal, 100 kJ.

USES: fresh as a dessert fruit, canned or in preserves, prepared as a juice and sold in cans or cartons.

grape-seed oil A high quality oil with a delicate flavour extracted from grape seeds.
NUTRITIONAL VALUE: high in unsaturated fats.
ENERGY per 100g: 900 kcal, 3766 kJ.
USES: in salad dressings, particularly vinaigrette, for cooking.

gratin A French term for foods prepared with a topping, usually of breadcrumbs and often with **cheese** and/or fat and browned under the grill or in the oven to produce flavours associated with **melanoidin**.

gravlax or **gravadlax** A speciality made with **salmon** fillets which are cured and pressed and usually eaten raw; of Scandinavian origin.

gravy A **sauce** made with the juices from roast meat. It may be thickened with flour or cornflour and darkened with fried onion, proprietary gravy browning, red wine.

green almond See **pistachio nut**.

green bean *Phaseolus vulgaris*. Alternative name for **french bean**.

greengage A sweet stone-fruit of the plum family, a variety of *Prunus interstitia*.
NUTRITIONAL VALUE: average: protein 0.6%, carbohydrate up to 7.9%, vitamin C, calcium.
ENERGY per 100g: average: 52 kcal, 218 kJ.
USES: as a dessert fruit and in preserves.

grenadilla See **passion fruit**.

grenadine A strong fruit-syrup made from **pomegranates** and sugar. Used to add colour and flavour to cold drinks.

griddle or **girdle** A flat, metal plate for cooking over direct heat such as hot coals or gas.

gridiron An iron frame with a base for cooking over hot coals.

grill To cook over or under a direct source of heat. The food sometimes being brushed with **fat** or **marinated**. See **Maillard reaction**.

grilse A young **salmon** returning for the first time from the sea to the river where it was spawned.

grind To wear down, break up or reduce to powder. The first grinding of corn was with a small oval stone moved around a larger saucerised stone called a quern; later, round mill-stones, one stationary with another above it which was rotated by horse, water or wind-power, were used. Small quantities of spices can be ground with a **pestle and mortar** while small hand or electrically-operated grinders with serrated steel discs are used for coffee, as well as spices. Small grinders are usually obtainable as attachments to modern **food processors**. Corn grinding requires a great deal of energy and is rarely carried out in the home, although grinders for this purpose are available, but expensive. See **milling**.

grissini Italian speciality of long finger-like sticks of bread cooked to crispness and served to accompany meals.

groats Coarse oatmeal, made from **oats** from which the **husks** have been removed.

ground-nuts See **peanuts**.

ground-nut oil Also known as peanut oil and arachis oil. A good all-purpose oil extracted from **peanuts**.
NUTRITIONAL VALUE: fat saturated 20%, monounsaturated 50%, polyunsaturated 30%.
ENERGY per 100g: 900 kcal, 3766 kJ.
USES: for cooking, in salad dressings, preserving such as in canned fish, in the manufacture of margarine.

grouper Name given to several varieties of

large fish of the **bass** family, with firm white flesh. Usually found in warm waters, including the Mediterranean.

NUTRITIONAL VALUE: protein 18%, fat 2–4%.

ENERGY per 100g: 89 kcal, 372 kJ.

USES: grilled or baked, suitable for kebabs and barbecues.

grouse *Lagopus scoticus*. A **game**-bird; usually refers to the red grouse which is only found in Scotland, parts of Northern England, Wales and the West of Ireland. It is considered the finest of all game birds.

SEASON: 12th August–10th December.

NUTRITIONAL VALUE: protein 20%, fat less than 4%.

ENERGY per 100g: roast: 196 kcal, 820 kJ.

USES: young birds are best roasted, whilst older birds, which may be tough, are used in such dishes as casseroles, raised pies, pates. They are sometimes marinated first.

gruel A thin soup-like food prepared by boiling **groats**; of Scottish origin. Other grains may be used. See **adlay**.

Gruyère A hard full-fat Swiss cheese, originally made in Gruyère, with a characteristic flavour. It takes 10 months to mature fully. It is sometimes confused with **Emmental**, but the latter has large holes in it and Gruyère should have none or only a few very small ones. Like most hard cheeses with a low water-content, it keeps well when wrapped to exclude air, under cool conditions. It can be refrigerated for storage. Mild and mature varieties are available. Two similar cheeses, made in France, are Gruyère de Beaufort and Gruyère de Comte.

NUTRITIONAL VALUE: average: protein 22%, fat 25%, mostly saturated.

ENERGY per 100g: average: 313 kcal, 1310 kJ.

USES: as a table cheese and in cooked dishes. It is an essential ingredient of Swiss cheese **fondue**.

guacomole A Mexican speciality **sauce** or **dip** based on ripe **avocado pear**.

guinea corn See **sorghum**.

guinea fowl *Numida meleagris*. A bird related to the pheasant, originally from West Africa. It has been domesticated in the UK since the 15th century.

NUTRITIONAL VALUE: protein 20%, fat content very low.

ENERGY per 100g: roast: 240 kcal, 1004 kJ.

USES: as the flesh is rather dry it is best **larded**, or stuffed with a fatty stuffing prior to roasting. It can also be casseroled.

gums Substances which are exudates from trees or shrubs or extracted from seeds and belong to the group known as non-starch polysaccharides; they cannot be digested in the small intestine but are fermented in the large bowel. They are hard when dry but become thick and viscous when mixed with water; widely used in commercial food preparations as **emulsifiers**, stabilisers and thickeners in sugar confectionery, delaying crystallisation and improving texture and smoothness in ice-cream, mousses, cream toppings. Generally they have little food value. Some 16 gums are listed as food **additives** within the range E400 to E416.

Those commonly used are:–

Gum arabic. Also known as Gum acacia. A naturally occurring gum from the stems of varieties of acacia.

Guar gum. Prepared from the seeds of a legume *Cyamopsis tetragonoloba*. It delays emptying of the stomach and is used in some slimming preparations.

Gum tragacanth. Prepared from the subtropical thorny shrub of Southern Europe, *Astragulus tragacantha*.

Gum-like materials are also obtained from seaweed and some gums are prepared synthetically. See **chewing gum**.

guarama A preparation from the seeds of a climbing shrub, *Paullonia cupano*, a native of tropical South America, used to make a beverage, because of its flavour and **caffeine** content, as an alternative to **cocoa**.

guava *Psidium guava* or *Psidium cattleyanum*. An exotic and highly aromatic tropical pear-shaped fruit with many hard seeds.

NUTRITIONAL VALUE: vitamin C up to 200mg per 100g.

USES: as a dessert, in fruit salads and for jams and preserves.

gumbo or **gombo** Another name for **okra**, *Hibiscus esculentus*, also known as lady's finger, bamya.

gunga pea See **red gram**.

gur A toffee-like concentrate made from the sap in sugar-cane, a form of crude sugar. Also known as **jaggery** in India and Sri Lanka where it is made from the sap of coconut palm.

gurnard A marine fish, small to medium in size with spiny fins, non-oily.

NUTRITIONAL VALUE: protein 18—20%, fat less than 2%.

ENERGY per 100g: 80 kcal, 335 kJ.

USES: baked, poached or steamed.

H

haberdine The fish **cod** which has been salted and dried.

hachis See **hash**.

haddock *Melanogrammus aeglefinus*. A small member of the **cod** family, slightly larger than **whiting** and common in the North Atlantic. It is often smoked. See **finnan**, **smokies**.

NUTRITIONAL VALUE: protein 16—18%, fat 0.5—1.0%, vitamin B complex, minerals.

ENERGY per 100g: average: 75 kcal, 314 kJ.

USES: lends itself to most methods of cooking.

haemoglobin An **iron**-containing **protein** which is the red colouring matter in red blood cells. As it passes through the lungs, haemoglobin combines with oxygen and carries it to tissues throughout the body. Oxyhaemoglobin, arterial blood, fully oxygenated, is bright red, but becomes dusky-blue when the oxygen is removed,

as in venous blood. **Anaemia**, a reduced level of haemoglobin in the blood, may be caused in several ways, one being lack of iron in the diet. Haemoglobin combines readily with the poisonous **gas**, carbon monoxide, forming carboxyhaemoglobin, causing the blood to become cherry-red in colour (when it may be confused with oxygenated blood). This prevents the blood from carrying oxygen to the tissues, with potentially fatal consequences.

haggis A Scottish dish made of chopped heart, lights, liver, onions, oats, suet and herbs packed into a sheep's stomach and boiled. Traditionally eaten on Burns' night, January 25th and 'addressed' by a speaker.

hake *Merluccius merluccius*. A marine demersal round-bodied **fish** of good flavour, related to **cod**. See **fish worms**.

NUTRITIONAL VALUE: protein 18%, fat 1%, vitamin B complex, vitamin D, calcium.

ENERGY per 100g: 80 kcal, 334 kJ.

USES: filleted or on the bone can be baked, grilled, fried, poached or steamed.

halal See **religious laws**, **Muslim**.

halam See **religious laws**, **Muslim**.

halva See **sesame**.

halibut *Hippoglossus hippoglossus*. The largest of the white flatfish, which can weigh from 0.75–180kg, found in the Atlantic. It has a dry, firm texture, coarser in larger fish.

NUTRITIONAL VALUE: protein 18%, fat less than 2%, vitamin B complex, vitamin D, calcium.

ENERGY per 100g: 160 kcal, 670 kJ.

USES: filleted, or on the bone, it lends itself to most methods of cooking.

halibut, Greenland A much smaller species of **halibut** with flesh of a softer texture.

halibut–liver oil One of the richest natural sources of the oil-soluble **vitamins A** and **D**.

USES: commonly used as a vitamin A and D supplement.

halophilic bacteria Bacteria which can survive in concentrations of up to 10–25% salt, at which level other organisms are destroyed or suppressed. The group includes some **food poisoning** bacteria and **yeasts**.

ham The thigh or hindleg of a mammal, which has been cured after its removal from the carcass; generally from the **pig**, but traditionally has been made with mutton (it still is in Muslim countries) and, long ago, from badger. Those made from mutton are common in the Middle East where **religious laws** forbid pig meat. There are a large number of speciality hams which vary according to the method of preparation and **curing**. Districts and countries have developed their own versions, some being **smoked**. See **gammon**, **preservation**.

NUTRITIONAL VALUE: variable: boiled: protein 16–20%, fat 11–40%, vitamin B complex, iron, sometimes high in salt.

ENERGY per 100g: boiled: 166–440 kcal, 695–1840 kJ.

USES: often requires soaking for up to 12hrs to remove excess salt, although this depends on the curing method. It is cooked by boiling or roasting or a combination of the two, and served hot or cold.

hamburger A flat, circular cake made of finely minced or ground meat, named after Hamburgh steak. It is associated with the USA, and is traditionally made with 100% lean beef, grilled over charcoal and served between the two halves of a large bread roll with raw or fried onions and tomato ketchup or relish. Hamburgers can be purchased ready to cook but this should be from a reliable source; they have been a cause of **food poisoning**, due to being kept for too long, in too high a temperature, before cooking or to inadequate cooking, particularly in fast-food outlets. They are sometimes called beefburgers.

hammer–mill A system for grinding **cereals** by repeated hammer blows. Essentially a mechanised version of grinding by pounding in a mortar.

hand The foreleg and adjacent meat of the pig.

hangi A method of cooking in New Zealand, using the natural steam of a geyser. The food is wrapped in cotton and placed in a pit over a source of steam escaping from the ground, covered and left for several hours.

hanging The suspension of **meat**, or a whole animal or bird, for a period to allow for natural tenderising processes of **autolysis** to take place. Game animals and birds are usually hung before they are eviscerated in order that they can develop flavour.

hangover See **congeners**.

hardening of oils See **fat – hardening of**.

hard water See **water**.

hare A wild rodent, related to the rabbit but usually larger and with long hindlegs. Considered a delicacy but requires **hanging** and long, slow cooking to tenderise it. See **jugged hare**.

haricot bean *Phaseolus vulgaris*. The **French bean**, kidney bean or haricot vert. The term usually refers to the .dried seeds, which keep well in dry conditions in closed containers at room temperature. They are usually white, but there are a number of varieties such as **flageolet**, **brown Dutch beans**.

NUTRITIONAL VALUE: cooked: protein 6.5%, carbohydrate 16%, calcium, iron.

ENERGY per 100g: cooked: 100 kcal, 418 kJ.

USES: soaked for up to 8 hours and then boiled until soft as a vegetable, in casseroles, for baked beans. Salt should not added until after they are cooked.

harissa A strong mixture of spices and herbs with hot chilli, used in North African cooking, where it is a form of **garam masala**.

hash A mixture of meat and/or vegetables which have been cut up into small pieces.

haslet A form of large **faggot** made with added spices and herbs, cooked together in a **caul**, and sliced to be eaten cold.

haybox cooking A method whereby food is partly cooked and placed hot in a well-insulated container, retaining enough heat for cooking to be completed.

hazelnut *Corylus avellana*. The round edible nut of a member of the birch family and extensively grown. It keeps well in its shell under cool dry conditions. Shelled it tends to become **rancid** and should always be stored in an airtight container under cool

conditions. Nuts which show a growth of mould may contain **mycotoxins** and should not be eaten.

NUTRITIONAL VALUE: average: protein 18%, fat 50%, mostly unsaturated, carbohydrate 5%, vitamin B complex.

ENERGY per 100g: average: 540 kcal, 2259 kJ.

USES: as a dessert nut, in sweetmeats and in various sweet, savoury and vegetarian dishes.

head–cheese Another name for **brawn**, so called because it is made of meat from the pig's head.

health food A term coined for a range of foods prepared from crops which are grown without the use of artificial fertilisers, pesticides, fungicides and weed-control chemicals, or from animals reared under natural conditions without artificial diets or hormone supplements; also known as organically produced foods.

It also covers food supplements such as **vitamins**, **amino acids**, **minerals**, **ginseng**, **royal jelly** and **evening primrose oil**. There is no sound evidence that those who have a well-balanced diet would be healthier if they took such supplements. They are only required by those whose food supplies are inadequate and lacking in essential substances, by reason of disability, disease or opportunity. There is indeed a risk of taking too much of some of these substances. Particular care is required with babies and children who are less tolerant of some food supplements than adults. See **organic**.

heart The muscular organ responsible for the circulation of blood. Those of animals and used as food are classed as offal. Heart can be tough unless taken from a young animal; that from pig or lamb is best for eating. It can be tenderised by **marinading**.

NUTRITIONAL VALUE: protein 20%, fat variable, but relatively high, mostly saturated (much can be cut away in preparation), vitamin B complex, iron.

ENERGY per 100g: 108—180 kcal, 451—753 kJ.

USES: usually stuffed and baked or braised, in casseroles.

heavy metals A group of metals including **lead**, **mercury**, **cadmium**, **arsenic**, which are intensely poisonous. They get into the food chain, affecting crops and seafood, mainly through water which has been polluted by sewage and smoke from industrial effluents.

hemlock The true hemlock, *Conium maculatum*, is a common, attractive, hardy, and highly poisonous herb with purple stems, growing wild, up to 2 metres in height, with clusters of small blue flowers. All parts of the plant are poisonous. The poison can get into the food chain through **quail**, which are tolerant of it and eat the seeds. There have been fatalities from excessive consumption of quail in areas where hemlock abounds.

The conifer, *Abies mariana*, known as Hemlock Spruce is unrelated and the growing tips of its leaf shoots are used as a flavouring agent for **beer** in Northern Europe, particularly in Norway and Russia. Another conifer, *Tsuga canadensis*, is the source of hemlock-oil, also used for the same purpose. The flavour is resinous in character, similar to the flavouring used in Retsina wines of Greece.

hen A female domestic fowl or game-bird and also sometimes refers to female fish and crustaceans. See **pullet**, **capon**, **chicken**, **broiler**.

henbane *Hyocyamus nigra*. A hardy herb found in the wild, with about 4—5 coarse teeth on the leaf edges, bearing yellowish, trumpet-shaped flowers and black berries. It contains hyoscine, which has valuable medicinal properties similar to the related

drug, atropine, found in **deadly-night-shade**. An overdose, of these drugs, is highly poisonous.

hepatitis A serious infective disease of the **liver**, characterised by damage to liver function and by jaundice. There are at least five forms of infective hepatitis, named A, B, C, D and E. Hepatitis A is the most common and least-serious, causing a lower mortality than the others. It is transmitted through water polluted by sewage, and from food contaminated by such water, particularly seafood such as **molluscs**. Hepatitis A is avoided by taking the usual precautions of drinking safe water and, if abroad, consuming hot food, or cold food only where there are high standards of **hygiene**.

Hepatitis B,C,D and E are more serious and acquired by contact with blood of a carrier, gaining entry through a wound of the skin or from a contaminated syringe needle; hence it is common among drug addicts. Damage to the liver may occur from several other infections and chemical agents, in particular **alcohol**. See **travel**.

herbal remedies Many plants contain substances of medicinal value which have been used over the centuries. Unfortunately the content of active ingredient may vary with growing conditions, variety, and time of harvesting. Some of the active ingredients have great potency and, although they are valuable as drugs, they can cause serious harm in the wrong dose; few of the popular herbal remedies are standardised. Some should never be used, these include **cannabis**, foxglove, poppy. All herbal remedies should be taken with care and purchased from reliable sources.

herbivore An animal which only eats food of vegetable origin such as grass, leaves, roots, seeds and fruit, as opposed to a carnivore which eats other animals.

herbs Botanically, plants which do not have

a woody stem and are neither trees nor shrubs; exceptions include mint, thymes, sage and marjoram which do develop hard stems as they mature. In the culinary sense, the term refers to plants chosen for the flavour and aroma imparted by the **essential oils** present in their leaves and sometimes stems. Many have a long history of use since biblical times and are of mediterranean origin, although most will grow in temperate climates. They include:—

ANNUALS: **basil, borage, clary, chervil, coriander, dill, parsley, savory** (summer).

PERENNIALS: **angelica, balm, burnett, catmint, chive, fennel, horehound, hyssop, lovage, marjoram, mint, oregano, rosemary, rue, sage, southernwood, sweet-cicely, tansy, tarragon, thyme, savory** (winter).

USES: to enhance the flavour of food, for garnishing.

herring *Clupia harengus*. The largest **fish** in the group which includes sprats, pilchards and sardines. All are pelagic and have oily flesh. They used to be common around European coasts and were once the commonest and cheapest of **protein** foods but they have become more rare, due to over-fishing. However, recently supplies have improved because of controls on catches. **Kippers**, and **bloaters** are herring, variously salted and smoked. Herring is occasionally infested with the herring-worm, anisakiasis which is killed by cooking or pickling. See **fish worms**.

NUTRITIONAL VALUE: protein 18%, fat 15—20%, vitamin B complex, rich in vitamin A and vitamin D, calcium, iron, iodine.

ENERGY per 100g: average: 230 kcal, 962 kJ.

USES: cooked by grilling, frying or baking, pickled or cured in various ways.

hexamine (E239) Permitted food **preservative** prepared from benzene. May cause intestinal irritation and skin rashes in some individuals.

USES: in processed cheeses, preserved herring and mackerel.

hickory The family of *Carya*, which includes the **walnut, pecan nut**, and **mockernut** trees. They are mostly natives of North America.

higher alcohols A number of alcohols, more complex than **ethanol**, which are produced in small quantities during the fermentation process in the manufacture of wines and spirits and concentrated by distillation. See **congeners, fusel oil**.

hind A female deer. See **venison**.

hindberry See **bilberry**.

hindu See **religious laws**.

hob A heated surface for cooking by methods such as frying, boiling, simmering; may be heated by gas, oil, solid fuel or electricity using a heated element, high intensity tungsten halogen lamps or induction. See **ceramic hobs, inductive hobs**.

hock The hindleg of an animal.

hock A white wine originating in Hochheim, Germany and now refers to white wine produced in the Rhine Valley. It is always bottled in brown bottles.

ALCOHOL CONTENT: average 9%.

hollandaise sauce A sauce made with eggyolks and butter; usually served with fish, vegetables and eggs. There are a number of variations such as **béarnaise, mousseline**.

hominy A prepared form of **maize** or sweetcorn, which has been hulled by boiling or some other process and sometimes dried and ground.

NUTRITIONAL VALUE: almost pure **carbohydrate**.

USES: as an alternative to potatoes. Dried and ground, it is used in puddings or as a form of bread.

honey A sweet, syrupy and semi-solid substance which bees produce from **nectar**, secreted by the nectuary glands of flowers, or less often from **honeydew**, by removing some of the water and inverting any **sucrose** present. Each different source of nectar can influence the type of honey, although bees often collect from more than one source and the result is a mixed honey.

It contains a mixture of sugars, mainly **glucose** and **fructose** and when it has a high glucose content, such as that from **rape** nectar, it tends to crystallize very fast, whereas when it has a high fructose content, such as that from **lime**, it remains smooth and fairly liquid. Bees reduce the water content of nectar and honeydew to 18% or less and the resultant honey will keep indefinitely.

Honey from ragwort (*Senecio jacobaea*, poisonous to animals) nectar has an unpleasant bitter taste and is unsuitable for human consumption and that from rhododendron nectar is poisonous, causing headaches, dizziness, vomiting. Hemp-flower honey contains **cannabis**.

Bees are subject to disease which can have serious consequences for the beekeeper; this can usually be traced to infection from containers, previously holding imported honey, which are left exposed and unwashed. All used containers should be cleaned or destroyed to prevent the spread of disease. See **honeycomb, royal jelly**.

NUTRITIONAL VALUE: carbohydrate (sugars) 80–85%, vitamin B complex.

ENERGY per 100g: 320–340 kcal, 1339–1422 kJ.

USES: mainly as a spread on bread, to sweeten stewed fruits, cakes and biscuits, drinks; also to make **mead**.

honeycomb The wax cells in the beehive in which the bees store **honey**. They are sealed with wax when they are full; it is also used to raise brood from eggs laid by the queen bee.

NUTRITIONAL VALUE: the wax cannot be digested and has no value.

USES: honey is sometimes sold in the comb and the wax is normally eaten with it. It is available in different forms:—
1. Individual wooden frames approximately 12cm square.
2. Cut from a large frame into blocks approximately 8 × 5cms.
3. In irregular chunks packed into a jar.

honeydew The secretion of aphids feeding on leaf-sap. Aphids extract the **protein** and discard the excess sweet sap which is collected by bees; in some areas it may replace nectar as the major source of sugars. In one area of New Zealand there is a particular source of honeydew from a unique aphid feeding on the trunks of a type of beech tree. Most honeys produced from honeydew are darker in colour and have a stronger flavour than those from **nectar**. Honey collected from conifer honeydew is bitter.

hop *Humulus lupulus*, a hardy perennial climbing plant related to the **mulberry** and grown for the bitter extract contained in the female flowers and used to flavour **beer**. The active principle is a mixture of **essential oils** and **resins** containing humulone and adhumulone. Most hops for making British beer are grown in the UK and several varieties are used for different types of beer. The hop extract used for **lagers** is imported.

horehound *Marrubium vulgare*. A half-hardy perennial herb of temperate zones; once used medicinally as a remedy for coughs but not nowadays.

hormones Chemical 'messengers', produced in the body by endocrine glands and transported in the bloodstream to other organs whose functions they control; similar agents in plants are called auxins and control plant growth. Examples of hormones are insulin, adrenaline, thyroxine, growth and sex hormones and **steroids**. Hormones have been used in farming to increase carcass weight and for the chemical castration of cockerels to produce **capons**. An experimental trial using hormones to increase milk production in dairy cows has recently been abandoned. Hormones can be present in meat and milk from treated animals and it is now illegal to administer them to animals whose meat or products are to be used for human consumption. See **thyroid gland**.

hors d'oeuvres A dish, usually savoury, served to whet the appetite before the main course of a meal: it can be a single item such as asparagus, globe artichoke, smoked salmon or a selection of six to eight different dishes including meat, fish, eggs and salads.

horse bean *Vicia faba*, another name for **broad bean**.

horse gram See **Madras gram**.

horse mackerel *Trachurus trachurus*. A distant relative of the common mackerel. Though abundant it is a large bony fish and not favoured for eating.

horsemeat Not commonly available in the UK for human consumption but is consumed on the continent. It has similar characteristics to **beef** but a lower **fat**-content.

NUTRITIONAL VALUE: protein 20%, fat 2–3%, vitamin B complex, calcium, iron.

ENERGY per 100g: 102 kcal, 427 kJ.

USES: as steaks and in casseroles. Also for pet food.

horse parsley See **alesander**.

horseradish A hardy perennial, *Cochliaria amoracia*, grown for the swollen root which has a pungent flavour due to an essential oil released by the enzyme **myrosinase** and activated during preparation.

USES: shredded and used as a condiment with meat, made into a sauce with butter or cream; traditionally served with roast beef, but also with fish such as mackerel.

horseradish tree *Monga oleifera*, a tropical tree which is a native of India. The roots are scraped and used in curries for their horseradish-like flavour.

hot cross bun A sweet bun risen with **yeast**, containing currants, candied peel and mixed spices, marked with a cross and glazed with sugar-syrup after cooking, while still hot. It is traditionally eaten on Good Friday.

hot dog An American fast-food; a **frankfurter** sausage cooked and put inside a bread roll, sometimes with fried onion and sauce, to be served hot.

hot-pot A traditional stew from the north of England cooked in an oven. Originally made with alternate layers of meat, mushrooms and oysters and topped with sliced potatoes. The term is used today for a simpler version without oysters but with onions and root vegetables added.

house wine Ordinary wine of the establishment.

Hovis A proprietary brown **bread** made with added **wheatgerm**, giving it a distinctive flavour and relatively high content of **vitamin B** complex and vitamin E.

huckleberry Another name for the whortleberry and **bilberry**.

humectant A substance which retains **water**. Used in products as different as tobacco, glues, inks and cakes. Humectants used in food preparation include glucose syrup, honey, glycerol and sorbitol.

humus or **hummus** A Middle Eastern dish

made of pureed **chick peas** and **tahina**, a preparation of crushed sesame seeds, flavoured with garlic and lemon.

husk The outer hard coat of **cereals** removed by threshing. It has no food value.

huss See **rock-salmon**.

hyacinth bean *Dolichos lablab*, sometimes known as *Lablabia vulgaris* and lablab bean. A tropical member of the pea and bean family and a native of India.

NUTRITIONAL VALUE: similar to other beans.

USES: grown for its edible leaves, pods and small black or brown beans which are used dried.

hydatid cyst The larval stage of the dog tapeworm, *Echinococcus*, and also found in related animals (fox and wolf). The eggs of the tapeworm are passed in dog faeces, they may then be swallowed by an intermediate host (sheep or some other herbivorous animal), and develop into larvae which form cysts in the liver and other organs. Dogs become infected by eating the entrails of infected animals. Man can also become infected by swallowing eggs of the tape worm passed in dog faeces. At first small, they may grow slowly over the years and become very large, sometimes containing many litres of fluid, with fatal results. The disease is now rare in Britain but still prevalent in some tropical countries where there is sheep-farming on a large scale. Dogs should be treated regularly with worming powders as a precaution and good **hygiene** observed.

hydrochloric acid A strong acid present in diluted form in the stomach and essential for the action of **pepsin**, a proteolytic enzyme, which operates only in an acid medium. A normal content of hydrochloric acid gives some protection against the common **food poisoning** organisms. People with a low level of acidity in the stomach, such as children, the elderly and infirm are more vulnerable to infection. The stomach is naturally protected from the acid but if it leaks upwards into the oesophagus, hydrochloric acid causes the painful condition known as heartburn. Occasional attacks can be treated by sitting upright and taking an antacid tablet. Medical advice is required for recurrent attacks.

hydrogen See **gas**.

hydrogenated vegetable oils Vegetable oils, high in polyunsaturated fats are treated by hydrogen, in the presence of a nickel **catalyst**, to harden them, by increasing the saturation, to form hard fats. They are used for **margarine**, **shortening**, **vegetable suet** and in place of **cocoa-butter** in the manufacture of **chocolate**.

hydrogen bonds Chemical bonds which are capable of linking **protein** molecules in such a manner that they can form a stable network. During the rapid beating of egg-white the bonds are temporarily broken and reform creating an environment favourable for the inclusion of air-bubbles to form a foam.

hydrolysed vegetable protein Known as HVP. A salty **protein** concentrate made by hydrolysing vegetable protein with **hydrochloric acid** and then neutralising with caustic soda. The usual source of protein is brewers' **yeast**. HVP has a meaty and salty flavour and contains **monosodium glutamate**; it is classed as a food rather than a food additive. It is the principle agent in flavouring concentrates such as **Marmite**, OXO, **stock cubes**.

NUTRITIONAL VALUE: protein 50%, vitamin B complex.

ENERGY per 100g: 200 kcal, 837 kJ.

USES: in flavouring sauces, soups, canned foods, proprietary meat products, pies.

hydrolysis The splitting of a substance into two or more parts by the addition of water, the process being activated by an **enzyme** or an acid. Hydrolysis is one of the essential processes that takes place in cooking, such as the breakdown of **starch**. It can also cause deterioration of food which contains **protein** or **fat**.

hydrometer An instrument for measuring the density of a liquid. Based on the principle that a suitably weighted glass float will submerge, according to the density of the fluid in which it is floating and so determine the specific gravity. Fluids containing substances denser than water, such as sugar, salts and acids, will cause the glass float to rest higher in the liquid than in a liquid containing alcohol, with a density less than water, which will allow the glass float to sink lower. The instrument has a stem marked in degrees of specific gravity and calibrated to read accurately at a stated temperature, usually around room temperature; errors occur if readings are taken at other temperatures. Hydrometers are used in wine and beer-making, to determine the concentration of sugars available for fermentation and to determine when fermentation has been completed. It is also used to check milk for dilution with water.

hygiene Named after Hygiea, the Greek Goddess of Health. The science of health, which, in the context of food, means scrupulous cleanliness of equipment used at all stages of production, to the final product for the table, the absolute cleanliness of hands and clothes of people involved, the purity of water and all food supplies.

Carriers of hazardous **bacteria** should not be allowed to handle food until they are free of the carrier state. However, the **staphylococcus** is so commonly present on the skin of healthy individuals that elimination of carriers of this organism is often impracticable. Pets should not be allowed in areas set aside for food storage, production or consumption.

All food must be fresh and free from any harmful bacteria, **moulds, parasites** and toxic chemicals. Strict rules are applied to storage of food in shops and institutions by refrigeration and guidance is readily available on the proper use of frozen food, chilled food and **microwave ovens**. See **food poisoning**. Travellers are at risk where high standards of hygiene are not practised (see **travel**).

hygroscopic The property of a substance to take up water from the air. Many food substances are hygroscopic, some strongly, such as common salt, calcium chloride and silica. The latter two are used to keep the contents of containers dry, preventing damp from damaging equipment and preventing foodstuffs such as biscuits from becoming soft.

hyper A prefix denoting an excess above normal and often used in connection with chemical substances circulating in the blood or body fluids. Thus:—

Hypercalcaemia is an excess of calcium salts in the blood, which can be due to too much **vitamin D**.

Hyperchlorhydria is an excess of hydrochloric acid in the stomach which may cause duodenal ulcers.

Hyperglycaemia is an excess of glucose in the blood and an indication of **diabetes**.

Hypertonic is a solution strong enough to gain water through a membrane which separates it from a weaker solution.

Hyperthyroidism is an excess of the **thyroid** hormones.

Hypervitaminosis is an excess of **vitamins**.

hypo A prefix which denotes below normal, the opposite of **hyper**. Thus:—

Hypokalaemia is a deficiency of potassium in the blood which may cause muscle weakness and heart irregularities. The condition is rare and in the UK is most commonly due to the effects of taking diuretic drugs.

Hypoproteinaemia is a deficiency of **protein** in the blood. This can result from famine and a variety of medical conditions, including liver disorders and impairment of absorption.

Hypotonic is a weak solution, the reverse of hypertonic.

hyssop *Hysoppus officinalis*. A perennial **herb** related to thyme. It is hardy in Southern Europe, with blue flowers and aromatic leaves.

USES: the leaves were used more often in the past for such foods as soups. The oil distilled from the leaves is used in liqueurs such as Chartreuse.

I

Iberian moss Same as **carrageen**.

ice Water which is cooled to below 0°C or 32°F, and becomes solid; in this state its volume is increased. Extensively used for conserving foods at a low temperature where refrigeration is inappropriate, such as fish caught at sea, in transit or on sale in fishmongers. Also used for cooling drinks and, mixed with common salt, as a refrigerant for ice-cream making where it is possible to achieve a temperature as low as −21°C (−5.8°F).

Ice used in drinks should be made from water safe for drinking, otherwise it may become a source of **food poisoning**. See **dry ice**, **travel − risks of disease**.

Iceland moss *Cetraria islandica*. A **lichen** and not a plant or moss; the only lichen used as a food. It requires repeated soaking to remove a bitter taste before being dried and ground into a flour to make a form of bread, or boiled with water to form a jelly.

ice-cream A confection variably based on fats, sugar, milk, flavourings and sometimes colouring, then frozen. The formation of ice crystals is prevented by stirring during freezing and by the addition of such substances as **gelatine**, **gums**, emulsifiers and stabilisers such as **carboxymethyl cellulose**. Most ice-cream is whipped to incorporate air, reduce density and improve texture. Ice-cream sold in multiple-helping packs must have the contents listed. The **fats** in most ice-creams are of vegetable origin; only milk-fats are used in the manufacture of **dairy** ice-cream.

NUTRITIONAL VALUE: protein 7−20%, fat 5−12%, carbohydrate 10−22%.

ENERGY per 100g: 110−270 kcal, 460−1130 kJ.

icing Sugar-based topping for cakes; also known as frosting.

ignition point See **fat − effects of heat** and **safety in use**.

immunity The ability of the body to defend itself against infection. A reduction in immunity may have a number of causes of which undernourishment is one.

Indian corn See **maize, corn**.

Indian cress See **nasturtium**.

Indian date See **tamarind**.

Indian fig See **prickly pear**.

Indian hemp See **cannabis**.

Indian rice See **rice, wild**.

Indonesian food Highly-spiced food usually served in many individual dishes for each person. In restaurants, 20–40 separate dishes may be served in a full meal.

inductive cooker-hobs Hobs powered by a recently introduced form of energy transfer, whereby an intense magnetic field is created at a frequency of 25 Hertz, developing heat in iron saucepans. The hob itself does not get hot and it is ineffective with utensils made of non-magnetic metals such as aluminium. The system has a safety device which prevents operation unless an iron saucepan covers the inducer. The power used is in the order of 1100 watts. The makers, a well-known cardiology department and independent observers have carried out exhaustive tests and shown that there is no danger for users fitted with cardiac pacemakers.

ink fish A cuttlefish or **squid**.

insects Insects are animals with an external skeleton found on land and in water. Many are used as food in different countries, although most Europeans only eat those found in the sea such as **prawns**, **shrimps**. Larvae of the honey-bee and silk-worms are highly prized among some native populations of Africa. See **cochineal, colour, kermes**.

instant food Food dried in the form of powder or granules which can be rapidly reconstituted with water. The group includes milk, coffee, tea, fruit juices and foods such as soups and potato.

insulin A **hormone** secreted by specialised cells in the pancreas which controls the metabolism of glucose. Deficiency of insulin occurs in **diabetes**.

intestine The digestive tract beyond the stomach, divided into two parts: the small intestine, where food is digested, includes the duodenum, jejunum and ileum, totalling about 4–5 m in length and the large intestine, about 1m in length, which includes the caecum, colon and rectum, where water and some salts are absorbed. Recent work has shown the importance of the large intestine as a digestive zone where complex polysaccharides, known collectively as **dietary fibre**, together with some proteins, are broken down.

inulin A polysaccharide sugar, composed of fructose molecules, naturally present in the tubers of **Jerusalem artichokes** and some **pulses**. It is not affected by the digestive enzymes but passes through to the large bowel where it is fermented by bacteria normally present. See **dietary fibre**, **flatus**.

inversion See **invertase**.

invert sugar A syrupy mixture of glucose and fructose, so called because the optical rotation of sucrose is inverted by the more highly laevorotatory power of fructose and distinguished by polarised light. Invert sugar is 30% sweeter than sucrose. Inversion of sugar takes place during cooking and this accounts for the difference in taste of food according to whether sugar is added before or after cooking. See **sugar**.

USES: to sweeten drinks and in the manufacture of confectionery to prevent crystallisation.

invertase An **enzyme** which can convert the double molecule of sucrose to two single molecules glucose and fructose, a process known as inversion. Invertase occurs naturally in plants and digestive juices of animals, including bees. See **invert sugar**.

iodine A **trace element** essential to the functioning of the thyroid gland, present in seafoods, meat, milk and milk products. A deficiency in the diet can result in the condition known as **goitre**.

iodine value An index of the degree of saturation of fats determined by the uptake of **iodine** by 100g of fat. The greater the proportion of unsaturated fats present, the higher the value. Examples:– coconut-oil 15–20%, butter 26–38%, lard 47–67%, vegetable-oils 80–100%, olive-oil 80–90%. See **fat, oil.**

iodised salt Common **salt** to which 1 part of potassium iodide has been added to 25–50,000 of parts of salt. Used in areas deficient in **iodine** to prevent **goitre.** See **potassium.**

Irish moss A seaweed with green or purple fronds which grows on rocks in deep water and is harvested at low spring tides. See **carrageenan** *(E407).*

NUTRITIONAL VALUE: none.

USES: as a gelling agent and thickener for mousses, cakes, desserts ice-cream and many other proprietary products.

Irish stew A stew made with mutton, onions and potatoes and sometimes pearl barley.

iron An element essential for the formation of **haemoglobin**, the oxygen-carrying component of blood and myoglobin, a similar red pigment in muscle. It is also essential in some **enzyme** systems. Iron is present in all red meats, liver, most fish, dairy products, cereals and some vegetables. A low intake of iron is one of the causes of **anaemia.** There is sufficient iron present in a mixed **diet** and supplements are not normally necessary. Iron deficiency can occur with repeated blood loss as with heavy menstrual periods, disorders of the intestinal tract, in strict **vegetarians**, and others for any reason on a restricted diet. In the past, the use of iron cooking-vessels compensated for any iron deficiency in the diet by dissolving slowly in the food being cooked. Iron is toxic when taken in excess which can then have serious consequences, particularly in children and infants.

iron oxides (E172) Permitted red, orange or black food colouring from naturally occurring oxides.

irradiation Treatment of food by exposure to ionising radiation (X-rays) is a recently introduced method of food **preservation.** In relatively small doses ionising radiation kills **micro-organisms, insect pests** and **parasites** and retards ripening processes in fruit and vegetables. By this method food can be made safe, **food poisoning** and food-borne diseases prevented and shelf-life extended. Irradiated food is safe, there is no residual radio-activity and the taste is not impaired.

Strict regulations are in force throughout the EEC to control irradiation of food and ensure that only fresh, high-quality produce is treated and ultimately sold to the public.

ischaemic heart disease Partial or complete blockage of one or more of the coronary arteries which supply the heart muscle with blood. The disease is due to an accumulation of fatty substances in the walls of the vessels, together with blood clots. The condition is often associated with a high level of **cholesterol** in the blood, other main risk-factors being raised blood pressure, smoking and **diabetes.** Prevention of the disease is the main reason for trying to reduce the prevailing **fat** intake to, at most, 35% of energy and for the substitution of saturated fats by unsaturated fats. **Diet** should be mixed and include **dietary fibre** and the anti-oxidant **vitamins A, C** and **E.**

isinglas A pure form of **gelatine** prepared from the swim-bladder of sturgeon and other fish.

USES: mainly for clarifying **beers** and **wines.**

isomer Molecules made of the same atoms but arranged in different order. Some have altered properties while others are similar.

isotonic Having the same osmotic pressure (the same power to attract a weaker solution). Two isotonic solutions separated by a semipermeable membrane will not move through it. Thus, fruits cooked in an isotonic solution of sugar remain whole, but in a hypotonic (weak) solution they burst their skins and in a hypertonic (strong) one they shrivel.

isotopes Elements which have the same chemical properties but exist in more than one form, having different atomic weights. Isotopes are often unstable and radioactive. Radioactive isotopes are used as markers to trace biological pathways and have a major role in investigating normal and abnormal functions in human, animal and plant systems.

J

jack bean *Canavalia ensiformis*, a tropical bush or climbing plant; a native of Brazil.

NUTRITIONAL VALUE: similar to **runner beans** when fresh, **haricot beans** when dried.

USES: cooked in the pod when fresh and as **haricot beans** when dried; also sometimes used as a coffee substitute.

jackfruit The large fruit, weighing up to 50kg, of the tropical tree *Artocarpus intergrifolius*, which is closely related to the **bread fruit**; it has a nutritious pulp and large seeds.

NUTRITIONAL VALUE: pulp: protein 2.5%, carbohydrate 10%, vitamin B complex. Seeds: protein 3.5%, carbohydrate 30%.

ENERGY per 100g: pulp, 50 kcal, 209 kJ. Seeds, 134 kcal, 560 kJ.

USES: if eaten raw, it is best soaked overnight to remove a bitter taste and unpleasant smell; it can be cooked and used as a vegetable. The seeds are roasted and may be ground into flour. The fruit and seeds are used in curries.

Jaffa orange A premium grade orange from Israel and named after the port from which it is traditionally exported. See **citrus fruits**.

jaffarine A cross between a **grapefruit** and **tangerine**.

jaggery A coarse, dark, unrefined sugar made from the sap of some palm-trees, including the coconut palm, often aromatic and used as a flavouring in Indian dishes, such as curry and in sweetening milk.

jam A **preserve** of fruit and sugar cooked to a temperature of 104°C (220°F), known as setting-point, so that it produces a **gel** when cold. This is due to the **pectin** present in the fruit. Fruits which have a low natural pectin-content, such as strawberries, require additional pectin to aid setting and this can be added in the form of purified pectin or another fruit with a high pectin-content, such as lemon. Minimum fruit contents in commercially-made jams are legally enforceable and vary with the fruit; they include strawberry 38%, blackcurrant 25%, gooseberry 30%, raspberry 30% and marmalade 20%.

jam keeping Jam can be contaminated by **moulds** or **yeasts** normally present in the air, but not if the jar is sealed immediately while the jam is still hot, so that any moulds on the surface are killed. Moulds will grow at any time after the container has been opened. Some jam-covers allow the evaporation of water and crystallisation occurs, which is not harmful. Jams made with a low sugar-content are more likely to grow moulds or ferment and those made with uncooked fresh fruits, known as freezer jams, must be kept frozen until required. Moulds may produce dangerous **mycotoxins** capable of seeping into the jam and there is a theoretical risk of poisoning. However, most people are prepared to take the very slight risk of removing the mould, together with an underlying layer of jam, and heating the remainder to destroy any residual spores rather than destroying all the contents of the jar.

Jamaica pepper See **allspice**.

Jamaica sorrel *Hibiscus sabdariffa*, a tropical annual plant with yellow flowers, which have a fleshy calyx with an acidic flavour.
USES: the calyces can be made into a **jelly** preserve.

jamberry See **tomatillo**.

Japanese medlar See **loquat**.

Japanese parsley See **coriander**.

jardinière A mixture of spring vegetables.

jaundice A state of yellowing of the skin and eyes, due to a build up of natural bile pigments, as a result of obstruction to the biliary system, liver diseases such as viral **hepatitis** or an increase in pigment due to excessive breakdown of blood.

jelly A clear sweet or savoury substance which is solid or semi-solid when cold; it becomes liquid when hot. Its main constituent is **gelatine** and forms when meat or poultry containing skin and bones are boiled in water and the resultant liquid cooled. Sweet jellies are made by boiling strained fruit juices with sugar and adding dissolved proprietary gelatine, or by dissolving a proprietary, flavoured gelatine product, available in block or liquid form, in boiling water.

Fruit jellies are also made, as **preserves**, by dissolving sugar in strained fruit juice and boiling until setting point is reached (104°C, 220°F); the **pectin** present in the fruit acting as the gelling agent. See **aspic**.

USES: meat and poultry based jellies as a basis for sauces, moulds containing meat, fish, chicken, vegetables, as a glaze. Sweet jellies based on proprietary gelatine products are often set in decorative moulds and served as desserts. Fruit jellies are used as jam, glaze, and sometimes as an accompaniment to meat dishes, particularly redcurrant jelly, traditionally served with roast lamb and game.

jelly-bag A bag made of finely woven cotton, wool or synthetic fibres used for extracting clear juice from fruit in the making of **jelly** preserves.

jeroboam A large wine-bottle equal to 6 ordinary wine or 4 champagne bottles.

jeropiga See **geropiga**.

Jerusalem artichoke *Helianthus tuberosus*. See **artichoke, Jerusalem**.

Jesuits' bark See **quinine**.

Jesuits' bread See **water-chestnut**.

Jew's ear Also known as Judas' ear fungus and jelly fungus, *Himeola auricular*. A soft floppy reddish fungus which grows on dead trees and is considered a delicacy.

jicana See **water-chestnut**.

Job's tears See **adlay**.

John dory *Zeus faber*. A marine fish with a

large head, which may reach a weight up to 9kg. The flesh is white and has a fine flavour; some say that this is improved if the fish is kept refrigerated for two or three days before cooking.

NUTRITIONAL VALUE: protein 18%, fat 1–2%, calcium, iron.

ENERGY per 100g: 85 kcal, 355 kJ.

USES: lends itself to most methods of cooking but is best poached or baked.

joule The international unit of energy. The joule itself is too small for practical purposes and the kilojoule, written kJ, equal to 1000 joules is generally used. There are 4.184 kJ in one kcal (1000 **calories** = 1 kcal).

jowar Indian name for **sorghum**.

jubjube A subtropical deciduous tree or shrub, *Zizyphus jubjuba*, also known as the lotus tree, which produces edible and pleasantly-flavoured fruits. The fruit of another closely related species, *Zizyphus lotus*, is eaten as a cult, because it is reputed to induce forgetfulness and indolence. The latter is the most likely food of the Lotus Eaters of mythology.

USES: eaten fresh or preserved in sugar-syrup and dried. Jubjubes are sweetmeats made to look like these fruits.

jugged hare A classic method of cooking **hare**. Traditionally, the jointed animal was packed in a stoneware jar or jug with beef gravy, port or other red wine, flavouring such as cloves, lemon peel, then the jar was immersed to its neck in a pan of boiling water for 2–4 hours, depending on the age of the animal. When cooked the gravy was thickened with the hare's blood. It may also be cooked directly in a stew-pan, but long, slow cooking and the use of the blood are essential to the authenticity of the dish.

junket Milk coagulated with **rennet** to form a curd. See **religious laws – Jewish**.

USES: eaten sweetened as a dessert.

juniper *Juniperous communis*. A hardy member of the *Pineae* family producing small cones which contain the fruits or berries. A fragrant **essential oil** can be distilled from the wood of some varieties and from the cones of others.

USES: as a flavouring in the making of **gin**. The dried berries are sometimes used to flavour casseroles and other savoury dishes.

K

K The chemical symbol for **potassium**.

kabab See **kebab**.

kaffir corn See **sorghum**.

kaffir beer Beer brewed from **sorghum** and malted sorghum.

kai-kai A New Zealand term for a feast.

kaoliang The Chinese variety of **sorghum**.

kakee The Chinese **persimmon** or date-plum, *Dyospyros kaki*. A sweet, yellow-orange coloured, many-seeded tropical fruit; although, if the fruit is not fertilised, there may be no seeds. Exported from Israel under the name Sharon fruit.
USES: as a dessert fruit and in fruit salads.

kale *Brassica olereacea acephala*. A hardy member of the cabbage family grown for its edible curly leaves; available during winter and spring.
NUTRITIONAL VALUE: protein 1%, vitamin A, vitamin B complex, vitamin C, dietary fibre.
ENERGY per 100g: negligible.
USES: cooked as a vegetable.

kangaroo An Australian marsupial.
USES: the large tail is the only part tender enough for human consumption and is used for soups; the rest is used for pet foods.

karo syrup A proprietary syrup based on starch, dextrin, maltose, glucose and sucrose; used to modify milk preparations for infant feeding.

karya gum (416) A gum prepared from varieties of the *sterculia* family, tropical trees and shrubs of South-East Asia.
USES: as a stabiliser in processed cheese, sauces and piccalilli and to prevent ice-crystal formation in sorbets and ice-cream.

kasha See **buckwheat**.

katemfe A tropical fruit, *Thaumatococcus danielli*, which contains an intensely sweet substance called thaumatin. See **artificial sweeteners**.

kebab or brochette. Pieces of meat, fish, vegetables placed on a skewer and cooked under a **grill** or on a **barbecue**. Fruits are sometimes cooked in the same way.

kedgeree The name is derived from the Indian 'khicri' which is basically a dish of rice and pulses cooked together, with various spices. The British version, traditionally a breakfast dish, is made with fish, usually smoked **haddock**, with rice and chopped hard-boiled egg.

keeling A Scottish variety of **cod**.

kelp Seaweed with large broad fronds used as a source of **alginates** both for food and in commerce.

keratin An insoluble, tough **protein** found in hair, nails, feathers and the outermost layer of skin. Feathers can be processed for animal feed.

kermes A red dye extracted from the dried body of the female of the insect, *Coccus ilicus* which lives in the kermes or holly-oak.
USES: as a colouring agent similar to cochineal and in Kermes, a red, bitter-sweet French liqueur.

kernel The edible part of a nut which lies within a hard shell.
NUTRITIONAL VALUE: all contain protein

about 15%, fat about 50%, vitamin B complex.

keta See **sockeye**.

ketchup Also known as catchup or catsup. An oriental word now used to describe any spicy sauce based variously on fish, tomato, mushroom.

ketones A group of organic substances such as acetic acid and acetone which are normal breakdown products of fats and usually only present in small quantities.

ketosis The production of an excess of **ketones**, a state which occurs when there is a high dependence on fat for energy and in diabetics whose disease is not controlled.

kewra *Pandanus tectorius*, also known as screwpine, a tropical tree of South-East Asia and North Australia with aromatic male flowers and an edible stone-fruit; the flesh tastes somewhat like pineapple.
USES: as a flavouring in sweet dishes or dried and used in curries.

kid A young **goat**.

kingfish *Lamprisi*. The opah, a large marine **fish** found off the West African coast.

kidney One of a pair of organs which, in mammals, eliminate waste products of the blood and control fluid balance by excretion of urine. Reptiles and birds have comparable organs but they function in a different way and produce semi-solid residues. In the culinary context it is classed as offal.
NUTRITIONAL VALUE: protein 16%, fat 2–3%, vitamin B complex, iron.
ENERGY per 100g: raw: average: 87 kcal, 364 kJ.
USES: lambs' and calves' kidneys are best for frying and grilling; those of the pig and ox have a stronger flavour and are more suitable for the traditional steak and kidney pie or pudding, casseroles and soups. The strong flavour can be reduced

by soaking in milk or water with a little vinegar.

kidney-bean See **haricot bean**.

kilderkin A **barrel** or cask for **beer** which holds 18 gallons.

kinase A group of substances responsible for the activation of precursors of **enzymes**.

kipper A **herring** split open, salted and cool-smoked, giving it a strong flavour. There is a slight risk of parasitic worms being present that are not killed by the **smoking** process, and therefore, all kippers should be cooked. See **bloater**, **fishworms**.
NUTRITIONAL VALUE: protein 20%, fat 20%, mostly polyunsaturated, salt, calcium, iodine.
ENERGY per 100g: 260 kcal, 1088 kJ.
USES: poached or grilled, it is a traditional breakfast food in the UK. Also used in fish-pies and pâtés.

kirsch Also known as kirschwasser. A **liqueur** distilled from fermented wild cherries.
ALCOHOL CONTENT: 40%.

kiwano Also known as the horned melon. A tropical fruit, variety of *Cucumis melo*, the size of a small melon with a yellow skin bearing multiple horns. The flesh and seeds are edible. Recently introduced to the UK it has similar nutritional values and uses to **melon**.

kiwi fruit The name given in New Zealand to the Chinese gooseberry, *Actinidea chinensis*. A vigorous semi-hardy climbing plant bearing plum-sized, seeded fruits with a slightly acid flesh. The thin brownish skin is not edible. They are available throughout the year and are now also grown in Southern Europe and the Channel Islands. They can be grown in sheltered areas of the south of England but do not make a reliable commercial crop.

NUTRITIONAL VALUE: significant vitamin C content.

USES: as a dessert fruit, in fruit salads and other desserts and in preserves. Not suitable for jellies made with gelatine.

knacker One who slaughters animals unfit for human consumption. Animals suspected of, or suffering from, **bovine spongioform encephalopathy** must be incinerated and not used for animal or pet food.

kneading The process of energetically stretching bread dough in order to develop the gluten and rearrange the molecules; it increases the strength of the dough, enabling it to retain the maximum number of gas bubbles produced in the fermentation of yeast, to make a light textured loaf. See **Chorley Wood process**.

knocking back The process of compressing bread dough after the first rising, to eliminate any large gas bubbles and produce an even texture in the second rising.

kohlrabi *Brassica oleracea caulorapia*. A member of the cabbage family with an expanded stem looking like a turnip but growing above ground level; it has a mild turnip-like flavour

NUTRITIONAL VALUE: protein 2%, carbohydrate 6%, vitamin C 50–70mg per 100g.

ENERGY per 100g: 33 kcal, 138 kJ.

USES: boiled as a vegetable, sliced finely or grated and used raw in salads.

kola nut See **cola nut**.

kosher or **cosha** See **religious laws**.

koumiss A fermented drink made of soured mare's and cow's milk; it contains about 2% alcohol. A speciality of Eastern Russia.

kromeski Minced meat, chicken, ham or game made into small balls, wrapped in bacon then dipped in batter and deep fried. May be served as a savoury or main course.

kumara A New Zealand (Maori) term for the **sweet potato**.

krynga Similar to **koumiss** but made with all cow's milk.

kummel A liqueur made with **cumin** or **caraway** seeds. See **spirits**.

kumquat *Fortunella japonica*, also known as *Citrus japonica* and closely related to the **orange**; native of China, Japan and Malaysia. The trees produce very small, orange-like fruits.

NUTRITIONAL VALUE: including skin: vitamin C.

ENERGY per 100g: 30 kcal, 125 kJ.

USES: fresh fruit is eaten whole or sliced in fruit salads and other desserts and cooked in some savoury dishes.

kwashiorkor See **protein**.

L

lablab bean See **hyacinth bean**.

lacquer The protective coat on the lining of cans to protect against the corrosive action of food-acids. Also the glossy coating on certain food substances such as sweets and medicinal tablets, for protection or decoration. Lacquers are classed as food additives and include **beeswax (901)**, **carnauba wax (903)**, **shellac (904)**.

lactase An **enzyme**, secreted by glands of the small **intestine** which splits **lactose** into **galactose** and glucose. It is also present in some plants.

lactic acid (**E270** and related compounds **E472b**) The **acid** formed in **milk** by the action of the *lactobacillus* on lactose. The process is associated with the production of some butyric acid, which accounts for the rancid smell of sour milk. Lactic acid is made commercially by the **fermentation** of **carbohydrate**; it is also formed in the manufacture of **yoghurt**, hard **cheeses** and of **sauerkraut** (when this does not depend on vinegar), assisting in their keeping qualities.

Lactic acid is formed in muscles when they contract and use up **glycogen** for energy; it is then carried away in the bloodstream. Its accumulation is one cause of muscle fatigue. Farmed animals slaughtered in the normal way have a reserve of glycogen which changes after death into lactic acid and tenderises the meat. Animals killed in sport have used up much of their glycogen before being killed, leaving little lactic acid, which necessitates using other means of tenderising the meat, such as **hanging**.

USES: as a preservative and for its **anti-oxidant** properties in foods such as confectionery, carbonated drinks, salad dressings, pickled red cabbage. Also used for its acid flavour.

lactose A **disaccharide** sugar consisting of one molecule of **glucose** and one of **galactose**; present in **milk** at a concentration of 5%. Lactose is only a quarter as sweet as sucrose and cannot be fermented by ordinary yeasts. It is converted to **lactic acid** in souring of milk, **cheese** and **yoghurt**-making.

USES: to sweeten wine without stimulating late fermentation, as a filler in medicinal tablets.

lactose intolerance A condition in which there is inability to digest lactose. Treated by a lactose-free diet. See **disaccharide intolerance**.

lactulose An **isomer** of lactose, produced when milk is heated or stored. It is less sweet than sucrose and is split by digestive enzymes into lactic and pyruvic acid. It has laxative properties.

ladies' bedstraw *Galium verum*. A hardy wild plant, often found as a garden weed. The flowers contain the enzyme rennin, known as vegetable rennet. See **junket**, **rennet**.

lads' love See **southernwood**.

laevulose Alternative name for **fructose**.

lager A light **beer** of German origin. It is prepared from the female flowers of a special variety of hops, using a process of deep fermentation with a heavy **yeast**, over a period of 10–12 days, at a lower temperature than that for beer. It is allowed to mature slowly for several months before being sold.

ALCOHOL CONTENT: 3−4%.

ENERGY per 100g: 30−60 kcal, 125−250 kJ.

lamb A sheep, less than one year old, which has not been pregnant. Spring lamb must be less than 6 months old. Also refers to the **meat**.

NUTRITIONAL VALUE: protein 13%, fat 7−10%, vitamin B complex, iron.

ENERGY per 100g: average: raw: 295 kcal, 1234 kJ.

USES: the meat can be grilled, roasted, used in casseroles, depending on the cut.

lambs' lettuce Corn salad. *Valerianella oblitoria*, a hardy annual leaf vegetable.

NUTRITIONAL VALUE: vitamin C and dietary fibre.

USES: available from successive crops all the year round for salads.

lamprey *Petromyzon marinus* , known as the sea lamprey and *Lampetra fluviatilis;* small primitive eel-like fish. Both varieties are native to Britain inhabiting the sea and estuaries. All belong to the family of *cyclostome*, with a cartilaginous skeleton and suckers in place of jaws. They are considered a great delicacy but are only rarely available for sale.

langouste *Palinurus elephas*; also known as crawfish. A spiney lobster found in the warmer waters of the south and west coasts of the UK and on the coasts of France and the Mediterranean. It is similar to lobster but does not have big claws.

NUTRITIONAL VALUE, ENERGY, and USES: See **lobster**.

langoustine A large **prawn** or small **lobster**; also known as Dublin Bay prawn or Norwegian prawn.

NUTRITIONAL VALUE: protein 20%, fat 3%, vitamin B complex, iron.

ENERGY per 100g: 107 kcal, 448 kJ.

USES: only the tail is eaten and is usually eaten dipped in batter and deep fried as scampi.

lanoline The **fat** extracted from the fleece of sheep. It is high in **cholesterol** and unsuitable as a food; used in the cosmetic industry for skin-creams.

laos See **galangal**.

lard Fat taken from around the kidneys and stomach of the pig; sometimes sheep. Vegetable lards are made from hardened vegetable oils. See **fats − hardening of**.

NUTRITIONAL VALUE: saturated fat 35−40%, unsaturated fat 50−55%

USES: for frying and roasting, in pastry and cakes. Also for greasing baking-tins and dishes.

larding The moisturising of lean, dry meat such as venison, veal, poultry and game, prior to roasting, by threading strips of fat, or **lardoons**, through it with a needle made for the purpose (larding needle).

lardoons or **lardons** Strips of pork or bacon fat used for **larding**.

lasagne Flat sheets of **pasta** layered with a meat and/or vegetable sauce, covered with cheese sauce and baked.

laver An edible seaweed, also known as blackbutter and sloke. It is cultivated in Japan, as nori. Green and purple varieties are found round the coasts of the UK on rocks near low tide mark. It requires soaking, to remove salt, and prolonged cooking which produces a gelatinous mass.

USES: a traditional food of South Wales and parts of Scotland; it is served as a vegetable, usually cooked with oatmeal to form laverbread.

laverbread See **laver**.

lax Scandinavian term for **salmon**.

laxative A substance which increases the rate of the passage of food through the bowel. It can act in a number of ways:−

1. Adding bulk to the **faeces**, by increasing the amount of **dietary fibre**.
2. Reducing the resorption of water, with such agents as magnesium sulphate, Epsom salts.
3. Increasing the natural activity of the bowel muscles (peristalsis), by drugs and substances such as cascara, senna, **rhubarb**, **castor oil** (this should be used with great caution).

lead A poisonous heavy-metal. Concern has arisen because of the amount of lead in the environment from industrial and motor-car fumes, from lead-based paints, lead water-pipes, lead-based solders used for joining water-pipes and sealing cans and containers used for food. It causes long-term nerve damage, weakness, vomiting and dental decay. Lead water-pipes are usually protected in hard-water districts by lime deposits, but lead can dissolve out slowly in areas where the water is soft or acidic. Strict regulations are now in force to control the amount of lead in the environment. New water-pipes must be made of other materials, lead-free solders used for joints and lead-based paints are used only rarely and then permits are required. Wine should not be stored in lead cut-glass decanters and old **pewter** never used for food or drink (modern pewter is lead-free). Some cosmetics from the East contain lead which can be absorbed by the skin.

leaven To lighten **bread** (also some cake) and cause it to rise; usually by the action of **yeast**. Unleavened bread is flat and does not contain yeast.

leberwurst A German liver-sausage.

lecithin (E322) One of the naturally-occurring **lipids** containing **phosphorus** and known as a phospholipid. It is present in egg yolk and vegetable oils, but is usually prepared from soya and other oily seeds. It has no known adverse effects.
USES: as an **emulsifier** and stabiliser. The lecithin present in egg yolk is important in the preparation of **mayonnaise**.

lectins A group of poisonous substances, widely dispersed in nature, but only found in significant quantities in red, brown and black beans, and which can cause **diarrhoea** and vomiting. They are destroyed by cooking the beans in boiling water for at least 10 mins.

leek *Alium porrum.* A hardy member of the onion family grown for its long leaves, tightly-packed in the form of a cylinder; milder in flavour than the onion. The part which grows below ground-level is white and more tender than the green top. It was cultivated as food in ancient Egypt.
NUTRITIONAL VALUE: protein 2%, carbohydrate 6%, vitamin C up to 20mg per 100g, minerals, dietary fibre.
ENERGY per 100g: raw: 30 kcal, 125 kJ.
USES: cooked by boiling or steaming, used as a vegetable alone or dressed with a white sauce or cheese, in soups, casseroles, gratin dishes and pies.

lees The sediment that falls to the bottom of a fermented liquor.

leg Traditionally refers to the hindleg of a mammal.

legume Botanically any vegetable that grows a seed-pod, such as the pea or bean; collectively known as **pulses**. Legumes are grown for the high food value of the seeds. Some are eaten fresh when young; mature seeds are dried, keep for long periods and provide the principal source of protein in vegetarian diets.

lemon *Citrus limona.* A fruit grown extensively in Southern Europe and in similar frost-free climates elsewhere. It has a thick skin containing an **essential oil** and a strongly acidic, juicy flesh held in segments. See **lime**.
NUTRITIONAL VALUE: vitamin C 50–100mg per 100g, citric acid 3–7%. The pH lies between 2.5 and 3.5.

ENERGY per 100g: negligible.

USES: the juice, sometimes together with the grated skin (**zest**), in desserts, drinks, cakes, savoury dishes. The juice is used for its vitamin C content and antioxidant properties to prevent discolouration of fruits such as apples, pears.

lemon balm *Melissa officinalis*. A perennial herb of Southern Europe with small leaves which have a smell of lemon when crushed. See **balm**.

lemon curd A rich **preserve** made with egg, butter, sugar and lemon.

USES: as a spread on bread and in tarts.

lemon-grass *Cymbopogon citrata*. A tropical grass with a smell of lemon. An **essential oil**, which is poisonous, is extracted from the roots.

USES: the leaves are used, fresh or dried, in curry dishes particularly in Sri Lanka and South-East Asia. The essential oil is used in soaps, perfumes and cosmetics.

lemon sole *Microstomus kitt*, also known as the smear dab. A **flatfish** found in coastal waters, mainly off the south coast of the UK.

NUTRITIONAL VALUE: protein 18%, fat 1–2%, calcium, iodine.

ENERGY per 100g: 86 kcal, 360 kJ.

USES: usually grilled or fried, sometimes poached.

lentil *Lens esculenta*, an annual legume of Mediterranean origin extensively grown in the Middle East and Southern Europe. Its multiple, small, highly-nutritious seeds are dried, store well and are relatively inexpensive. They are brown or green when whole (known as German lentils), but red or orange with the outer skin removed (known as Egyptian lentils). They are classed as **pulses** and there are a number of different varieties.

NUTRITIONAL VALUE: average: protein 7.5% (marginally greater in the green and brown varieties), fat 3.7%, carbohydrate 17%, vitamin B complex, minerals.

ENERGY per 100g: average: cooked: 100 kcal, 418 kJ.

USES: they should be well washed and boiled for 20–30 mins until soft (presoaking is not necessary). Much used in soups, European, Middle Eastern and Indian dishes. Can be used in place of meat as a source of protein; often mixed with other pulses and various herbs and spices.

lettuce A composite plant, *Lactuca satica*, grown for its edible leaves. Many varieties are cultivated; some are hardy for winter use but most are tender for spring and summer use. Cabbage varieties have soft leaves and those of the iceberg type, crisp. The cos variety is tall and the leaves less tender than others.

NUTRITIONAL VALUE: protein 1%, vitamin C, minerals.

ENERGY per 100g: 10 kcal, 42 kJ.

USES: raw as a basis for a variety of salads and hors d'oeuvres, as a garnish, cooked in soups.

lettuce laver *Ulva lactuca*. A bright-green edible seaweed which looks like lettuce. Also known as green lava. It is not as important as the red or common **laver**.

leveret A **hare** less than a year old.

libation Wine served in honour of a god. Facetiously used for wine served for other purposes.

lichen A primitive form of life. A fungus growing in harmony with algae. Found on trees and rocks in areas free of atmospheric pollution, and thus it is an index of air purity. Only one form, known as **Iceland moss**, has any food value.

Liebig A German chemist who invented the first meat extract, known as Liebig's Beef Extract. This provided a valuable export for the beef-producing countries, particularly the Argentine, before canning and refrigeration were introduced. The meat was ground, soluble matter dissolved out with cold water and then concentrated by prolonged boiling until a thick dark extract was formed. A pure beef extract such as this would be too expensive to market today on any scale. See **Bovril**, **OXO**.

lights The lungs of a mammal, classed as offal and named because of their very light sponge like texture.

USES: sometimes used in **faggots**, but mainly in pet food.

lignin See **connective tissue**.

lima bean See **butter-bean**.

lime *Citrus aurantiifolia*. Very similar to the **lemon** but a little smaller and green in colour and with a sour flavour. Grown in tropical countries as an alternative to lemon which prefers a cooler climate.

NUTRITIONAL VALUE: vitamin C 50–100mg per 100g, citric acid 3–6%.

USES: first used by the British to prevent **scurvy** on long sea-voyages, hence the word 'limey' applied to British sailors. Used now in lime-cordials, marmalade, some sweet and savoury dishes.

lime Calcium oxide. The product of heating limestone, marble or chalk to a high temperature; it is highly caustic. Calcium oxide hydrated with water forms calcium hydroxide, which combines slowly with carbon dioxide (see **gas**) in the air to form **calcium carbonate**; it is used in some air purifiers. Lime is responsible for the deposits in kettles and hot-water-pipes, and shares with **magnesium** the power to precipitate soap so reducing its effectiveness. See **calcium**, **lead**, **water**.

lime-tree A member of the *Tilia* family. A tall, hardy, deciduous tree producing bunches of small green flowers, in July, which have a valuable flow of **nectar** making them attractive to bees. The resultant **honey** is of good quality, with a high **fructose** content, a faint greenish tinge and a delicate minty flavour; it is slow to crystallise. Lime leaves are often infested by aphids which excrete **honeydew**, also attractive to bees; this accounts for the sticky deposits which fall from the trees during the summer. The flowers are dried and used to make a **tisane** which is reputed to have a calming effect. One variety, *Tilia petiolaris*, is poisonous to bees.

limpet *Patella vulgata* , the common limpet is a conical marine **mollusc** with a ribbed shell which adheres to rocks and becomes exposed at low water. It is edible but rarely eaten. It lives by filtering water to feed and so must be purified before being used as food, to prevent **food poisoning**.

NUTRITIONAL VALUE: protein 15%, fat 2%, calcium, iron.

ENERGY per 100g: 78 kcal, 318 kJ.

USES: mainly in soup.

linoleic acid The principal unsaturated **fatty acid** in vegetable oils. See **fats**.

linamarin A poisonous **glucoside** related to cyanide, present in **cassava (manioc)** and destroyed by processing and cooking.

lipase A naturally occurring **enzyme** present in some seeds, including flour made from them, and in the intestinal tract which breaks down **fats** into fatty acids and glycerol; it accounts for rancidity in fat-containing products. The process is retarded by **tocopherol** and other **anti-oxidants**.

lipids Compounds of **fatty acids**, insoluble in water but soluble in fat-solvents such as petroleum products, ether and chloroform. They comprise, simple lipids (oils, fats and waxes) and compound lipids such as **lecithin** and other phosphatides. They are found in a wide range of plants, seeds and animal fats. Lipids circulate in the blood as part of the process of digestion and conversion to energy and the blood levels should be within an accepted range for health. See **cholesterol**.

lipolytic activity The cause of fats becoming **rancid** due to bacteria and enzymes which, in the presence of air and moisture, break down the fats, causing changes in taste and smell. The process occurs naturally during digestion of fats, but is a cause of wastage in stored food. See **preservatives, antioxidants**.

lipovitellin and **lipovitellenin** The two main **proteins** present in egg yolk; both contain phosphorus and account for 30% of the yolk.

liqueur Alcoholic drink with over 15% and up to 40% alcohol; usually sweet and flavoured with fruits, herbs, spices. The formula is often a trade secret.

USES: usually drunk after a meal, often with coffee. Also used as a flavouring in a variety of dishes and sweetmeats.

liquidiser See **blender**.

liquid paraffin A purified, colourless, transparent, refined mineral oil which cannot be absorbed and has no food value. It is used for coating dried fruits to prevent sticking and as a laxative, acting by lubrication. In regular doses can absorb fat-soluble **vitamins** and lead to deficiency. It should not be used for cooking.

liquorice *Glycyrrhiza glabra*. A hardy plant grown for its root, from which the extract known as liquorice is made.

USES: in sweetmeats such as 'pontefract cakes', 'liquorice all sorts', in a liqueur, Strega, and for its medicinal properties.

Listeria monocytogenes A **bacterium** present in the intestines of various animals and widely distributed in the environment, water, vegetation, soil, excreta of man and animals. Unlike other **food poisoning** organisms it can grow at low temperatures and refrigerated foods should be kept below 5°C (41°F). Some exposure is unavoidable but fortunately only rarely causes food poisoning. It is usually destroyed by the acid in a healthy stomach and by normal cooking practices. It can cause vomiting and fever, and has been known to cause abortions in pregnant women, meningitis, collapse and occasionally fatalities. Babies, the elderly, pregnant women, those with a reduced stomach-acidity or with some deficiency of their immune system, are most vulnerable.

Contamination of food by listeria occurs through poor **hygiene** and handling of foods which are not naturally acidic. Hard **cheeses** are protected by their low water-content and the presence of **lactic** acid, but soft, ripe cheeses with a higher water-content, other milk products and meat pâtés offer a medium for the survival and multiplication of the bacteria. Reheated food must be fully heated through and leftovers discarded. Special care is needed when using **microwave ovens** to ensure that the temperature reaches at least 80°C (176°F) in the centre of the food. The practice of cooking for large numbers in canteens, hospitals, hotels and restaurants, with the need to prepare food in advance and reheating before consumption (**cook-chill**), has greatly increased the risk and accounts for the serious rise in outbreaks of all types of food poisoning.

litchi See **lychee**.

litmus A dye extracted from a **lichen**, which has the property of turning red in an acid environment and blue in an alkaline one. Commonly used in the form of an impregnated paper strip. Other dyes with colour-changes over a range of pH are more often used today. See **pH**.

litre The international metric unit of volume. 1 British gallon equals 4.55 litres, 1 USA gallon equals 3.785 litres.

liver A large organ in the upper abdominal cavity of mammals and birds, with multiple functions. It produces bile, a viscous yellow fluid, secreted into the upper bowel and essential for emulsifying fats to allow their absorption into the bloodstream. It also processes the products of digestion for use by the body for energy, growth and repair, and it neutralises some substances that are poisonous to render them harmless.

Liver has a high content of **vitamin A** which, in large doses, is teratogenic, that is, capable of causing congenital deformities in babies, so that pregnant women should avoid eating too much of it or taking vitamin A supplements without medical advice. Liver can be used fresh or frozen and all should be cooked because there is a slight risk of ingesting live **parasites** when it is uncooked. People should be wary of eating liver where there is a low standard of meat inspection.

NUTRITIONAL VALUE: protein 15%, fat 5%, high in vitamin A, vitamin B complex and vitamin D (fish livers are the highest known natural source of vitamins A and D), iron, calcium.

ENERGY per 100g: raw: 140 kcal, 586 kJ.

USES: the liver of calves, lambs, and young pigs are most suitable for frying and grilling and the more fully flavoured ox-liver for casseroles. Pigs' and chickens' livers are used in liver sausages and pâtés. Oil extracted from the livers of fish, such as cod, halibut, shark are an important source of vitamins A and D and used as food supplements. See **pâté de foie gras**.

liver fluke *Fasciola hepatica*. A parasite which mainly affects sheep and cattle. Short flat worms hatch from eggs deposited on grass and when eaten by animals migrate to their livers. Human infestation is rare but can occur from eggs of the parasite contaminating food through unhygienic food-handling and from wild **watercress**.

liver sausage Sausage, usually made with liver from pigs and/or chickens and mixed with herbs and spices. There are many regional variations.

loaf The regular shape in which certain foods are prepared and cooked for serving; usually refers to **bread** but also to savoury mixtures such as meat-loaf, nut-loaf.

loaf-sugar Sugar formed into small cubes. Originally it was processed into very large blocks, shaped like an inverted U.

lobster *Homaris vulgaris*. A large marine crustacean with heavy claws, found widely distributed around Atlantic coasts; much prized for the meat found in the tail and claws. Related to prawn, **langouste** and freshwater **crayfish**. It must be fresh and is often sold alive; it is killed by plunging in boiling sea- or salt-water.

NUTRITIONAL VALUE: protein 20%, fat 3%, vitamin B complex, calcium, iron.

ENERGY per 100g: 107 kcal, 448 kJ.

USES: cooked by simmering for 10–15 mins according to size and served hot as a main course, or cold, usually with mayonnaise.

locust bean The bean of the **carob** tree.

loganberry A seeded fruit, thought originally to be a cross between blackberry and raspberry, but may be a cultivar of a variety of blackberry. It is red to dark-red in colour, and more acid than either raspberry or blackberry. See **tayberry**.

NUTRITIONAL VALUE: vitamin C 40mg per 100g.

USES: most suitable for preserves, but can be eaten fresh or stewed.

lollipop A sweetmeat on a stick. Frozen varieties are called iced lollies.

loquat The sweet acidic fruit of a subtropical tree, *Eriobotrya japonica*, a member of the apple and rose family; also known as the Japanese medlar. It does not travel well and is not often available in the UK.

lotus A common name for various members of the water-lily families *Nymphaea* and *Nelumbo*. *Nelumbo nucifera* is the name of the sacred lotus of China and India. It has expanded edible rhizomes and the flowers produce large edible seeds. *Nelumbo lutea*, the American lotus is grown for its rhizomes.

NUTRITIONAL VALUE: rhizomes: protein 1.7%, carbohydrate 11%, vitamin B complex, calcium, iron.

USES: both the seeds and rhizomes are used, mainly in Asiatic and in particular Chinese and Japanese cookery. The aromatic leaves are used as a wrapping for steamed pork and fish dishes.

lotus tree See **jubjube tree**.

lovage *Ligusticum scoticum*. A hardy perennial herb with a strong flavour of celery.

USES: both the fresh leaves and dried seeds are used sparingly as a flavouring in soups, casseroles.

love-in-a-mist *Nigella sativa*. See **fitches**.

low-salt The name given to a **diet** low in **salt** or sodium chloride and desirable for those who have a raised **blood pressure** or suffer from some heart and kidney diseases. The important factor is sodium and not the chloride content. Salt-tasting substitutes are prepared with **potassium** or **ammonium chloride**, and have a similar, although weaker flavour. Some are a mixture of salt with either or both of the others. They can be used in cooking or at the table, as many foods taste bland without salt.

Those on a low-salt diet should be aware of the relatively high salt content in processed foods such as cooked meats, pies, soups, sauces, **stock cubes**, flavouring concentrates.

luce Another name for **pike**, a freshwater edible fish which preys on other fish. Rarely available.

lucerne See **alfalfa**.

lugasnega An Italian **sausage** in continuous form and not divided.

lumpfish *Cyclopterus*. Variously known as lumpsucker, hen-fish or sea-hen. Only the roe is eaten; it is used as a mock **caviar**, dyed black or red.

lungs The large pair of organs within the chest cavity responsible for bringing inspired air into close association with blood, for the removal of carbon dioxide and uptake of oxygen. They are sponge-like structures through which the blood circulates in capillaries; air enters through the bronchi which end in minute cavities where it is separated from the blood by only a thin membrane, thus enabling the exchange to take place. For culinary purposes lung is classed as offal and called **lights**. See **gas – carbon dioxide, oxygen**.

lutein (E161B) Permitted yellow to red food colouring; a derivative of **carotene** and present in egg-yolks.

lychee Also known as litchi. A seeded fruit of the tropical evergreen tree, *Litchii chinensis*, with a thin, brown skin, soft, white flesh, mildly acidic flavour and a hard kernel. It is available fresh and **canned**.

NUTRITIONAL VALUE: protein 1%, fat 0.5%, carbohydrate 15%.

USES: as a dessert fruit, alone or in fruit salads.

lycopene (E160D) Permitted red food colouring prepared from tomatoes.

lye peeling The commercial process of removing skins of fruits and vegetables for preserving by soaking them briefly in caustic soda, then tumbling in fresh water.

Lyonnaise Description of dishes which are specialities of the Lyonnais region of France and characterised by the use of **onions**.

lyophilise To **freeze-dry**.

lysine An essential amino acid. In a mixed diet, the low lysine content of cereal foods is compensated for by the high content in dairy products and meats.

M

macadamia nut Nut of the large evergreen tree, *Macadamia ternifolia*, a native of tropical North Australia; it is sweet with a very hard shell which is difficult to remove, so making it expensive.

NUTRITIONAL VALUE: average: protein 20%, fat 50%, vitamin B complex, minerals.

ENERGY per 100g: 530 kcal, 2218 kJ.

USES: eaten as a dessert nut for its fine flavour and chopped in ice-cream and other desserts.

macaroni A type of **pasta** extruded in the form of pencil-sized tubes; of Italian origin. Sold dried and keeps well, best in airtight containers.

NUTRITIONAL VALUE: average: cooked: protein 6%, carbohydrate 25%, vitamin B complex, vitamin E, calcium, iron, dietary fibre. Uncooked: protein 13%, carbohydrate 77%.

ENERGY per 100g: average: cooked: 130 kcal, 545 kJ. Uncooked: 365 kcal, 1527 kJ.

USES: cooked by boiling and served as a vegetable, often with cheese sauce as a complete dish. Also cooked with milk and sweetened as a dessert.

macaroon A small biscuit-like cake made of sugar, ground almonds and egg white.

mace A spice; the outer coat of the **nutmeg** and with a different flavour.

macedoine A mixture of fruit or vegetables cut up into small equal-sized pieces.

macerases The **enzymes** produced by the *Aspergillus* mould and used to break down pectin in fruit to increase the extraction rate of juice. See **pectinase**.

macerate To soak and soften by immersion in a liquid, usually water. It also means to soak fruits in an appropriate liqueur, after sprinkling with sugar, to soften them and add flavour.

Mâcon Red or white wine from the Mâcon district of France.

mackerel *Scomber scombus*. A surface-feeding or pelagic shoal-fish common around the coasts of the UK and generally available all the year. It has a rich oily flesh with large bones and a full flavour. The fish must be very fresh and stored on ice, from the time of catching until it is sold, as it deteriorates more quickly than most other fish. See **fish, fish selection, fish worms, mackerel — smoked**.

NUTRITIONAL VALUE: protein 18–20%, fat 15–20%, almost all unsaturated, vitamin A, vitamin D, calcium, iron, iodine.

ENERGY per 100g: average: 282 kcal, 1180 kJ.

USES: cooked by frying, grilling or baking.

mackerel, smoked Mackerel split open, salted and hot smoked; it does not require cooking prior to serving.

USES: eaten cold as a starter, in salads, made into pâté, fish pies.

macrobiotic diet A diet advocated by Zen Buddhists. It consists of a 7 stage system of eating, the last stage being restricted to **cereals** and unpolished **rice**. It is based on the 'yin' 'yang' concept where everything in life is one or the other and must be balanced. It can lead to severe **malnutrition**.

madagascar bean See **butter-bean**.

Madeira Fortified rich sherry-like wine from Madeira.

ALCOHOL CONTENT: up to 17%.

Madeira cake A plain sponge-cake decorated with candied peel, so called because it was originally served as an accompaniment to Madeira wine.

Madeira sauce Brown **sauce** to which **Madeira** wine has been added.

madeleine An individual sponge-cake coated with jam and coconut.

Madras A state in Southern India which has given its name to certain types of **curry** dishes and chutneys.

Madras gram *Dolichos biflorus*, the same as horse gram, a tropical climbing plant of the pea and bean family producing pods with small seeds.

USES: the whole young pods may be eaten freshly cooked. The seeds are variously coloured and cooked as **pulses**.

maggot The grub or larva of a **fly**. Eggs are laid on exposed food, most commonly by the blue-bottle fly, in warm weather, and hatch into grubs in 2–3 days; the fly is particularly attracted to meat. The maggots themselves are harmless but the fly can carry disease.

magma The sticky mixture of sugar crystals and syrup which occurs during the refining of sugar.

magnesium A very light metal essential to plant and animal life, where it plays a part in bone formation, nerve and muscle function and some **enzyme** systems. The body contains the equivalent of about 25g of the metal in the form of magnesium salts. It is a component of **chlorophyll** and present in milk, cereals and meat. Although there are raised requirements for magnesium in periods of growth, pregnancy and lactation, there are adequate quantities in a diet containing green vegetables, cereals and dairy products, thus a deficiency is unlikely to occur in man, but it can occur in cattle.

Magnesium is toxic in large quantities and supplements are not required. Toxic levels are highly unlikely to occur in a normal mixed diet. See **trace elements**.

magnesium carbonate (540) A naturally-occurring mineral, prepared as a fine powder and used in small quantities as an **anti-caking** agent in salt and icing-sugar, to regulate the acid content in some processed foods, in indigestion tablets.

maidenhair tree See **ginkgo**.

maid of honour A small tart with a **macaroon** filling.

maigre Made without meat.

Maillard reaction A chemical process that takes place when **proteins** and **carbohydrates** are heated above 100°C (212°F), producing the brown pigment called melanoidin, which has a characteristic flavour. This change occurs on the surface of **bread** (crust or toast), cakes, pastries, and other foods cooked in an **oven**, under a **grill** or **fried**. There is slight loss of nutritive value but the gain in character, attractiveness and flavour offsets the slight loss.

maître d'hôtel The French term for the head waiter in a restaurant, who is in full charge and responsible for completing the cooking, at the table, of dishes such as, **crêpes suzettes**.

maize *Zea mays*. Also known as Indian corn or corn. A tall food grass of great importance and widely grown in both tropical and temperate climates. It probably started as a weed in Mexico from which the present day varieties have been developed. The seeds, larger than other grain seeds, form in a tight and heavy head and ripen to a golden yellow. It is low in **protein** and **fat** but high in **carbohydrate** and those who subsist mainly on maize may suffer deficiency diseases, unless their diet is supplemented by other foods to provide fat and protein. Special varieties are cultivated for various purposes. See **sweetcorn**.

NUTRITIONAL VALUE: average, protein 5%, fat 3%, carbohydrate 25%, carotene.

ENERGY per 100gm: average, 145kcal, 607kJ.

USES: To make cornflour, for breakfast food (cornflakes), popcorn, polenta, farina, animal feed.

Malaga A rich heavy Spanish wine, sweetened with a variety of additives, such as raisins of the muscatel grape, boiled grape juice, fortified grape juice; a speciality of Malaga in south east Spain.

ALCOHOL CONTENT: 14–15%.

malic acid (E296) Acid occurring naturally in apples, pears and other fruits. It is used as an acid flavouring.

During storage of wine malic acid may be fermented by micro-organisms and converted to lactic acid which, being less sour, reduces the acidity and improves the quality of the wine.

Malmsey A strong sweet wine made from the momonvasia grape; of Cretan origin.

malnutrition A state of food deprivation with weight loss, general poor health, reduced resistance to infection, retarded growth in children, swelling, bleeding, skin disorders, blindness, disorders of the nervous system, defects in the skeleton and teeth, sterility and shortened life-span. Malnutrition can arise from a number of causes as well as dietary deficiency, such as disorders of the digestive system, chronic illness, infections, **parasites**.

malt The concentrated thick extract of malted **barley**, or other **cereals** containing the sugar, **maltose**, together with small quantities of other breakdown products of **starch**, giving a sweet characteristic flavour. Varieties of barley are selected for their low **protein** and high **diastase** content. The grain is germinated and the young rootlets gently warmed, so that the enzyme diastase can convert starches into maltose; the grain is then heated in a kiln and dried. The degree of heat employed produces different types of malt, ranging from almost clear crystal malts to very dark ones with a strong flavour, used for brewing stouts. See **flour – malted**.

USES: in the manufacture of **beer**, **gin**, **whisky**.

maltase An **enzyme** present in saliva, and pancreatic and intestinal juices, which splits **maltose** into two molecules of **glucose**.

malt flour See **flour**.

maltose A natural **sugar** formed by the action of the enzyme, **diastase**, on starches. A **disaccharide** consisting of two molecules of **glucose**. The source of **malt** in germinating seeds.

manchet Ancient name for the finest wheat bread.

mandarin A small sweet orange with loose skin. See **citrus fruits**.

mandolin A simple, hand-held, adjustable, food-slicing device with stationary blades that cut, either straight or ribbed, when the material to be sliced is moved across the blade.

USES: for slicing vegetables such as carrots, cucumber.

manganese An essential **trace element** in a number of **enzyme** systems; adequate amounts are present in a normal diet and deficiency has not been observed in man. It is one of the least toxic minerals because of its low rate of absorption and rapid excretion in the bile and urine.

mangetout See **pea**.

mango A large stone-fruit, sometimes

weighing up to 3kg, of the tropical tree, *Magniflera indica*. It has an aromatic soft, sweet, slightly acidic flesh when ripe.

NUTRITIONAL VALUE: protein 0.5%, carbohydrate 15%, vitamin A, vitamin B complex, vitamin C 20–30mg per 100g.

ENERGY per 100g: 60 kcal, 250 kJ.

USES: the ripe fruit is eaten in its natural state, alone or in fruit salads; the juice is extracted as a drink, and used for flavouring ice-cream and sorbet. Unripe or ripe, it is used in **chutney**.

mangold or mangel-wurzel. A large form of turnip, *Beta vulgaris rapa;* rather a coarse vegetable and grown mainly as cattle feed. Of no culinary importance.

mangosteen *Garcinia mangostana.* A tropical tree of Asia producing purplish-brown orange-like fruits with edible segments and a good flavour.

NUTRITIONAL VALUE: vitamin C 10 mg per 100 g.

USES: usually eaten raw but may be cooked.

manioc See **cassava, tapioca**.

manna The term is applied to two different naturally-occurring exudates of trees:—
1. The food of the Bible which nourished the Israelites in the wilderness and 'fell from heaven' is probably the sugary secretion, formed on leaves and branches of thorny shrubs, called *Alhagi maurorum*, which dries and is then blown by the wind.
2. A sugary extract from the sap of the subtropical Manna ash-tree, *Fraxinus ornus*, cultivated in Sicily and has mild laxative properties; it is about 60% sugar, mostly **mannitol** with some **mannose**.

mannitol (E421) Also known as **manna** sugar; a **polysaccharide** sugar found naturally in the wood of some coniferous trees and as a natural exudate from the tree, *Fraxinus ornus*.

USES: as an anti-caking agent, sweetener and dietary supplement.

mannose A form of sugar, similar to **glucose** and found in **manna**.

mantis shrimp *Squilla mantis*, a marine crustacean; a type of large **prawn** with front legs which resemble those of the insect, praying mantis, found around the coasts of the Mediterranean and other warm seas.

NUTRITIONAL VALUE: protein 20%, fat 2%, rich in minerals.

USES: only the tail is eaten and cooked as for prawns.

maple syrup Sap from the maple-trees, *Acer saccharum* and *Acer nigrum*, concentrated to form a syrup containing 60–70% sucrose.

USES: as a spread, particularly on **pancakes** and **waffles** and also as a sweetener.

maraschino A liqueur made with the wild black cherry, including the kernels which give it a nutty flavour. A speciality of Dalmatia.

ALCOHOL CONTENT: 40%.

USES: drunk as a liqueur and also used to preserve cherries.

marasmus A wasting disease due to **malnutrition**.

marc A form of **brandy** made from the fermented residue of grapes, including the pips and skins, after pressing for wine-making. It varies in quality and can be drunk as well as being used in cooking. See **congeners**.

mare Same as **marc**.

marengo Originally said to be a dish made for Napoleon during the battle of Marengo, with veal, garlic, tomatoes, mushrooms. Nowadays it is more commonly made with chicken rather than veal.

margarine A cheap substitute for **butter** first made during the mid 19th century, by emulsifying beef fat with milk. It is now made from a variety of hardened unsaturated fats of vegetable or fish origin emulsified with water. Margarines are usually coloured, flavoured with salt and **diacetyl** and fortified with **vitamins A and D**. Increasingly, soft margarines are made with a variable content of up to 60% unsaturated vegetable fats, to meet the demand for a reduced consumption of saturated fats. Most of them also contain **antioxidants** and **preservatives**. They keep well under cool conditions, wrapped to exclude air.

margarine, kosher Margarine made wholly with vegetable oils and with added **carotene**.

marigold *Calendula officinalis*. A half-hardy annual plant. The petals of the flowers are sometimes used as an inexpensive source of yellow colouring in place of **saffron** but lacking its flavour.

marijuana See **cannabis**.

marinade The liquid, cooked or uncooked, used to **marinate** (or marinade).

marinate or **marinade** The process of soaking food such as fish, meat, poultry or vegetables, prior to cooking, in a liquid such as vinegar, lemon juice or wine and sometimes oil, flavoured with seasoning, herbs, spices, onion. Used to tenderise and enhance flavour.

marinière The term for **shellfish**, usually **mussels**, cooked in wine with shallots and herbs.

marjoram An aromatic herb of Mediterranean origin; two main varieties are *Oreganum vulgare*, the wild form known as **oregano**, and *Origanum marjorana* (sweet marjoram).
   USES: used widely in a variety of meat, fish, vegetable and cheese dishes, especially in Italian cooking.

marmalade The name, from the Portuguese word for **quince**, for a preserve or sweetmeat made from that fruit. It now usually means the preserve made from **seville oranges**, or other **citrus fruits**, eaten with toast as part of the traditional British breakfast. Legally marmalade must contain not less than 20% fruit. Occasionally it still refers to a fruit sweetmeat, but not necessarily made of quince.
   ENERGY per 100g: average: 261 kcal, 1092 kJ.

marmalade fruit *Lucuma mammosa*. A tropical tree bearing large, sweet egg-shaped berries which are eaten raw.

marmite A cooking vessel for **soups** made of metal or earthenware. Also the tradename for a hydrolysed extract of **yeast**, with a high vitamin B and salt content, used as a flavouring for meat, vegetable dishes and soups; contains **monosodium glutamate**. See **hydrolysed vegetable protein**.

marrons The French for **chestnuts**.

marrons glacés A sweetmeat made by boiling whole **chestnuts** in successive solutions of **sugar-syrup** of increasing concentration, finally dipping them in a well-beaten strong-sugar syrup and allowing them to cool and crystallise.

marrow or vegetable marrow. *Cucurbita pepo ovifera*. A half-hardy trailing annual plant which produces cylindrical fruit which can grow to a large size. It belongs to the family *Cucurbitacae* which includes **courgette, cucumber, melon**. All have many seeds.
   NUTRITIONAL   VALUE: negligible. Vitamin C about 10mg per 100g.
   ENERGY per 100g: 8 kcal, 33 kJ.
   USES: classed as a fruit but usually eaten as a vegetable and suitable for boiling, steaming and stir-frying; requires peeling to remove the tough skin, unless very young. It may be stuffed whole or cut into rings. It can be cooked with sugar and an

acidic flavouring, as a dessert; also used for jam (with ginger), chutney and pickle.

marrow-bone Long bones of mammals containing the soft reddish material, known as bone-marrow, where production of blood cells takes place.

NUTRITIONAL VALUE: high fat content and rich in vitamin B complex, iron, calcium.

USES: for the preparation of meat stock, by prolonged boiling of the bones, previously broken to expose the marrow, for soups and casseroles; the stock usually forms a jelly when cold and any solidified **fat** can be lifted off.

marsala A fortified sherry-like Sicilian wine.
ALCOHOL CONTENT: up to 18%.

marzipan Also known as almond paste. A firm paste made from ground **almonds**, **sugar**, **egg**, **lemon** juice and **almond essence**. Marzipan ready-prepared for sale must be made with **pasteurised** egg-yolk to prevent the spread of **salmonella** infection. Some is made with **glucose syrup** in place of egg. It becomes hard on exposure to air and the **fats** may become **rancid** after a month or more. Keeping qualities are improved when it is covered in **icing** to exclude air.

NUTRITIONAL VALUE: high in monounsaturated fat, protein and carbohydrate.

USES: for decorating cakes, making sweetmeats, artificial fruits, as a filling in small cakes and tarts and as a base for icing on celebratory cakes.

matelote A dish made of fish, onions, herbs, cooked in wine.

matzoon A form of **yoghurt** from Armenia.

mayonnaise A stable **emulsion** of almost jelly-like consistency, made of egg yolk, olive or other vegetable oil and vinegar, often flavoured with mustard, garlic and salt. Mustard itself has emulsifying proper-

ties, which, together with the **lecithin** in the egg-yolk, assist in forming the emulsion. Commercially produced mayonnaise must be made with **pasteurised** egg yolks to prevent the spread of **salmonella**. It should be stored in a refrigerator.

NUTRITIONAL VALUE: traditional mayonnaise has up to 70% fat, but commercially-produced reduced-fat products may have as little as 25% (salad-cream, a similar product, has a lower fat-content).

ENERGY per 100g: 250–630 kcal, 1046–2636 kJ.

USES: as a dressing on salads, fish, meat and egg dishes.

mead A **wine** made from fermented **honey**, usually with lemon juice or other acid.
ALCOHOL CONTENT: variable, 8–14%.

meal A preparation of ground **cereal** or other starchy food or **pulses**.

meal-worm The larva of the **flour** beetle. A big problem in flour mills before the days of **roller-milling**. Modern milling involves heat which kills the eggs, and shorter periods of storage interfere with the breeding cycle of the insects.

measurement See Appendix.

meat The striated **muscle** of mammals, excluding **heart**, **poultry** and **fish** muscle. (In the USA it includes the muscle of poultry and fish). Meat from **cattle**, **sheep** and **pigs** has a high **fat**-content, some lying on the surface and clearly visible and some lying among the muscle fibres. In response to the advice on reducing dietary fat, farmers are producing leaner meat but it has less flavour. Meat from the deer, **venison**, naturally has less fat than other meat. All meat must be fully cooked to prevent **food poisoning**.

NUTRITIONAL VALUE: protein about 20%, fat-content varies from about 5% to 30%, vitamin B complex, vitamin E, iron.

USES: as an important source of **protein** in a mixed diet.

meat conditioning The process of allowing meat time, after slaughter of the animal, for desirable changes to take place, both tenderising it and enhancing its flavour. The process begins with **glycogen** changing to **lactic acid**, which has a softening effect, followed by the slower process of **autolysis** due to natural **enzymes** present in the meat breaking down the **proteins**. The time taken for the maximum benefit varies with temperature but may extend to 3 weeks. A good butcher will see that meat is fully conditioned before sale, although this will add to the cost of the product.

meat extract Concentrated water-soluble components of meat, originally patented by **Liebig**. Most present-day meat extracts are mixtures of meat extracts and **hydrolysed vegetable proteins**, known as HVP, to reduce cost. Tradenames of products include **Bovril**, OXO.

meat olives See **olives − meat**.

mechanically-recovered meat, also known as MRM. The parts of the carcass, not removed by a butcher by knife, are recovered by subjecting it to special machinery involving high-power, centrifugal force and possibly ultrasound. The product includes a variable mixture containing gristle, cartilage and **fat** and sometimes only a small proportion of muscle. The prevalence of **bovine spongioform encephalopathy** places a major responsibility on meat inspection services and MRM has no place in meat products for human consumption.

medallion Food which has been cut into rounds or ovals. Usually refers to meat but may also be used to describe rich desserts decorated with chocolate and or coloured **icing**.

medlar The fruit of *Mesphilus germanica*, related to the **pear** and **apple**. It is the size of a small apple, brown-skinned with a leafy calyx at the top. It is unusual in that it must be allowed to become soft before it can be eaten. The ripe flesh is brown, the consistency of an over-ripe pear and slightly acid. In warm climates the fruit softens on the tree but often in the UK only after storing.
USES: for making preserves.

Médoc Wine produced in the district of Médoc in SW France.

melanoidin The brown pigment produced when food is exposed to direct heat or hot **fat**, as in **grilling, baking, frying, toasting**. See **Maillard reaction**.

Melba toast Wafer-thin slices of bread lightly toasted. Originally made for Dame Nellie Melba, the opera singer.

melon The large sweet many-seeded fruit of the annual *Cucumis melo*, with a high water content (90%). Grown in warm climates and under glass in cooler areas. There are a number of varieties differing in shape, size, colour and flavour such as, honeydew, cantaloupe, galia. See **water melon**.
NUTRITIONAL VALUE: protein 1%, carbohydrate 2−5%, carotene in some, vitamin C 10mg per 100g. Seeds: protein 20%, fat 20−40%.
ENERGY per 100g: flesh: 12−23 kcal, 50−96 kJ. Seeds: 260−440 kcal, 1088−1840 kJ.
USES: as a dessert fruit, in fruit salads, ice-cream. The seeds are roasted and used in cooking or as nibbles.

menhaden *Brevootia tyrrannus*. A marine fish of the **herring** family, living in waters off the East coast of the USA and used mostly for the oil extracted from its flesh.

menu A prepared list of dishes available, on the day, for a meal; also known as Bill of Fare. See **à la carte, table d'hôte**.

mercury One of the heaviest and most toxic

of metals, seen as a silvery liquid. It has no essential role in the body, although some may be present. Mercury finds its way into the food chain from industrial pollution and sewage where it is picked up by marine life. It is poisonous and a cause for concern where heavy and chemical industries do not take strict precautions in waste disposal. Its use as a pesticide has been banned.

meringue An aerated preparation of **egg-white** with a high proportion of sugar, lightly cooked to solidify the egg **proteins** and dried in a cool oven to remove remaining moisture and develop crispness. Commercial meringues must be made with **pasteurised** egg white to prevent the spread of **salmonella**, as the cooking temperature may not be high enough to kill the bacteria. One infected egg can contaminate a large batch of meringues. Meringue mixture used as a dessert topping as in lemon meringue pie is cooked at a higher temperature for a shorter time and needs less sugar.

ENERGY per 100g: average: 400 kcal, 1673 kJ.

USES: made in individual portions, sometimes flavoured with coffee or chocolate, sandwiched together with cream, as containers for fruit, and in other desserts such as Pavlova, hazelnut meringue, lemon meringue pie.

metabolism The term for the chemical and physical changes which take place in all living matter. It involves the breakdown of foodstuffs and old tissue to release **energy** (catabolism) and the synthesis of complex molecules such as **proteins**, **carbohydrates** and **fats** to form new tissue (anabolism). The rate at which metabolism takes place increases with exercise and in response to fever and injury. All metabolic processes are controlled by **enzymes**. The minimum amount of energy to maintain vital processes is known as the basal metabolic rate.

methaemoglobin The result of an irreversible chemical change in **haemoglobin** which renders it no longer capable of carrying oxygen. It can be caused by excess of nitrates and nitrites used as **preservatives** in food, or in water supplies. However, the risk to adults is small and unlikely to cause problems. The young are more vulnerable and there is concern that levels of nitrates and nitrites in water supplies may pose a health hazard for babies. See **nitre**.

methane See **gas**.

methanol Methyl alcohol, the simplest **alcohol**; it is highly poisonous and capable of causing blindness, mental disturbances and fatalities. It is present in **methylated spirit** and has been put into cheap wines and alcoholic drinks, causing mass poisoning. Small quantities are present in scrumpy **cider**.

methionine A sulphur-containing **amino acid**, one of the eight essential to life and the one in which a poor **diet** is most likely to be deficient. dairy products, cereals and meat contain a significant amount. A commercially prepared form is added to some animal feeds.

methylated spirit A mixture of **methanol** and **ethanol** which is highly poisonous. It is coloured violet and given an unpleasant taste to try to prevent people from drinking it. It is inexpensive, readily available and used by some as a cheap substitute for alcohol.

USES: as a solvent for domestic purposes and a fuel for small portable cookers and heating-lamps.

methylcellulose (**E461** and related compounds **E460**, **E462–466**) Preparations made from wood-pulp.

NUTRITIONAL VALUE: none.

USES: as bulking agents in some proprietary 'slimming' foods, binders, stabilisers.

metre The international standard of length. One metre equals 39.38 inches. See Appendix.

meunière Fish fried in butter and served with lemon juice and herbs.

mewling Another name for **whiting**.

meze An appetiser of the Eastern Mediterranean, similar to **hors d'oeuvres**.

Michigan banana See **papaw**.

microfiltration The process of filtration under pressure, by forcing a liquid through a very fine filter, such as porous ceramic or microcrystalline glass, holding back minute particles and **bacteria**. Used for clarifying and sterilising wines, beers, pharmaceutical products.

micro-organism A single-cell plant, animal or **bacterium** visible only through a microscope; it can be a **parasite**, **fungus** or **mould**. Micro-organisms play an essential part in life; many are beneficial but others cause disease and destruction of plants and food. All have the ability to increase rapidly, some doubling their number every 20 minutes in favourable conditions.

microwave oven An oven where the food, which must contain moisture, is heated by radio-frequency electromagnetic radiation, causing intense agitation of individual molecules, generating heat within the food. Microwaves cannot penetrate more than about 3 cm and so thick items will cook only if sufficient time is allowed for heat to be transferred to the inside by conduction or convection; thus if the process is carried out too fast, as when the power is set at high for too a short time, it is possible for the outside of the food to over-cook while the inside is inadequately cooked. No microwave ovens heat evenly, although those with a turntable or stirrer distribute the heat better than those without, but nevertheless, time must be allowed for the heat to spread through the food items. As long as manufacturer's instructions are clear and adhered to, micro-wave cooking is safe. Special **thermometers** are made for use in microwave ovens.

Metallic containers or objects must not be put into microwave ovens; neither should coloured china or earthenware dishes be used if they have a coating of metallic oxides (as these are also electrical conductors), unless they can be filled with liquid to distribute the heat.

Although some of the older microwave ovens may have leaked, with the theoretical risk of damaging the eye, modern ovens are safe, as their doors are screened against leakage and have automatic safety switches which operate when the doors are opened. Modern domestic microwave ovens, in good working order, should not interfere with most heart pacemakers but there is a possibility of interference from high-powered commercial microwave ovens.

Power in microwave ovens is controlled by a system which switches it on and off several times a minute; the ratio of 'on' to 'off' determines how much power is being used. The fast-heating times can cause intense local heating in liquids, resulting in a higher temperature zone below the surface, and if this is disturbed, as when the container is lifted out of the oven, or its contents stirred, this over-heated layer can have an explosive effect and cause serious burn injuries. Liquids are best heated in bowl-shaped containers rather than mugs or jugs with straight sides, and a rest period should be allowed before removing them from the oven. See **food poisoning**.

miel French for **honey**.

mignonette Coarsely ground **pepper**.

migraine A state associated with headaches, vomiting, visual disturbances. There is no absolute relationship with food, although it is thought that food substances which have a high content of the amino-acid tyramine such as cheese and chocolate may precipitate an attack in some individuals.

milanaise Dishes from Milan in Northern Italy, such as macaroni with cheese and tomato, meat dipped in egg and breadcrumbs, sometimes with parmesan cheese, and fried, a soufflé with a lemon flavour.

mildew See **mould**.

milk The secretion of the mammary glands of mammals; a complete diet for the infant until it is old enough to take other simple foods. Milk is an emulsion of **fats, carbohydrates** and **protein** with the sugar **lactose** in a ratio specific for each type of animal, so that milk of one animal is generally not satisfactory for feeding the young of another, without modification. Milk also contains minerals, vitamins, and antibodies from the mother to protect the infant from disease. All milk may contain drugs administered to the mother (human or animal) including **antibiotics**, which can be harmful.

All cow's milk on sale in the UK must be from cattle tested for, and free from, **tuberculosis** and almost all milk sold is **pasteurised**; this reduces the number of living organisms in it but does not sterilise it. All fresh milk should be considered to contain **micro-organisms** capable of converting lactose to **lactic acid** and it will keep longer if refrigerated to prevent multiplication of these micro-organisms.

Four main types of fresh milk are sold, and identified when bottled, by the colour of the cap. Thus:—

'Gold-topped' is full-cream milk from Jersey or other Channel Island cows.

'Silver-topped' is full-cream milk from other breeds of cows.

'Red-topped' is semi-skimmed milk, from which half the fat has been extracted.

'Blue-topped' is skimmed milk, from which virtually all the fat has been extracted.

Occasionally milk that has not been pasteurised is available and this is 'green topped'.

Fresh milk is sold in either bottles (1 pint), cartons or plastic containers (usually 1–4 litres). Milk in bottles sealed with coloured aluminium caps (see above) are liable to be punctured by birds, when left outside, and outbreaks of **campylobacter** have occurred from milk contaminated in this way. Vitamin C may be destroyed if bottles are left out in bright light.

NUTRITIONAL VALUE: average: human milk, protein 1.4%, fat 4%, carbohydrate 7%. Cow's milk: protein 3.4%, fat 1% (skimmed), 2% (semi-skimmed), 3.9% (standard full-cream), 4.2% (Jersey, Channel Island), carbohydrate 4.9%. All milk contains calcium, small quantities of vitamin A, vitamin B complex, vitamin C, vitamin D, minerals.

ENERGY per 100ml: skimmed: 32 kcal, 134 kJ, semi-skimmed: 47 kcal, 197 kJ, standard full-cream: 65 kcal, 272 kJ, Jersey, Channel Island 69 kcal, 289 kJ, goats': 69 kcal, 289 kJ.

Other forms of cow's milk available are:—

Condensed. Full-cream or skimmed milk, evaporated to less than 33% of its original volume, with sugar added as a preservative, and canned.

NUTRITIONAL VALUE: average: full-cream: protein 8.4%, fat 9%, carbohydrate 53.9%. Skimmed: protein 10%, fat 0.2%, carbohydrate 59.2%.

ENERGY per 100g: average: full-cream: 330 kcal, 1381 kJ. Skimmed: 280 kcal, 1172 kJ.

Dried. Milk, usually skimmed, from which all water has been removed, by **spray** or **roller drying**. Sometimes vegetable fat is added.

NUTRITIONAL VALUE: without fat: reconstituted: protein 3.5%, carbohydrate 5.3%.

ENERGY per 100ml: without fat: recon-stituted: 35 kcal, 146 kJ.

Dried baby milk. Usually a proprietary brand of milk, modified to have a similar concentration of nutrients to human breast milk. It should always be reconstituted strictly in accordance with the manufacturer's instructions. See **baby feeds**.

Evaporated (or unsweetened condensed). Milk evaporated to 45% of its volume and canned. Legally it must contain not less than 7.8% fat.

NUTRITIONAL VALUE: average: protein 8.2%, fat 9%, carbohydrate 12%.

ENERGY per 100g: 160 kcal, 669 kJ.

Homogenized milk. Milk in which the fat globules have been reduced to a small enough size to produce a stable emulsion without the fat separating out.

Long-life milk. Trade-name for a brand of UHT milk. See below.

Sterilised milk. Milk which has been heated to destroy all life within it.

UHT. Milk which has been heated to a temperature of 132°C (270°F) for a few seconds; it has a life of up to six months at room temperature, when sealed in the original container, but once opened should be treated as fresh milk. There is some alteration in taste. See **buffalo milk, ewe's milk, goat's milk**.

mille feuilles, 'Thousand leaves'. Iced cake made with layers of puff **pastry** and sandwiched with a filling of cream or custard and jam.

millet Seeds of *Sorghum vulgare* and other related grasses but not **wheat, barley, oats** or **rice**. Also known as **sorghum**, Kaffir corn, Egyptian rice or corn, Guinea corn, Tunis grass and African corn. It grows in warm climates and is the most important food crop in Africa as it grows rapidly and has a high yield.

NUTRITIONAL VALUE: protein 6–11%, carbohydrate 60–70%, fat 1.5–5%, vitamin B complex, iron.

ENERGY per 100g: 280–320 kcal, 1171–1339 kJ.

USES: ground into **flour** or a coarse **meal** for a porridge-type of food or unleavened **bread**. May be cooked and eaten as an alternative to **rice**. Also used for local beers, animal feed in the USA and bird seed in the UK.

milling The processes of grinding **corn** and other **cereals** by hand or machine to produce degrees of fineness, varying from coarse-ground **semolina**, to those of the finest quality flour.

The practice has been carried out since earliest times, when seeds were collected from the wild for food. Originally the grains were ground on a saucerised stone, with a smaller stone moved around by hand, known as a **quern**. Later the Romans introduced water-power to drive a round, rotating stone, set above a stationary stone of the same size. Windmills, invented by the Persians in the 7th century, became a common sight in the middle ages, operating grind-stones. Stone-ground flour remains cool and the natural **yeasts** remain active and could be used to start the fermentation process of bread-making but modern high-speed roller-mills grind fast and the heat produced kills the yeasts.

Milling also involves separating the various components of grain to produce a wide range of products, which include **bran, wheatgerm**. See **ageing, extraction rate, flour, grind, protein**.

milt or **melt** The soft **roe** of male **fish**; also the **spleen** of mammals.

mimicry A defence process whereby one species copies the look of another. For example, where a highly poisonous fungus (toadstool) may look very similar to an edible one.

mince To chop or grind finely (usually meat); generally in a hand-operated appliance or in a **food processor**.

Mince commonly means minced meat, raw or cooked and served as a meat dish on its own or used to stuff vegetables and in pies.

mince-pie Originally an individual pie containing minced meat and dried fruit but has come to mean a similar pie containing a mixture of dried fruits, candied peel, suet and sugar. Traditionally eaten hot at Christmas.

mineral An inorganic substance found naturally in water or extracted from mines, such as sodium chloride (common salt), metals.

mineral salts Inorganic salts which have an essential role in body function. The most important are those containing **calcium**, **iron**, **phosphorus**, **potassium** and sodium (see **salt**). Others, known as the **trace elements**, are only necessary in small quantities and include **chromium**, **cobalt**, **copper**, **iodine**, **magnesium**, **manganese**, **molybdinum**, **selenium** and **zinc**. They are widely present in nature and deficiencies in the UK are unlikely. Some minerals are toxic in larger than necessary doses; supplements are only rarely required and then strictly on medical advice. See **heavy metals**.

mineral waters Untreated natural spring waters which are sold under many names. Some are still, some mildly alkaline, while others are naturally or artificially carbonated (**effervescent**). They are claimed to have beneficial qualities because they contain essential minerals and have a high degree of purity. The best known in the UK include Buxton, Malvern, Perrier and Vichy. See **water**.

mint A member of the *Mentha* family, of common hardy **herbs**. There are some 40 known varieties, most having a characteristic flavour. The family includes:–

Mentha alopecuroides. An all purpose culinary mint.

Mentha citrada. Bergamot mint.

Mentha piperata. Peppermint mint. Used only for its peppermint flavour.

Mentha rotundifolia. Apple mint. Particularly favoured for mint sauce.

Mentha sicasta. Spearmint. The most widely grown for culinary purposes.

USES: mint leaves are widely used for flavouring vegetable and savoury dishes, for the sauce or jelly traditionally served in the UK with roast lamb. Oil extracted from *Mentha piperata* is used in sweetmeats, desserts, the liqueurs crème de menthe and royal mint chocolate. Also used for flavouring toothpaste and some medicinal products.

mirabelle A small yellow cherry-like plum, *Prunus insitia*.

USES: for making the liqueur Mirabelle, and in desserts and preserves.

miraculin A glycoprotein present in the fruits of the tropical flowering tree, *Richardelli dulcifera*, which has the property of making some acidic fruits taste sweet. The taste lingers on the tongue and has been tried as a sweetening agent but found to have no commercial value.

mites Minute members of the animal kingdom, often too small to be seen by the eye. They abound in homes and on the body and can be responsible for disease and **allergies**. Cheese-mites are found on mature cheeses and are harmless.

mixed spice Generally a mixture of **cloves**, **ginger**, **cinnamon** and **nutmeg** in the ratio of 1,2,4 and 4 parts respectively. Spices loose their potency by evaporation of the **essential oils** and are best when freshly ground. They should be kept in the dark in airtight containers and are best refrigerated.

USES: in cakes, puddings and biscuits.

mocca A mixture of **coffee** and **cocoa** used as a beverage and in confectionery.

mocha or **moka** Coffee from Moka in the Yemen, where it was probably first grown and used.

mockernut The sweet hard-shelled nut of *Carya tormentosa*, a tall tree of the Eastern United States. Now more widely grown.

NUTRITIONAL VALUE: protein 15–20%, fat 40–60%, carbohydrate 15–20%.

ENERGY per 100g: 476–695 kcal, 1991–2908 kJ.

USES: as a dessert nut.

molasses A crude, dark, sweet and strongly-flavoured syrupy extract obtained during the refining of **sugar**, which does not crystallize. See **treacle**.

NUTRITIONAL VALUE: about 65 % sucrose with glucose, fructose and dextrin, iron and other minerals.

USES: in making ginger biscuits, puddings, toffee, rum; also, mixed with grains for animal feed, and for making silage.

mollusc A large group of invertebrates found on land, in freshwater and seawater. Most have shells but some are soft-bodied. The land **snail** and the freshwater **mussel** found in rivers, are the only edible molluscs not found in the sea. The majority of edible molluscs are found in coastal waters worldwide. The most important are **clams**, **cockles**, **cuttlefish**, **mussels**, **oysters**, **squid** and **winkles**.

All except the cuttlefish, octopus and squid, live by filtering sea-water and are liable to contamination by chemical pollutants, viruses and **bacteria** present in sewage effluents. All molluscs must be taken from water free of contamination and kept alive in clean water for 24 hours, to allow them time to cleanse themselves. They should then be cooked to destroy any residual **micro-organisms**. Outbreaks of **cholera**, **poliomyelitis**, **typhoid** and **hepatitis** have all been reported from contaminated molluscs.

They should be purchased from a reputable dealer. See **red tide**.

NUTRITIONAL VALUE: protein 10–15%, fat 0.5–2%, vitamin B complex, calcium, iodine.

ENERGY per 100g: 45–78 kcal, 188–326 kJ.

USES: as first courses, main courses and in soups.

molybdenum A **trace element** essential to **enzyme** systems. Adequate quantities are present in a mixed **diet** and supplements should never be required.

monosaccharides A group of simple sugars, which includes **glucose** and **fructose**. See **disaccharides**, **polysaccharides**.

monosodium glutamate (E621) The sodium salt of glutamic acid, naturally present in many foods, including **milk**, **cheese**, **tomatoes**, **mushrooms** and **peas**. It has little flavour of its own but has the ability to enhance the flavour of any food to which it is added. For this reason, it is extensively used in processed, canned and packaged foods, particularly soups and pies, and in **seasoning salt**. It is safe in the recommended concentration of 0.1–0.3%. Excessive use can upset some people and it should never be added to food for babies and young children. See **Chinese food syndrome**.

monounsaturated fat See **fat**.

monstera *Monstera deliciosa*. A tropical evergreen climber, native of Mexico and tropical America, producing a fruit which, when ripe has a soft acidic flesh with a hint of pineapple flavour; only rarely available in the UK.

montilla A variety of dry **sherry**.

mooli A winter variety of **radish**, *Satanus sativus*. Also known as Japanese radish. The roots are white and the shape of a large carrot, growing to 30—40cms in length. It has a pungent, peppery flavour and is best harvested before it reaches full maturity.

USES: sliced or grated in salads, with vinegar as an alternative to horseradish sauce with roast beef or fish such as mackerel.

morel *Morchella conica* and the very similar *Morchella esculanta*, two edible **fungi** found wild in the spring in pastures, hedges and woods. They have a characteristic conical cap and must, on no account, be confused with the deadly false morel, *Gyromitra esculanta;* expert advice should be sought for identification.

mornay A plain white sauce flavoured with cheese and sometimes with fish stock.

morphine Also known as opium. A powerful alkaloid extracted from the juice of the head of the opium poppy, *Papava somniferum* and used to relieve pain. The drug is strongly addictive. It is not present in poppy seeds which are used as a source of oil and for flavouring and decorating bread, cakes.

mortar See **pestle and mortar**.

Mosel A light white **wine** from the district of that name in Germany.
ALCOHOL CONTENT: 7—8%.

mother of vinegar The slimy culture of the bacterium, *Acetobacter aceti*, which converts **ethanol** (ethyl alcohol) into vinegar (**acetic acid**).

mould A common name for a **fungus** widely present in nature, and which proliferates to form the powdery growth or mildew which appears on stale bread, cheese, preserves and other foods. Some moulds are highly poisonous, producing **mycotoxins** which include the **aflotoxins**, associated with mouldy **peanuts**, and rye (**ergot**); others are of medicinal importance and some of food value. The group includes the mould *Penicillium*

notatum from which the drug **penicillin** is extracted, and the blue mould *Penicillium roquefortii*, used for **Danish Blue**, **Roquefort** and **Stilton** cheeses, *Penicillium glaucum* for **Gorgonzola**. The white mould *Penicillium candidum* is used for **Camembert** cheese.

Moulds which grow on jam, cheese and foods left exposed to the air are potentially dangerous and as a general principle mouldy food should be thrown away, as the mycotoxins diffuse into the substance of the food. However many people have just removed the mould from jam and cheese and suffered no ill effects. Moulds which may develop in wine are controlled by **sulphur dioxide** before fermentation. See **jam keeping**.

mould A container in which jellies and various dishes such as mousses, puddings, pâtés are given a particular shape when turned out.

moules French for **mussels**.

moulin-légumes (or 'mouli'). Trade-name for a device for crushing and sieving cooked fruit and vegetables in the preparation of purees and soups.

mountain-ash See **rowanberry**.

moussaka A Greek speciality savoury dish based on minced mutton, layered with aubergines, tomato, spices and covered with a cheese sauce.

mousse A light-textured, uncooked dessert or savoury made with eggs and cream. Because of the risks of **salmonella** poisoning, from the use of raw eggs, various alternatives can be used, such as evaporated milk, proprietary egg-white substitutes.

mousseline A variation of **hollandaise sauce** with added whipped cream.

Mozzarella A soft, almost pure white, Italian cheese traditionally made with buffalo milk. It is protected by law and its manufacture must comply with certain standards and production methods. It is copied worldwide and similar cheeses are made from cow's milk. Mozzarella ripens rapidly and deteriorates within a few days even in a refrigerator.

NUTRITIONAL VALUE: average: protein 20%, fat 22%.

ENERGY per 100g: average: 279 kcal, 1167 kJ.

USES: as a table cheese, but more often in cooking, particularly Italian dishes.

mucin A clear, slimy, viscous complex of protein and carbohydrate secreted by glands throughout the intestinal tract. In the mouth, in the form of saliva, it contains starch-digesting enzymes and when mixed with food by chewing is the first stage in digestion, its lubricating properties assisting in swallowing. Mucin also assists in the passage of faeces. It is a constituent of egg-white.

mucor The family of fungi which produce **moulds**.

mucous membrane The delicate and sensitive lining of organs such as the nose, eyes, mouth, intestinal tract, and air passages, but not the chest cavity. It usually secretes mucous and is easily damaged. Cancers can develop in it from repeated irritation, by smoking, chewing tobacco and **betel-nut**.

muffin A bread-like cake eaten toasted and spread with butter.

mulberry A loganberry-like fruit which grows on the tall deciduous mulberry tree, *Nonus nigra*. The soft, somewhat acid, fruit falls to the ground when ripe. It does not keep and is rarely available for sale. The leaves are used as food for silkworms.

NUTRITIONAL VALUE: protein 1%, vitamin C 10mg per 100g.

USES: eaten raw or cooked and for preserves.

mull To heat and add spices; usually refers to wine (mulled wine).

mullet Two unrelated species of high quality non-oily marine fish with firm flesh; usually only available during the summer months. They are:—

Red mullet, also known as surmullet. *Mullus surmuletus* and *Mullus barbatus* are two similar species caught mainly in the Mediterranean and off the Atlantic coasts of Southern Europe. They are expensive and considered delicacies.

Grey mullet. *Mugil cephalus* is the common grey mullet found mainly in warm temperate seas and is also farmed. The roe is known as boutague and is a delicacy in Mediterranean countries.

NUTRITIONAL VALUE: All varieties: average: protein 18%, fat 1–2%, calcium, iron.

ENERGY per 100g: average: 86 kcal, 360 kJ.

USES: usually cooked whole and fried, grilled or baked. The liver of the red mullet is highly prized and left inside the fish or used for a sauce.

mulligatawny A curry soup, originally from East India.

mung bean *Phaseolus aureus*. A very small olive-green bean, usually dried and sold as a pulse.

NUTRITIONAL VALUE: dried: cooked: protein 7%, carbohydrate 11%, fat 0.5%.

ENERGY per 100g: cooked: 74 kcal, 310 kJ.

USES: cooked and used as pulse. Also sprouted and known as bean sprouts, eaten in salads or stir-fried as a vegetable.

muscat A type of white **grape**, used for wine of the same name.

muscatel A large strongly-flavoured **grape**. Dried for muscatel raisins which are traditionally sold on the stalks. Also spicy wine of that name.

muscavado A type of unrefined **sugar**, dark brown and sticky.

muscle The part of mammals, birds and fish

responsible for movement; it has a high protein content and is the principal source of animal food. Red muscle owes its colour to blood pigments and iron-containing molecules known as myoglobin which also store oxygen. The muscle of pork and veal owes its paler colour to the animal being bled after slaughter. The colour of ham and bacon is due to chemical changes caused by the action of nitrates and salt used in **curing**. Birds and some fish have reddish-brown and white muscle, each having a different function. Muscle which is not used very much, except in short bursts, does not need to store oxygen, thus it has little myoglobin and is white. Brown muscle however, burns fat slowly to provide energy and contains myoglobin in order to store oxygen and this gives it its colour. Hence, in domestic birds which do not fly very much, such as chicken and turkey, the breast muscle is white and the leg muscle brown because they stand around a lot. Game birds which are free-flying have brown breast and leg muscles. Brown muscle tends to have a fuller flavour than white.

mush Meal (a coarse flour) boiled to form a pulp.

mushroom The commonest of the edible **fungi**, *Psalliota campesta*, found growing wild in old pastures where horses are grazed and no fertilisers have been used. Today the majority are cultivated and sold young as button mushrooms, but the larger open mushrooms have the best flavour. The flavour of mushroom soups may be due to varieties of *boletus edulus*. They are sometimes dried.

NUTRITIONAL VALUE: protein about 2%, vitamin B complex, trace of iron and vitamin C.

ENERGY per 100g: raw: 18 kcal, 75 kJ.

USES: chopped raw in salads or cooked and eaten as a savoury, as an ingredient in sauces, casseroles, soups.

Muslims See **religious laws**.

muslin Finely woven cotton fabric. Used for wrapping cheese and straining liquids.

mussels Bivalve **molluscs**. Common edible species are *Mytilis edulis*, found round the coasts of Europe and *Mytilis galloprovincialis*, the Mediterranean variety. They cling to rocks, ropes and underwater structures. *Margaritifera, Unio* and *Anodonta* are freshwater species and found on river-beds. Sea-water species are now extensively farmed in mussel-beds.

Only live mussels with tightly-closed shells, taken from unpolluted waters, should be eaten. Before cooking they should be left in fresh water for several hours in order to clean themselves. The thread-like hairs, known as **byssus**, with which they attach themselves, should be discarded. Mussels can cause **food poisoning** if these precautions are not taken. See **red tide**.

NUTRITIONAL VALUE: protein 15%, fat 2%, calcium, iodine, iron.

ENERGY per 100g: 78 kcal, 326 kJ.

USES: cooked by boiling, eaten as a separate dish or with other foods.

must The term used for new **wine**, grape juice that is unfermented or incompletely fermented, or the pulp to be fermented.

mustard The powder prepared by pounding or milling the pale seeds of *Sinapsis alba* and/or the yellow seeds of *Brassica juncea*, both of which are members of the same family and widely grown in temperate climates; introduced by the Romans. The seeds contain an **essential oil**, a **protein**, a **glucoside**, the enzyme **myrosinase** and an emulsifying agent. *Brassica juncea* is now being grown for its fleshy leaves and is among those vegetables sold as spring greens.

The potency of mustard only develops in the presence of water, which allows the enzyme to react with the glucoside and produce the characteristic flavour. The yellow seed, usually known as brown mustard, is responsible for the pungency felt in the nose, because of the volatile oil, while white mustard is felt more on the tongue. The two types of seed are blended to give the best condiment mustard.

USES: as a condiment made up with water; it is best mixed 10 minutes before it is required. Mixed with herbs and vinegar to prepare special varieties such as Dijon mustard. Used in mayonnaise both as an emulsifier and to give flavour. Used in cooking, heat drives off some of the volatile oils, which reduces the pungency. The seeds are used in curry dishes.

mustard and cress A salad grown from the seeds of *Brassica alba* (mustard) and *Lepidum sativa* (cress) and cut at the cotyledon stage, a few days after germination.

NUTRITIONAL VALUE: protein 1.5%, vitamin C up to 80mg per 100g, carotene, calcium, iron.

ENERGY per 100g: negligible.

USES: in salads, sandwiches especially with egg, as a garnish.

mustard oil Cooking oil used in the East, extracted from mustard seeds. In tropical countries there is some risk of contamination with other seeds, such as *Argemonee mexicana*, which contain a poisonous alkaloid.

mutton Meat from a sheep between 1–2 years of age.

mya A form of **clam**, a marine bivalve found off the North American coasts.

mycoprotein Also known as quorn. A food prepared from the fungus *Fusarium graminearum*, now grown in an artificial medium for its **protein** and **dietary fibre** content. It is firm, pale grey in colour, cuts in a similar way to tender cooked **meat** and is used as a meat substitute. It has little taste but readily takes up flavours from marinades, **sauces, seasoning**. Keeps refrigerated for 2–3 days, freezes well and can then be stored for several months.

NUTRITIONAL VALUE: protein 12%, fat 3.2% , mostly unsaturated, carbohydrate 1.8%, fibre 4.8%.

ENERGY per 100g: 84 kcal, 352 kJ.

USES: as a meat substitute in dishes such as pies, casseroles, risottos, pasta dishes, stir-fried dishes.

mycotoxin A poison produced by a variety of **fungi** of all sizes, including some **moulds**, and large toadstools. The poison can be rapidly fatal (even in small doses), and positive identification is essential when selecting fungi for food. Highly toxic mycotoxins may be present on mouldy **peanuts, dried figs** and **rye**. Moulds flourish under warm, damp conditions. If poisoning occurs, or is suspected, medical advice should be sought urgently.

myogen A form of albumen in which muscle fibres are embedded; it accounts for up to 20% of total muscle protein.

myosin. A **globulin** which constitutes the major form of muscle protein.

myrosinase An **enzyme** present in **mustard** seeds which activates the pungent **essential oils** in the presence of water. Also found in **horseradish**.

myrrh Also known as **sweet cicely**, *Myrrhis odorata*. A native wild aromatic perennial herb.

USES: cultivated for use of the leaves, roots and seeds for salads.

myrtle *Myrtum communis*. An evergreen shrub, just hardy in the South West of England, bearing small edible black berries.

USES: the berries may be used for flavouring pork and chicken, in a similar way to **juniper**, and the aromatic leaves used to wrap pork and chicken for roasting. Also used to make a liqueur, Myrtille.

myrtle pepper See **allspice**.

Mysost A Scandinavian cheese made by concentrating **whey** by boiling until it sets on cooling. The flavour depends on the amount of **lactose** it contains. It can be quite sweet if the natural lactose is unaltered, but acid if there has been conversion to lactic acid.

N

naseberry *Achras sapota*, also known as sapodilla, zapota. A tropical tree, native of South America and West Indies, producing a potato-like seeded-**fruit** which ripens with a soft, sweet, yellow flesh, translucent and low in acidity but with some **tannin**.

USES: fruit, usually eaten fresh as a dessert. The trunk produces a latex substance chicele, used for chewing-gum.

nasturtium *Tropaeolum major;* also known as Indian cress. An annual creeping plant with trumpet-shaped flowers.

USES: the leaves have a pungent flavour and may be used in salads; the flowers as a decoration on salads; the seeds can be pickled in vinegar and used as a substitute for **capers**.

natural A term used for some food substances, but which has no legal definition. It implies that it is a biological product in its natural state; however, the term has been widely interpreted by food manufacturers to include biological materials which have been modified to alter their characteristics. It is also used to describe flavourings and colourings of foods which would not normally be found in them, such as **annato**, a vegetable dye, used to colour some cheese and smoked herrings (kippers). There is no evidence that there is any health risk.

navarin A stew of mutton or lamb, often with haricot beans.

neapolitan ice An **ice-cream** made in a square or rectangular mould, in layers of several colours and flavours.

neat's foot jelly From the word neat meaning a member of the cattle family. See **calves' foot jelly**.

Nebuchadnezzar A very large wine bottle equal to 20 ordinary (75cl) bottles, usually of **Champagne**. Named after a King of Babylon.

nectar The sugary secretion from the nectuary glands of flowers, which attracts pollinating insects and birds; it is the principal source of sugars for honey-bees. The water content varies from 20–50% with a variable mixture of pollen, mineral substances, **essential oils** and different sugars characteristic of each source. Nectar from some heathers is thixotropic, that is a **gel**, which flows when disturbed and then returns to a jelly state. The nectar of some flowers is unfit for human consumption and some is poisonous such as that from rhododendron and ragwort. See **honey**, **honeydew**.

nectarine A variety of peach, *Prunus persica*, with a smooth skin.

NUTRITIONAL VALUE: carbohydrate 5–

8%, vitamin C up to 5mg per 100g, carotene.

ENERGY per 100g: 20–32 kcal, 84–134 kJ.

USES: as a dessert fruit, in fruit salads and other desserts.

neep Another name for **turnip**.

nephelium See **lychee**.

neroli oil See **seville orange**.

Nescafe See **instant food**.

nettle The common stinging nettle, *Urtica dioica;* a wide spreadspread weed.

NUTRITIONAL VALUE: negligible.

USES: the top few leaves of the young shoots can be used as a spinach-like vegetable and for soup; once washed, they lose their ability to sting.

niacin Also known as niacinomide and **nicotinic acid**.

nickel. A trace element essential in life but in such small quantities that there is sufficient in a normal diet and deficiency does not occur. The metal is a component of the alloy nickel-silver, used as an inexpensive substitute for silver for spoons, cutlery; it lacks the warm colour of silver. Also used on copper and other metals in electroplating alone or as a first stage in silverplating. It is relatively non-toxic but carries a high risk of inducing dermatitis when it is in prolonged contact with skin; for this reason it is no longer used for fastenings on clothing or buckles where they may touch the skin. Also used commercially in the hardening of fats.

niçoise À la Niçoise means prepared as in the Nice district of France, usually salad, with garlic, tomatoes, black olives, anchovies and olive oil.

nicotinic acid (375) One of the 12 **vitamins** which form the vitamin B complex and essential for health. It is used as a food **additive** to protect colour in bread, cereals and flour but has not yet been given the 'E' prefix of full approval. It is present in **cereals** (not **maize**) but with the highest concentration in meat, fish, liver and yeast and adequate quantities are contained in a mixed diet. It is fairly stable and not destroyed by cooking. Deficiencies cause a condition called **pellagra**, with disorders of the skin, intestinal tract and the nervous system. It is unrelated to nicotine, the drug present in tobacco.

Niersteiner A light, white wine from around Nierstein in Germany, sold in brown bottles.

ALCOHOL CONTENT: about 8–9%.

nigella See **fitches**.

nisin (E234) An antibiotic prepared from *Streptococcus lactis*, and occuring naturally in cheese. It is not used in the treatment of human disease and is the only antibiotic permitted as a food **preservative** in the UK.

nitrates See **nitre**.

nitre In the form of sodium nitrate (Chile saltpetre) or potassium nitrate (saltpetre), nitre occurs naturally in some common vegetables, up to 1g per kg, and gets into other foods through the use of preservatives and through water supplies. Its use as a food **preservative** in meat, canned foods and sausages is strictly controlled. The action of heat and the brining process convert nitre rapidly to nitrites which prevent the growth of the most serious **food poisoning** bacteria, *Clostridium botulinum* and *perfringens*. Nitrites are themselves poisonous to mammals, but the low concentration necessary to protect food from the growth of bacilli is within the limits of tolerance and it is generally considered that their advantages outweigh their disadvantages. Nitrates get into water supplies from modern farming practices involving intense cultivation, heavy dressings of nitrogenous fertilisers and ploughing of arable pastures. To avoid excesses their concentrations are regularly monitored. See **methaemoglobin**.

nitrites See **nitre**.

nitrogen See **gas**.

nitrogen trichloride Also known as agene; one of the bleaching agents formerly used to remove the yellow colour of carotene and xanthophyll from flour to make it white, but now abandoned.

nocake Meal made by grinding Indian corn (**maize**).

nog A drink made with egg and hot beer or spirits; also the name of a strong ale brewed in Norwich.

noggin A mug holding a gill which is a quarter of a pint (approximately 145ml); also refers to a drink such as beer, spirits.

noisette Made, or flavoured, with **hazelnuts**. Also refers to small pieces of butter (beurre noisettes), or lamb chops or cutlets boned and rolled (noisettes of lamb).

non–dairy creamer A powder preparation made with **hydrogenated vegetable oils, dextrin, casein**, emulsifiers, antioxidants and used as a milk substitute in coffee and tea.

nonstick A heat-resistant plastic coating known as PTF (polytetrafluor-ethylene). It is a product of space research. Now applied to cooking vessels to prevent food sticking, and can be used for frying pans, saucepans, baking tins. It should not be overheated and it is damaged by metal and abrasive cleaners and only wooden or plastic spoons should be used for stirring. If the coating becomes damaged by rough treatment or overheating, the pan should not be used. Generally any food that sticks is removable with warm water, detergent and a soft cloth or brush; a plastic scourer should be used only if this is unavoidable.

noodles A form of **pasta** made in short flat strips. In oriental cooking noodles may be made with many different starchy substances such as wheat flour, rice flour, mung beans, sometimes with egg, and in a variety of shapes.

nopales Mexican name for the edible pad-like leaves of several varieties of the cactus, *Opuntia platyopuntia*. It grows wild in subtropical and arid areas. See **prickly pear**.

USES: the young tender leaves can be cooked and used in soups or as a vegetable. Rarely available in the UK.

Normandy pippins Whole apples, peeled, cored, sliced and dried. They may then be soaked and cooked as for fresh apples. They are usually treated with **sulphur dioxide** to prevent brown discoloration.

Norwegian prawn See **langoustine**. Same as Dublin Bay prawn and scampi.

nougat A chewy sweetmeat made of sugar, starch, nuts and sometimes egg and/or gelatine and dried fruit.

noyau A liqueur flavoured with almond or peach kernel. During preparation a **glucoside** present in the kernels, reacts with water to form the dangerous hydrocyanic acid, which must be removed by boiling the liquid before using it to make the liqueur.

nutmeg The **kernel** of the fruit of a tropical tree, *Myristica fragrans;* the outer case is **mace** which has a different flavour. Both are used as spices with sweet and savoury dishes.

nut Any seed which has a hard shell or outer coat and an edible centre or kernel. Nuts vary considerably in flavour and are an important source of nourishment, especially in a vegetarian diet. Once they are shelled they can be kept for several months if in airtight containers, in cool conditions, preferably a refrigerator or freezer; when they are exposed to the air, the oils tend to oxidise and become rancid. Nuts, especially **peanuts**, which develop a mould may contain dangerous **mycotoxins** and should be discarded (not even fed to birds). See **protein**.

NUTRITIONAL VALUE: most nuts are similar. Protein 15–20%, fat 40–55% of which about 20% is **saturated**, carbohy-drate 15–20%, (much of which is not digestible). The four exceptions are:— **coconut**, **cocoa**-bean, **chestnut** and **palm-kernel**.

ENERGY per 100g: 480–590 kcal, 2008–2468 kJ.

USES: eaten alone, in vegetarian and other savoury dishes, sweetmeats, cakes, biscuits, desserts; also in the production of cooking oils.

oat The seed of a hardy grass, *Activa sativa;* a **cereal** with a relatively high **fat** content. It contains **phytic acid** which can reduce the absorption of **calcium**. **Vitamin D** and calcium should be given as **supplements** where oats are the main food source, to prevent bone thinning.

NUTRITIONAL VALUE: average: protein 13% (low in gluten), fat 7.5%, carbohy-drate 73%, vitamin B complex, calcium, iron.

ENERGY per 100g: average: 393 kcal, 1644 kJ.

USES: ground as oatmeal for **porridge**, **oatcakes**, cakes and biscuits. Unsuitable for bread-making on its own, but can be mixed with wheat flour to give flavour. Also an important food for animals.

oatcake One of the oldest and simplest forms of unleavened bread, which is made from oatmeal, water, salt and fat, pressed into thin biscuits and cooked in an oven.

oatmeal See **flour** and **oats**.

obesity A state of fat accumulation, due to an excess of **energy** intake over energy requirements. A person is generally consid-ered obese when their weight is 20% or more above the standard for age, sex, height and build. It is the commonest nutritional disorder of affluent societies, in which up to 45% of men and 35% of women may be overweight. Obesity has an adverse effect on many diseases, and slows recovery from injuries and surgical procedures.

Weight reduction is the commonest reason for controlling food intake. The diet should be designed to restrict energy intake and replace high-energy foods with low-energy foods. The diet should be broadly based and include vegetables, fruit and some whole-grain foods to provide sufficient vitamins and minerals. Exercise increases energy output and can play an important part in weight reduc-tion. The following is a basis for weight reduction:—

1. Weight loss should be gradual, with a change in eating habits, aiming at a loss of approximately 2.0kg (4.4 lb) per month; a slow reduction is more likely to be permanent.

2. Consumption of high-energy foods,

particularly pastries, cakes, biscuits, confectionery, snacks and all foods which contain a high proportion of fat and sugar should be cut to a minimum.

3. White meat or fish should replace red meat.
4. Intake of leaf and root vegetables, whole-grain foods, pulses and fruit should be increased.
5. Regular exercise should be taken.
6. Low-energy fluids (including skimmed instead of whole milk) should be drunk.
7. Medical advice should be sought if the individual is unwell in any way.

oca A South American plant, *Oxalis sativa*, used for its edible tubers as an alternative to potato.

octopus A marine cephalopod with eight legs or tentacles and related to the cuttle-fish and squid. There are many varieties but *Octopus vulgaris* is the one most commonly found. Normally only the tentacles are eaten, but they are tough and require long cooking.

NUTRITIONAL VALUE: protein 18%, fat ` 1–2 %, calcium, iodine.

ENERGY per 100g: 79–88 kcal, 330–368 kJ.

USES: braised or poached as a fish or main course.

oedema The collection of tissue fluids in and under the skin, particularly in the lower parts of the body and around sites of infection. Generalised oedema occurs with failure of the heart or kidneys, with **protein** deficiency due to starvation, and disorders of the liver and kidneys. Oedema may be aggravated by excessive intake of **salt**.

oestrogens The female sex **hormones** secreted by the ovaries. Oestrogens given to animals used for food can enter the food chain through meat and dairy products and their use is now banned in the EEC and most other developed countries.

offal Edible parts of an animal that are not part of the main carcass. Offal includes **brains, chitterling, heart, kidney, liver, lights, tongue, spleen, sweetbreads, tripe.** See **bovine spongioform encephalopathy.**

ohmic heating A process used commercially for rapid heating, by passing an electric current through the food, which must contain water.

ohmic sterilisation A sterilisation process in which an electric current is passed through a column of food; the electrical resistance to the passage of the current causes heat, in the same way as the element of an electric fire. When the operation is carried out under precise conditions, the heat of the food can be raised to the correct sterilising temperature. The method is efficient, safe, and increasingly used commercially, but has no place in the home.

oil Fat and oil are interchangeable substances depending on temperature; oil, which is usually liquid at room temperature, becomes solidified to form fat as the temperature drops and the point at which this change takes place varies according to the source of the oil. The main oils used in cooking are **corn, groundnut** (peanut), **olive, rape, soya, sunflower**; vegetable oil is a mixture of some of these with others. Speciality oils with distinctive flavours are extracted from **sesame seeds**, nuts such as **walnut, hazelnut.** See also **coconut oil, cottonseed oil, grapeseed oil, mustard oil, poppy-seed oil.** See **fat – effects of heat** and **safety in use.**

ENERGY: all oil has a value of 9 kcal, 37 kJ per gram.

USES: for frying, baking, roasting, in salad dressings, for greasing baking tins and dishes to prevent sticking.

oka See **yam.**

okra *Hibiscus esculentus*, also known as lady's

fingers or gumbo; a native of tropical Africa. The plant is now grown around the Mediterranean for its edible seed pods.

USES: cooked as a vegetable, or used in sauces for its viscous juices. The pods are soft, rather mucilaginous and considered a delicacy.

old man See **southernwood**.

oleic acid The predominant monounsaturated **fat** in the diet, present in butter, vegetable oils; **olive-oil** is the richest source.

olive The fruit of a Mediterranean tree widely grown as food from the earliest days of civilisation. The commonest olive is *Olea europaea*, but there are hundreds of different varieties producing different qualities of fruit. Some olives are harvested in the unripe state in September, when they are green, whilst others are left to ripen and turn black, dark brown or purplish, in the winter; both are soaked in water, or dilute caustic soda (for a quicker result), to remove the bitterness and then preserved in brine, if not being used for the extraction of **oil**.

NUTRITIONAL VALUE: average: protein 0.9%, fat 11%, carbohydrate trace, calcium, iron.

ENERGY per 100g: 103 kcal, 430 kJ.

USES: in a variety of snacks, savoury dishes from the Mediterranean. Sometimes they are stuffed with sweet red pepper.

olive-oil The oil extracted from crushed olives has been used for some 5000 years in countries around the Mediterranean, where it is a food-stuff of fundamental importance. The many grades, rated according to their acidity, depend on the olives used, climate in which they are grown, soil conditions and method of extraction; 'extra virgin oil', the finest (from Italy or the South of France), made simply by pressing the olives, is pale green; 'refined' is a lower quality and is made from a second pressing of the olives; and oils that do not qualify for the top grades because of high acidity and/or defective flavour, are often blended. Olive oils are expensive compared with other vegetable oils.

NUTRITIONAL VALUE: has the highest percentage of **monounsaturated fats** (about 70%) of all foods.

ENERGY per 100g: 900 kcal, 3766 kJ.

USES: for cooking it is considered to be superior to all other oils and can be used for **mayonnaise**, salad dressings such as **vinaigrette**, in **marinades**, shallow-frying, grilling, and roasting. It should not, however, be used for deep-frying because of its low **flash-point**. It is also used in **canning** fish.

olives, meat Small stuffed rolls of meat (usually beef), which are cooked by **braising**.

oloroso In Spain, a dry **sherry**, but elsewhere, medium sweet.

omelette An **egg** dish. The egg is lightly beaten, spread over the greased base of a shallow pan and lightly cooked without disturbance and finally folded in half, sometimes over a sweet or savoury filling. In a souffle omelette the separated egg whites are whisked and folded into the beaten yolks. Young children, the elderly, infirm and those on immunosuppresive drugs are at some risk of **food poisoning** if the omelette is not fully cooked.

omentum A large fold of fatty tissue in the abdomen, sometimes used as a membrane for wrapping **faggots** in place of **caul**.

omnivore One who eats both animal and vegetable food as opposed to a vegetarian who does not eat meat.

omophagia The consumption of raw animal as flesh. See **cooking** for prevention of disease.

omum See **ajowan**.

onion *Allium cepa*. A hardy bulbous plant which is widely grown and used for its remarkable flavouring qualities. There are a number of different varieties which vary in shape, size and flavour, some being mild and more digestible than the strong ones. The **essential oil** contained in the bulb is a strong irritant of the mucous membranes, particularly the eyes, but this oil is lost in cooking. Onions also contain anthoxanthin, a stable yellow flavone dye. Heated above 140°C (284°F) browning takes place. See **Maillard reaction**.

NUTRITIONAL VALUE: protein 1%, carbohydrate 5%, vitamin C about 25mg per 100g, calcium, iron, dietary fibre.

ENERGY per 100g: 23 kcal, 99 kJ.

USES: one of the most widely-used vegetables; boiled or baked whole, stuffed, sliced or chopped in stews, meat and vegetable dishes, soups, sauces. The flavour is best extracted by gently heating in oil (**sweating**). Also the milder varieties can be sliced and eaten raw in salads, as a garnish. Small varieties are **pickled** as a savoury.

opah The king-fish, a large African marine fish.

opium See **morphine**.

optical activity The property of certain substances to rotate the plane of **polarised light**. Those, such as **fructose**, which rotate it to the left are known as laevorotary, denoted by a (−) sign, whilst those which rotate it to the right are dextrorotary, such as **glucose**, denoted by a (+) sign. Optical activity is dependant on the asymmetry of the molecule and is measured by a **polarimeter**. **Sucrose**, a chemical compound of fructose and glucose, is dextrorotary but becomes laevorotary when it is split into its two components because of the higher optical activity of fructose over glucose. The process is known as inversion and the mixture is called **invert sugar**.

orange *Citrus sinensis*, a member of the citrus family, widely grown in areas where there is a frost-free climate and an adequate water supply. The thick skin contains **essential oils** and the pith, the white soft coat under the outer skin, contains **pectin**. Most varieties are relatively sweet. In tropical countries the varieties of orange grown are ripe when they are green. Blood oranges contain a natural red pigment, anthocyanin. Almost all oranges sold are coated with a wax emulsion containing **diphenyl**, a fungicide, to prevent the growth of **moulds**, and this can be only partly removed by washing; the quantity consumed even when the grated peel (**zest**) is used is unlikely to be harmful. See **mandarin, ortangue, satsuma, seville orange, tangerine**.

NUTRITIONAL VALUE: average: carbohydrate 8%, vitamin C up to 50mg per 100g.

ENERGY per 100g: average: 35 kcal, 150 kJ.

USES: mainly as a dessert fruit and for juice extraction. The grated peel and/or juice is used for flavouring cakes, desserts, sweetmeats, some savoury dishes. Also used for **marmalade, candied peel**, soft drinks (squash).

orange, bitter See **seville orange**.

orange-flower water A distillation of orange flowers used in perfumery and sometimes as a flavouring in desserts.

orcanella See **alkannett**.

oregano *Origanum vulgare*. A wild form of the herb **marjoram** which is common in Mediterranean areas. It has a stromg flavour and is used widely in Mediterranean cooking, particularly Italian pasta dishes and pizzas.

organic (chemical definition). A chemical substance which contains carbon, an essential component of all living matter.

organic The term used to describe foods

produced without the use of any artificial fertilisers, pesticides or fungicides and with only natural equivalents being accepted. The ground in which crops are grown must be free of residual substances which may have been used in the past. Organically-grown products are more expensive, due to lower yields and higher rate of rejection because of loss of quality; this may be due to size, blemish or irregularity. Improved flavour is claimed but is open to question. With reference to meat, (including poultry), the term implies that from animals which have been fed only on organically produced fodder.

It should, however, be pointed out that in countries with a high standard of monitoring food residues, there is no evidence that the quantities of chemicals consumed in non-organically produced food are harmful. The development of improved strains of crops with disease resistance and enhanced growth characteristics, together with a better understanding of the use of chemicals and the introduction of biological methods of disease control, is leading to a gradual reduction of the quantities of chemical substances used.

organism Any living animal or vegetable; a micro-organism is an organism too small to be seen by the naked eye.

orgeat A sugary drink made from **almonds**.

orgy Originally an ancient pagan rite. Now refers to a boisterous occasion and over-indulgence in food and drink.

ortangue A cross between an **orange** and a **tangerine**.

Orvieto A white **wine** from the district around the city of that name in Italy.

osmosis The diffusion of liquids through a porous membrane, an essential natural process in the response of plants to water and their soluble contents, affecting all stages of growth and the behaviour of vegetables and fruits during cooking. In principle, if two solutions containing differing concentrations of dissolved substances are separated by a semipermeable membrane, fluid will pass through the membrane from the weaker to the stronger solution until the two solutions are of equal strength. It is the way in which roots take up nutrients and leaves can take up moisture from the air or rain.

Using the principle of osmosis, vegetables which are limp can be made crisp and fresh-looking by immersion in plain water. Strong solutions of **salt** and sugar act as **preservatives** because they prevent water entering **micro-organisms** so that they cannot grow but are not necessarily destroyed. See **isotonic**.

osseter A type of **sturgeon**.

osteomalacia See **rickets**.

osteoporosis A thinning of bones causing a tendency to fractures. It is rare in men but common in women after the menopause, due to lack of **oestrogens**. It can also occur after prolonged bed-rest, as with delayed recovery from injury and some diseases. To reduce the risk, or delay onset, of the disease it is important to take as much exercise as possible and maintain an adequate **calcium** and **vitamin D** intake in the **diet**.

oven An enclosed cavity or space which can be heated for cooking by baking. Primitive ovens are made of brick or stone and heated by a wood fire, the fire being removed when the oven has reached the required temperature. Baking takes place with the heat retained in the oven.

Modern ovens are generally heated by gas, electricity or oil (some by solid fuel) and usually have a system of temperature control by **thermostat**. Food is cooked through the circulation of hot air and, to a small extent, by radiation from the heated walls of the oven; the temperature is higher at the top than the bottom. However, nowadays many electric ovens and a few gas ones are 'fan-assisted' and have an electric fan incorporated in them to give a more even heat throughout the oven (although this is disputed by some users), and to shorten cooking time. For maximum efficiency, manufacture's instructions should be adhered to. See **cooking, microwave oven**.

ovoid Shaped like an egg.

oxalic acid An acid found in small quantities in most vegetables, particularly **rhubarb**, **spinach** and **sorrel**; much of it combined with calcium, as calcium oxalate and not absorbed into the body. The highest concentration is in the leaves of rhubarb, which should never be eaten. Oxalic acid is potentially harmful except in small quantities, but there is no risk from foods containing it in the amounts normally eaten.

oxidases Enzymes which oxidise substances by removing a hydrogen molecule and converting it to water. They have an essential function in the body for the utilisation of food to provide **energy**, but are also responsible for deterioration of stored food. See **antioxidant**.

oxidation A chemical change which increases the oxygen, or reduces the hydrogen content, of a substance. The process may be associated with deterioration in the quality of foods, caused by **enzymes** in the presence of moisture, particularly those foods containing **fats** which become **rancid**. See **flour improvers, gas (hydrogen, oxygen)**.

OXO A proprietary product in the form of a cube, granules or paste made of **meat** extract, **hydrolysed vegetable protein**, and **monosodium glutamate** bound together with fat; in common with stock cubes and similar products it has a high salt content.

ENERGY per 100g: negligible.

USES: as a low-calorie hot drink and as flavouring for soups, stews, casseroles, gravy.

oxtail The tail of the ox, classed as offal, containing enough meat to make it a valuable source of meat for soups and stews but it usually has a high **fat** content.

ox tongue See **tongue**.

oxygen See **gas**.

oxyhaemoglobin See **haemoglobin**.

oyster There are some 300 species worldwide of this bivalve **shellfish**. *Ostrea edulis* is the native oyster found in European coastal waters where it has suffered a decline owing to pollution. Oysters feed by filtering sea-water and concentrate any **food poisoning** organisms or toxic chemicals present in the water. They must be harvested from clean waters and be cleaned before sale. At one time they were plentiful and among the least expensive of foods. They are now being farmed and becoming readily available again. They are also available frozen and canned. Oysters native to UK waters should not be harvested during the summer months which is the breeding season, the eggs within the shell give them an unpleasant taste. See **red tide**.

NUTRITIONAL VALUE: protein 10%, fat 1%, calcium, zinc.

ENERGY per 100g: 49 kcal, 205 kJ.

USES: traditionally eaten raw, when they should be alive and the tightly closed, opened only immediately prior to serving. They are also eaten cooked as in steak, kidney and oyster pie, wrapped in bacon and grilled (Angels on horseback), in sauces.

oyster plant See **salsify**.

ozone A form of **oxygen** with three oxygen atoms in its molecule, in comparison with oxygen which has only two. The gas is chemically highly active, a powerful **germicide** and **toxic** to all living cells. It is used commercially for **sterilisation** of water used in bottling and canning because of its lack of taste, for surface sterilisation of some foods and in ice to preserve fish.

Ozone is normally present in the upper atmosphere and reduces the amount of **ultraviolet light** (UVL) reaching the earth's surface, thus protecting living creatures from over exposure to these damaging rays. However, atmospheric pollution from factories, internal combustion engines and chemicals such as the gases known as CFCs (used in **refrigerators**), methane, nitrous oxides, is leading to a reduction in the ozone layer with the risk that high levels of UVL will reach the earth.

The most important steps to be taken to preserve the ozone layer, include the replacement of CFCs by other inert gases in refrigerators, reduction of pollution by industry and internal combustion engines. Old and discarded refrigerators should be sent to the local authority for safe disposal.

P

paëlla A Spanish dish of **rice**, sometimes coloured and flavoured with saffron, cooked in a shallow pan with vegetables, particularly peas, together with shellfish, chicken, garlic and herbs. There are many variations.

pak–choi *Brassica chinensis;* also known as Chinese mustard. It is similar to **Chinese cabbage** but with more loosely packed leaves.

NUTRITIONAL VALUE: protein 1%, vitamin C, minerals.

ENERGY per 100g: 12 kcal, 51 kJ.

USES: the central leaves are used raw in salads and the older outer leaves and stalks cooked by boiling, steaming or stir-frying. Sometimes the stalks are cooked separately.

palm A large group of tropical and subtropical branchless shrubs and trees, usually with fan-shaped leaves, including the **date** and **coconut**. Some are cultivated for their oil-seeds and others for the **pith**, an important source of **carbohydrate** in tropical countries. The terminal buds of many palms are edible and prepared in a variety of ways, particularly in the Caribbean. In Europe they are only available as a canned luxury food. See **cassava, sago** and **tapioca**.

palm–honey Sap of a **palm**, concentrated as a form of **sugar**.

palm–kernel oil Oil extracted from the nut of the tropical palm *Elaeis guineensis;* similar to **palm–oil**, but more delicate and pale in colour.

palm–oil Oil extracted from the pulp which surrounds the nut of the tropical palm *Elaeis guineensis*. It is reddish in colour with a high **carotene** content and one of the most important of the edible oils. It shares with coconut oil and cocoa-butter the highest saturated **fat** content of the vegetable oils.

NUTRITIONAL VALUE: fat almost 100%, of which 80–90% is saturated, carotene, tocopherol.

ENERGY per 100g: 900 kcal, 3766 kJ.

USES: commercial only; for manufacture of cooking fats, **margarine**, soaps, candles.

palm-wine Fermented sap from a **palm**.

pamplemousse French for **grapefruit**.

pan See **betel nut**.

panada Originally **bread** boiled to a pulp and flavoured. Also the term used for a thick sauce, used as a basis for cooked savoury and sweet **soufflés** or for binding mixtures such as **rissoles, croquettes**.

panary A store place for **bread**.

pancake A thin cake of flour, egg and milk fried in a shallow pan, sprinkled with sugar and lemon and rolled up. Alternatively served with a sweet or savoury filling. Traditionally eaten on Shrove Tuesday.

pancheon A dish or pan of simple earthenware.

pandore A highly-esteemed variety of **oyster** from the Forth estuary in Scotland.

pantothenic acid See **vitamins**.

papain A powerful proteolytic **enzyme** present in *Carica papaya*, the **papaya** fruit, used as a meat tenderiser. It may be injected into a live animal just before death. The enzyme is inactivated in the human digestive system. It destroys **gelatine** but not **agar-agar**. See **tender**.

papaw The fruit of a hardy North American deciduous tree, *Assimina triloba;* an ovoid yellowish berry with a yellow aromatic pulp, which is sweet and somewhat banana-flavoured. Also known as Michigan banana and is from the same family as the custard apple. It is distinct from **papaya**.

papaya Also known as **pawpaw**. An exotic aromatic fruit of the tropical *Carica papaya* tree. When fully ripe, the flesh is sweet and soft containing large numbers of hard round black seeds; it ripens after picking but does not keep well. The flesh contains **papain**. A recent introduction is **babaco**, a large seedless variety.

NUTRITIONAL VALUE: average: carbohydrate 9%, vitamin C 80mg per 100g.

ENERGY per 100g: average: 40 kcal, 167 kJ.

USES: eaten raw as a dessert fruit and in fruit salads.

papillote A method of cooking in paper or **aluminium foil** to preserve natural juices; whole fish or portions of meat are seasoned, wrapped in greaseproof paper, baking parchment or foil and baked. The food is usually served in its wrapping.

Also a curled paper frill used to decorate the bone or bones of meat or poultry, as on rack of lamb, whole ham, chicken legs for buffets.

paprika A powder ground from the dried ripe fruits of the sweet red pepper (**capsicum**); of Hungarian origin. The pigment, related to carotene, is oil-soluble and resists cooking and pH changes.

USES: to give flavour and colour to dishes such as Hungarian **goulash**, chicken paprika; also as a garnish on cheese, fish and vegetable dishes.

paraffin, liquid See **liquid paraffin**.

para nut See **Brazil nut**.

parasite A living creature which thrives on, or within, another animal, the host, from which it draws its nourishment. Parasites may be **micro-organisms (bacteria, fungi** or protozoa) or larger creatures such as insects, mites or worms. All insects, reptiles, birds, fish and mammals are liable to invasion by parasites. Some parasites are relatively harmless and even beneficial such as normal bacteria which colonise the mouth and alimentary tract, whilst others cause disease. Man is at risk by ingestion of eggs or immature forms of potential parasites in uncooked, or inadequately cooked food, particularly **meat** and **fish**; also from fruit and vegetables that have not been thoroughly washed, from contamination by pets, animal faeces or the hands of cooks or other food handlers. Some parasites can penetrate intact skin and so an individual can be infected by wading in infested water, particularly in warm climates. See **fish worms**, **giardia**, **hydatid cysts**, **tapeworms**, **toxacara**, **toxoplasmosis**, **trichinosis**, **malnutrition**.

paratha A thin cake made of flour, water and **ghee**; of Indian origin.

parboil To cook partially, by boiling; thus potatoes are sometimes parboiled before roasting. Whole rice may be parboiled to allow **vitamins** of the B complex to diffuse into the grain from the **husks** before these are removed.

parkin A form of **gingerbread** which contains **oatmeal** and **treacle** in addition to the other ingredients.

Parmesan, also known as Parmigiano regianno. A particularly hard, long-matured and strongly-flavoured speciality **cheese** from Italy.

NUTRITIONAL VALUE: protein 31%, fat 37%.

ENERGY per 100g: 457 kcal, 1912 kJ.

USES: used for cooking or grated on soups, pizzas, pasta dishes.

parsee See **religious laws**.

parsley *Petroselinum crispin*. A moderately hardy **herb**, which is either curly or broad-leafed. The broad-leafed variety has a slightly different flavour from the curly-leafed one. It can be dried for winter use although there is some loss of flavour, but it freezes well.

NUTRITIONAL VALUE: high in carotene and vitamin C.

USES: the leaves and stalks are used whole or chopped in **bouquet garni**, as flavouring in soups, savoury dishes and sauces and the leaves chopped or in sprigs as garnish.

parsley, Hamburgh A turnip-rooted variety of *Petroselinum crispinum*.

USES: as a root vegetable, in soups, casseroles.

parsnip A hardy starchy root vegetable, *Peucedum sativa*, white or pale yellow in colour. It was an important winter food in the past until potatoes were introduced. It grows wild but the roots are small; cultivated varieties have roots weighing up to 1 to 2 kg.

NUTRITIONAL VALUE: boiled: protein 1.3%, carbohydrate 13% and vitamin C up to 20mg per 100g.

ENERGY per 100g: boiled: 56 kcal, 234 kJ.

USES: a winter vegetable which can be boiled, steamed and baked. Also used in soups, casseroles and gratin dishes.

parson's nose The tail end of a fowl from which the tail feathers grow, considered a delicacy by some.

partridge A **game**-bird which although small, is highly prized for its flavour. Young birds should be hung for only 3 or 4 days, older ones for up to 2 weeks depending on temperature. See **hanging**.

SEASON: 1st September—1st February. Northern Ireland, 1st October —31st January.

NUTRITIONAL VALUE: protein 18%, fat 2–3%.

ENERGY per 100g: 90–97 kcal, 377–414 kJ.

USES: young birds are suitable for roasting and grilling, older ones for braising, pâtés, pies.

pashka A Russian speciality made with curd cheese, cream, chopped almonds and dried fruit set in a mould.

passion-fruit The seeded-fruit of *Passiflora edulus*, also known as grenadilla. A subtropical climbing plant, bearing ovoid berries about 5 cm long with a yellow or purple skin and an aromatic, soft, slightly acidic pulp. There is also a giant passion-fruit, a purely tropical plant, *Passiflora quadrangularis*, which bears fruits like large melons which have an inferior flavour.

NUTRITIONAL VALUE: average: protein 1%, carbohydrate 16%, vitamin C up to 20mg per 100g.

ENERGY per 100g: average: 64 kcal, 268 kJ.

USES: eaten fresh, cut in half and the flesh scooped out, in fruit salads as a garnish; also the juice is extracted as a drink and often mixed with juice of other tropical fruits.

pasta A food, probably of Chinese origin, but now associated with Italy. The dough is usually made from hard durum wheat, sometimes wholemeal, flour and water, sometimes with added **spinach** or **tomato**. It is produced in a wide variety of shapes, spirals, bows shells, tubes, long thin strands, flat sheets. It is generally sold dry and keeps for long periods in airtight containers, but freshly made pasta is becoming more widely available and should be cooked within one or two days of purchase or frozen. See **cannelloni, lasagne, macaroni, noodles, ravioli, spaghetti**.

NUTRITIONAL VALUE: average: cooked: protein 5.6%, fat 1%, carbohydrate 25%.

ENERGY per 100g: average: cooked: 130 kcal, 545 kJ.

USES: cooked in boiling water until it is **al dente** and served in a variety of ways such as with a simple cheese or tomato sauce, **pesto** sauce, or a rich meat sauce, vegetable sauce.

pasteurisation A method of partial **sterilisation** of dairy foods by heat treatment named after Pasteur, the famous French biologist. The temperature is raised and held at 55–65°C (131–149°F) for 30 mins; this does not unduly alter the character of the food but will destroy most non-sporing bacteria such as the *Tubercle bacillus* but not sporing bacteria such as *Clostridium botulinus* and *Clostridium perfringens*. The process is used for **milk, eggs** and **cheese** and but not for canned foods. Pasteurised milk will go sour, stored at room temperature, in 3–4 days owing to the presence of lactose-fermenting **bacteria**. See **botulism, food poisoning, Listeria monocytogenes**.

pastry A variable biscuit-like product made with **flour** and **fats** bound with water and sometimes egg; the proportion of fat ranges from about 1/5 to 3/4, resulting in very differing textures. The fat, known as **shortening**, which has the important characteristic of dispersing evenly in the flour, is traditionally lard or butter, or a mixture of the two, but specially formulated fats made from **hydrogenated vegetable oils**, of which some are mixtures containing 50% polyunsaturated fats, are available. As the lightness of pastry depends on the expansion of trapped air during cooking, it is very important to keep ingredients, utensils, and hands as cold as possible during its preparation; the cooler the air, the greater its potential for expansion. Most pastry freezes well, cooked or uncooked. Ready-mixed, uncooked shortcrust, fillo and puff pastry are available chilled or frozen.

There are many varieties of pastry but the main types are:–

Choux pastry. A very light rich pastry made with flour, hot water, fat and eggs, usually baked in bun or finger shapes, split and filled with cream, sweet or savoury fillings. Used for eclairs, profiteroles. See **beignet**.

Fillo pastry. A very low-fat pastry, of Greek origin, the name meaning 'leaf'. It is rolled out paper-thin, almost transparent, and becomes characteristically brown and crisp when cooked. Layers of pastry are rolled or folded into a variety of shapes round a filling, sweet or savoury, and baked or fried. It can be made at home, but is generally bought ready rolled out and frozen.

Flaky pastry. A high-fat (3 parts fat to 1 part flour) pastry with a brittle, layered consistency. The incorporation of air is achieved mainly by folding the dough over small lumps of fat and rolling it, repeating the procedure several times.

Puff pastry. Similar to flaky pastry but the fat is added in a smooth layer before rolling. Both are used for sausage rolls, savoury snacks, vol-au-vents, pie-toppings, tarts.

Raised pie or **hot water crust**. Pastry made with 1 part lard to 3 parts flour and bound with hot water, so that it is rolled out and moulded while still warm. Used for traditional pork pies, game pies.

Rich flan, pâté sucrée, biscuit crust. Sweetened pastries, bound with egg and used for fruit tarts and desserts.

Shortcrust pastry. Probably the most commonly used pastry, made with 1 part fat to 2 parts flour. The fat is rubbed into the flour and then mixed to a soft dough with water and rolled out thinly. Used for flans, tarts, fruit and savoury pies. The term 'short' refers to the crispness of the pastry.

Suet crust. Baked and steamed pastry made with suet and self-raising flour in a ratio of 2 parts fat to 2 parts flour, bound with water and rolled out to a greater thickness than short crust. Used for meat pies or puddings, fruit and syrup puddings.

ENERGY per 100g: 270–670 kcal, 1125–2803 kJ.

pâté or **terrine** A paste made of blended, chopped or minced meats, liver, fish, vegetables, sometimes with herbs, soft cheese. There is a risk of contamination by **food poisoning** organisms during preparation and all pâtés should be kept refrigerated and used within two or three days. See **Listeria monocytogenes**.

USES: served cold as a first course of a meal with bread rolls, toast, salad, as a snack on biscuits.

pâté de foie gras A French speciality **pâté** made with the **liver** of geese force-fed on maize, a high-carbohydrate and low-**protein** food, causing gross enlargement of the liver which degenerates, and the tissue is replaced by fat. The pâté has a high saturated-fat content.

pathogen A collective name for **bacteria** and other **micro-organisms** which cause disease, as compared with those which are harmless and even beneficial to man. See **food poisoning**.

patty A small, flat savoury cake made with minced meat or other food. There is a risk of contamination by **food poisoning** organisms during preparation and patties should be well cooked and refrigerated if not to be eaten immediately.

paunch The noun refers to the belly; the verb means to eviscerate, the act of paunching being the **drawing** of a bird in preparation for the table.

paupiette Slices of meat or fillets of fish rolled round a savoury stuffing, poached, and served with a sauce.

pawpaw See **papaya**.

paysanne A simple country style of cooking meat usually with onions, turnips, carrots, celery.

pea Any one of the large family of leguminous plants of the genus *Pisum*, grown worldwide, like beans, as an important source of protein. The most commonly grown variety is *Pisum sativum*, known as the garden pea. The seeds are round and keep well when dried; they are often split during the drying process. Pea pods are edible but not usually eaten, except those of the mangetout (flat podded) and sugar snap (round podded) varieties *(Saccaratum)* which are eaten whole when young.

NUTRITIONAL VALUE: fresh, cooked: protein 6–8%, carbohydrate 10–18%, vitamin B complex, vitamin C up to

30mg per 100g. Dried, cooked: protein 10.2%, carbohydrate 21.5%. (Vitamin C is destroyed by drying and canning).

ENERGY per 100g: average: fresh, cooked: 72 kcal, 301 kJ. Dried, cooked: 128 kcal, 536 kJ.

USES: eaten fresh, dried or canned as a vegetable, in savoury dishes, soups (sometimes including pods), dried for **pease pudding**, in other savoury dishes, soups.

peaberry A type of **coffee**. The beans are single seeds from the fruit of one variety of coffee tree, whilst in most other varieties they are in pairs or threes.

peach The sweet aromatic stone-fruit of *Prunus paria*, of which there are many varieties; rarer white-fleshed ones are considered superior. Dried, it keeps well and is usually **sulphited** to preserve its natural colour. Widely available **canned**.

NUTRITIONAL VALUE: average: fresh: protein less than 1%, carbohydrate 6.5%, vitamin C up to 8mg per 100g, carotene. Vitamin C is destroyed in the dried fruit.

ENERGY per 100g: average: fresh: 37 kcal, 155 kJ.

USES: fresh, as a dessert fruit; fresh, canned or dried in fruit salad and other desserts. Juice of the fresh fruit is extracted and preserved for drinking. See **pêche Melba**.

peanut Also known as ground-nut. The fruit of the annual subtropical *Arachis hypogea*. The flower-heads droop to ground level and the nuts are formed in soft shells underground. There are two varieties, Spanish with 2 kernels and American, with 3 kernels which have a slightly lower oil content. They are subject to the growth of a poisonous **fungus** or mildew producing a powerful toxin of the **aflotoxin** group, particularly if stored in damp conditions. Any nuts showing signs of this fungus must be discarded; not even given to birds. Shelled and roasted nuts share the tendency of all nuts to become **rancid**, due to the

breakdown of oils, and should be stored in airtight containers in a cool place, or refrigerated.

NUTRITIONAL VALUE: average: natural or dry-roasted: protein 24%, fat 49% of which 21% is saturated, 39% monounsaturated and 40% polyunsaturated, carbohydrate 9%, vitamin B complex, dietary fibre. Roasted and salted: fat 52%.

ENERGY per 100g: average: natural: 570 kcal, 2385 kJ. salted: 600 kcal, 2510 kJ.

USES: often roasted and salted for eating as snacks, such as with an aperitif, used fresh in sweetmeats, cakes, biscuits, salads, vegetarian dishes. Commercially, the source of **ground-nut oil** and **peanut butter**.

peanut butter A paste made of ground roasted peanuts mixed with extra oil, which has usually been hardened to prevent separation. It will keep in an airtight container for up to 3 months. Sometimes contains chopped peanuts to give a crunchy texture.

NUTRITIONAL VALUE: average: protein 25%, fat 50%, carbohydrate 13%.

ENERGY per 100g: average: 600 kcal, 2510 kJ.

USES: as a spread on bread or toast, as an ingredient in biscuits, cakes.

pear *Pyrus communis*. Over 1000 varieties of pear are listed; all have a common ancestor and have been grown for food since before Roman times. Of the same genus as the apple, the pear differs in shape and behaviour of the fruit. It ripens slowly at first but the last stages take only a few days; after a short time it passes its peak and deteriorates rapidly. It is sweet and juicy and at its best one of the most exotic fruits in the UK. Available fresh, **canned** and **dried**.

NUTRITIONAL VALUE: average: carbohydrate 10%, vitamin C.

ENERGY per 100g: average: 41 kcal, 172 kJ.

USES: as a dessert fruit, in fruit salads and

cooked in a variety of desserts. Special varieties are used in the manufacture of **perry**.

pearl barley Barley which has been husked. It stores well in dry conditions.

NUTRITIONAL VALUE: cooked: protein 3%, fat 1%, carbohydrate 28%, (most of the vitamin and mineral content is lost in processing).

ENERGY per 100g: cooked: 120 kcal, 502 kJ.

USES: traditionally used in lamb or mutton stews, in making **barley water** and soft drinks.

pease pudding Split dried **peas** which have been soaked then boiled, seasoned with pepper and salt, mashed with butter, placed in a cloth and boiled again; traditionally served with pork and ham.

pecan nut The hard-shelled sweet nut of *Carya pecan*, a tall hardy member of the walnut family; a native of North America. Related to *Carya tormentosa*, the **mockernut**.

NUTRITIONAL VALUE: average: protein 20%, fat 50%, vitamin B complex, minerals.

ENERGY per 100g: average: 530 kcal, 2218 kJ.

USES: a dessert nut and in desserts and cakes.

pêche Melba A classic dessert of peach, ice-cream and raspberry purée, created for Dame Nellie Melba, the opera singer.

peck A unit of measure, for dry gods, now obsolete; equal to 2 gallons.

pectin (E440a and **440b)** A food additive used to promote the setting of jams and preserves; also commercially as an **emulsifier** and stabiliser and to delay cakes becoming stale.

pectin A naturally occurring **polysaccharide**, present in the flesh and pips of many **fruits** and in the **pith** of **citrus fruits**, which has the property of forming a **gel** in an acid medium in the presence of **sugar**. It is not digested in the alimentary tract but is fermented in the large bowel and forms part of the complex known as **dietary fibre**. There are variations in the complexity and amount of pectin found in different fruits; the content is high in citrus fruits, apples and gooseberries but low in strawberries. Its potency falls as the fruit ripens, and thus it is better to use slightly under-ripe fruit for **jam** and **jelly**-making. Setting is aided, when using fruit with a low acid and pectin content for these preserves, by the addition of lemon juice, citric acid or a proprietary pectin concentrate made from apple pulp or citrus pith. See **pectinase**.

pectinase Also known as pectase and pectolase. An **enzyme** which hydrolyses **pectin**; used to increase the extraction rate of fruit juices and remove pectin from fruit wines as it prevents clarification.

pedicle The stalk of a fruit.

pekoe A type of **tea**.

pelagic See **fish**.

pellagra A deficiency disease caused by lack of the vitamin **nicotinic acid**. It may be seen in conditions of chronic starvation and in those who subsist on a high carbohydrate diet consisting mainly of polished rice or maize. It is associated with dementia, roughness of the skin and diarrhoea. It is rare, and prevented by eating a mixed diet which includes whole grain wheats and a proportion of meat, yeast, fish, potatoes.

pemmican A concentrated food made from powdered dried **meat**, mixed with melted fat, sometimes with dried fruits and sugar. Used by North American hunters and early explorers.

penicillin The first of the **antibiotics**, discovered by Alexander Fleming in 1928 from a chance finding of a **mould**, *Penicillium notatum*, contaminating a culture plate of *Staphylococcus aureus*. It was first extracted and used for medical purposes in 1941. Penicillin is one of the safest, and still a most important, antibiotic but unfortunately many *Staphylococci* are now resistant to it. Penicillin is used for the treatment of mastitis in cows, and **milk** from cows under treatment must not be sold for human consumption. Other varieties of penicillium mould, which have no medicinal importance, are used for the production of **cheeses** such as **Camembert**, **Gorgonzola**, **Roquefort** and **Stilton**. See **mould**.

penny bun See **boletus**.

pennyroyal *Mentha pulegium*. A prostrate creeping variety of **mint** with a special flavour used in north country (UK) **black pudding**.

pentosans Complex sugars present in some fruits and vegetables; they are not themselves digestible but may be broken down by acids and utilised.

pepinetto See **chayotte**.

pepper A condiment derived from the strongly aromatic berries of the tropical tree, *Piper nigrum*, a native of South America. The berries or peppercorns are green when unripe and turn black when dry; white peppercorns are riper and have the outer skin removed. Peppercorns contain the **alkaloids** (chemical substances) piperine and piperdine which provide the pungency of the condiment. The flavour of pepper is best when freshly ground in a small **peppermill** or with a **pestle and mortar**. It is available as peppercorns or ready ground. Common pepper is unrelated to **cayenne** or **chilli** pepper, sweet pepper (see **pepper, sweet**).

USES: in soups, casseroles, sauces, savoury dishes, as a table condiment. Black pepper is the most pungent and white milder. Green pepper is the mildest form but more aromatic and often used in oriental cooking.

pepper, red See **chilli**, **cayenne**.

pepper, sweet The fruit of the *Capsicum annum*, a subtropical annual. The plant grows to about 50–60cm and bears squat, oblong green fruits ripening to red, yellow or orange according to the variety. Also known as pimento and not to be confused with the **chilli**.

NUTRITIONAL VALUE: protein 0.9%, carbohydrate 2.2%, vitamin C 100mg per 100g, calcium.

ENERGY per 100g: 40 kcal, 167 kJ.

USES: chopped or sliced raw in salads when green or fully ripe, cooked whole and stuffed, chopped or sliced in many vegetable and meat dishes. Dried and ground when red to make **paprika**.

peppermill A small hand-operated disk mill for **grinding** fresh peppercorns at the table and in the kitchen.

peppermint *Mentha piperita*, a member of the hardy family of mints from which **oil** of peppermint is extracted and used as a flavouring in sweetmeats, chocolates, some toothpastes and medicines.

pepperwort *Lepidum sativum*. Also known as cress, as in mustard and cress.

NUTRITIONAL VALUE: vitamin C.

USES: used in the cotyledon stage in salads, sandwiches (particularly with egg), as a garnish.

Pepsi-cola An acidic refreshing drink similar to **Coca-cola**.

pepsin A **proteolytic enzyme** produced in the stomach and concerned in the digestion of proteins; it is only effective in an acid environment. The stomach wall is protected against its action.

perch *Perca fluvialis*. A freshwater fish, not of good eating quality and best known only to anglers.

percoct Well- or over-cooked.

percolate To pass through. A percolator is an apparatus for percolating, usually used for **coffee**. Percolators may be single- or continuous-cycle, but most recent ones are single-cycle, in which the boiling water is dripped through the ground coffee only once. Continuous-cycle percolators extract more **caffeine** and make a stronger drink, but the content of the essential oil, **caffeol**, responsible for the fine aroma and character of coffee is reduced.

pericarp The outer coat of a seed.

Périgord A district in south-west France famous for its **truffles**.

periwinkle See **winkle**.

periwinkle vinca One of a group of highly poisonous prostrate herbs, extracts of which have valuable medicinal properties. The most important is vinblastine, used in the treatment of cancers.

perk A kind of **perch**.

permanganate of potash Potassium permanganate, prepared as dark-purple crystals which dissolve readily in water. The solution is a powerful oxidising agent and used as a **disinfectant**. Acidified, it is used for rinsing salads and fruits to be eaten raw, where strict hygiene standards are not enforced, to reduce the risk of **food-borne diseases**.

perry A drink similar to **cider** but made from **pears**.

ALCOHOL CONTENT: up to 10%.

persimmon The fruit of *Diospyros kaki;* also known as kakee, Chinese persimmon, date plum and, in Israel, Sharon fruit. It looks rather like a tomato, is yellow/orange, very sweet and contains seeds. It may be grown in southern Europe.

pesticide A chemical substance that kills insects. Many plants are ecologically friendly and contain natural pesticides, which can be extracted and used to control insect pests. The most important of such pesticides include Derris, Pyrethrum and Nicotine.

A wide range of new synthetic pesticides were discovered after World War 2. These increased yields from food crops, making it possible to raise the standard of living of many populations, although a number of insects have since become immune to their effects. However, as well as the immense benefits of such pesticides, they have serious disadvantages too; many are persistent and enter the food chain through sprayed crops, and water-supplies through ground-water and rivers, thereby reaching coastal waters. Their consumption at any stage can cause harm to humans and wild-life, such as birds, bees and fish, which is a cause for concern.

There are now restrictions on their use and some of the most dangerous ones such as Aldrin, DDT, are banned in EEC countries. Fortunately, new and safer pesticides are becoming available and some biological measures are being introduced to replace chemicals. Fruit should always be washed before eating, and for total safety peeled, to remove both pesticides and **fungicides** used by growers. Instructions on the use of individual pesticides should be strictly adhered to.

pestle and mortar The pestle is the instrument used for pounding substances in a bowl known as the mortar; usually both are made of hard unglazed ceramic material.

USES: for grinding crystalline substances, spices and pulping fresh herbs, garlic.

pesto A sauce, of Italian origin, made with pounded pine-kernels, basil, garlic, parmesan cheese and olive oil.

USES: mainly with **pasta**.

pests

   Rats and **mice**. Both can contaminate food supplies through **faeces** and urine, causing **food poisoning**. Rats inhabit sewers and may contaminate water with the organism that causes Weils disease, a highly dangerous infection in animals and humans. Local authorities in the UK employ Pest-Control Officers to deal with infestations of these pests.

Cockroaches. *Blatta orientalis* and *Blatta germanica;* the commonest varieties of winged beetle-like insects, originally tropical, but now widespread which may infest dwellings, commercial establishments and any location where there is warmth, shelter and food. They feed on any food or food scraps left exposed and are active at night, hiding away in cracks and crevices by day. They have been found to frequent central-heating and service ducts in hotels, blocks of flats, catering establishments, factories and even hospitals. By depositing their faeces they can spread any of the diseases associated with food.

In the UK there are strict **hygiene** regulations and all commercial establishments which handle food are subject to inspection. Penalties may be severe if infestations are found.

pets, as a source of disease. Pets can be responsible for serious human diseases and strict hygiene should be practised at all times. No pets should be allowed in areas used for food-storage or preparation.

Dogs and **cats** can spread **tape worms** and other intestinal worms, **toxoplasma** and **toxocara**, by personal contact or through faeces on grass-land and playing areas, carrying a small risk of blindness, particularly in children. All dogs and cats should be treated regularly for worms, as recommended by veterinary surgeons.

Pets which are well fed and do not need to hunt for food are unlikely to harbour parasites, except fleas, which are associated with threadworms.

Parrots can be a source of **psittacosis**.

Tortoises and most other reptiles such as snakes and lizards can carry **salmonella**.

Animal bites and scratches can become infected and all but the trivial ones require medical advice. The most serious disease, rabies, has been eradicated in the UK, but travellers who have been bitten by an infected animal while abroad are at risk of developing it.

petits pois verts Small green **peas**. Usually sold frozen or canned.

pe-tsai See **Chinese cabbage**.

petticoat tails A corruption of petits gatels, old French for small cakes. The term is used for small pieces of shortcake or **shortbread**.

NUTRITIONAL VALUE: average: protein 10%, fat 40% (mostly saturated), carbohydrate 50%.

ENERGY per 100g: average: 587 kcal, 2456 kJ.

petit pain French for bread roll.

petits fours Very small fancy cakes or biscuits usually eaten at the end of a meal with coffee.

pewter An alloy of tin and antimony, formerly used for drinking vessels and plates. Old pewter contains **lead** and sometimes **arsenic** and should not be used for food or drink. Modern pewter is made from tin and antimony only and is safe to use.

pH The scientific term used to record the degree of acidity or alkalinity of a substance within the range 0–14. The neutral point is 7, above which is alkaline and below is acid. All fresh foods, including vegetables, are acid to some degree; the juice of a **lemon** may be as low as 3.0. The pH rises when food deteriorates and it affects the performance of **enzymes**, some of which require an acid and some an alkaline environment in which to be active.

Slight changes in pH may affect both the colour and flavour of foods, in their freshness, preparation and cooking. Changes in pH may be induced to enhance a desirable change or to prevent an undesirable one. A lowering of the pH is usually achieved by adding vinegar, citric acid (as lemon or fruit juice), **yoghurt** or **cream of tartar**. Raising the pH can be achieved with **chalk** or by milk as a **buffer**; **bicarbonate of soda** can be used but tends to leave a bitter taste. Fruit acids are readily oxidised in the body to become neutral or even alkaline and are not usually associated with changes in pH of tissue fluids or with stomach upsets. See pH values of common foods in appendix page 241.

phase inversion Refers to the relationship of oil or fat and water in an **emulsion** which, during processing, is inverted. Common examples are **milk** and **cream** in which the **fat** in droplets is in a continuous phase of water, but during processing to make **butter**, the oil becomes the continuous phase and the water is in droplets, accounting for the shiny surface of butter. In traditional **margarines**, water is the continuous phase and the surface is dull.

pheasant *Phasianus colchicus*. The most widespread **game**-bird, originally from the East but introduced into Europe many centuries ago. The female is smaller and rather plain compared with the larger and more colourful male. Like all game birds, the flesh has a low fat-content and the birds should be hung, before being plucked and drawn, for a period of a few days to two weeks, depending on temperature, to develop flavour and tenderise the flesh. The birds are traditionally sold as a brace, a hen and a cock, but those sold ready for cooking are available singly. See **hanging**.

SEASON: 1st October to 1st February (Northern Ireland 31st January). Deep-frozen birds are sometimes available out of season.

NUTRITIONAL VALUE: protein 18%, fat 2–3%.

ENERGY per 100g: 95 kcal, 397 kJ.

USES: young birds are suitable for roasting but older ones are better braised or casseroled in a variety of ways.

phenol Carbolic acid. Phenol is present in small quantities in wood-smoke and is poisonous in large quantities; it is not an approved substance for use as a food preservative. See **smoking**.

phenylketonuria An inherited disorder in which the metabolism of **proteins**, containing the essential **amino acid** phenylalanine, is defective. Treatment, carried out under medical supervision, involves restriction of protein foods which contain phenylalanine; these are meat, fish, cheese, eggs, soya, flour, bread and biscuits: permitted foods are most vegetables, fruits, salads, sugar, jams, butter, most fats, special low-protein flour and biscuits and cakes made with it, a limited amount of peas, cow's milk, cereals, rice, potatoes.

phosphoric acid (E338) A mild acid used as a souring agent in drinks such as **Coca-cola**, and as an **antioxidant**. It is safe in the quantities used for flavouring and enhancing the antioxidant effect of other substances such as those in meats, sausages, cheese.

phosphorus An element essential to all forms of life; in mammals it is a major component of bone and teeth, as calcium phosphate. It is necessary for nerve and muscle function and a variety of **enzyme** systems and present in all plant and animal tissues. There are adequate quantities in a mixed **diet** and supplements are not required.

photosynthesis The process that occurs in green plants whereby **chlorophyll** converts carbon dioxide from the air, by the action of sunlight, into **carbohydrates** and liberates oxygen into the atmosphere.

phylloquinone See **vitamin K**.

phytic acid A phosphorus-containing complex acid, present in variable quantities in **cereals**, particularly **oats**, some vegetables and nuts, which has the ability to bind **calcium** and limit its absorption from the small intestine, which may be important when there is a high intake of oats.

piccalilli A bright yellow **pickle** of mixed vegetables with **mustard**.

pickle (noun). A variable mixture of fruits and vegetables preserved with vinegar, often slightly sweetened and flavoured with herbs and spices.

pickle (verb). To preserve in **brine** or **vinegar**; a process used for meat, fish and vegetables. Vinegar discourages the growth of **bacteria** and **moulds**; **brine** preserves by an osmotic effect, which prevents **micro-organisms** from obtaining water. The container of pickled substances should be sealed to exclude air and stored in a cool place. See **osmosis**.

pie A variable mixture of meats, vegetables, fish or fruits cooked in a **pastry** case, or in a dish, and covered with pastry.

pig An omnivorous ungulate developed from the wild boar and a valuable source of **meat**, **offal** and **fat**. Appreciation of the need for a healthy diet has led to a demand for leaner carcasses with a minimum quantity of fat. See **pork**.

pigeon Any member of the large dove family of birds. The wild pigeon, *Columba oalumbas* is a pest which is very troublesome to farmers and gardeners, as it consumes large quantities of cereals, vegetables and fruits, often leaving little behind. Large houses used to keep pigeons in dovecots to provide a regular supply of meat and eggs. Pigeons can carry **salmonella** and infect exposed food and grain, and therefore may be a risk to health. They may also be contaminated through eating seeds poisoned with **pesticides**.

NUTRITIONAL VALUE: average: protein 18%, fat 2–3%.

ENERGY per 100g: average: 95 kcal, 397 kJ.

USES: young birds of about 4 weeks old, known as squabs, are best for eating and are suitable for roasting; they need to be well **barded** to overcome dryness. Older birds can be casseroled and need long, slow cooking.

pigeon-pea See **redgram**.

piggin A straight-sided vessel with a vertical handle used formerly in a dairy as a ladle and measure for milk.

pike *Esox lucius*. A carnivorous freshwater fish capable of eating small waterfowl. Considered a delicacy in France, but not often eaten in the UK.

pilaff A top grade of long-grain **rice** grown in India. In the West, the term more commonly means a dish prepared with rice.

NUTRITIONAL VALUE: See **rice**.

ENERGY per 100g: See **rice**.

USES: as a dish of rice alone or with added meat, chicken, fish or vegetables, with herbs and spices.

pilau See **pilaff**.

pilchard *Sardinia pilchardus*, an oily marine **fish**, like a **herring** but smaller and with a stronger flavour. The young are called **sardines**. *Clupea sprattus*, a closely related member of the same family, may be sold under the same name. See **fumado**.

NUTRITIONAL VALUE: protein 18%, fat 20%, mostly unsaturated, vitamin A, vitamin B complex, vitamin D, calcium, iron.

ENERGY per 100g: 250 kcal, 1046 kJ.

USES: usually canned and eaten cold with salad. See **canning**.

pimenta acris A tropical tree which produces an aromatic berry also known as bayberry, black cinnamon and wild clove. It is astringent, aromatic and sweet, but not often used.

pimento See **pepper sweet**.

pimms A strong beverage, the recipe for which is a carefully guarded trade secret. It is recommended that it should be drunk diluted with lemonade or ginger ale; garnished with cucumber, orange or mint and, traditionally, blue **borage** flowers. There are several variations but Pimms No.1 is the most popular.
ALCOHOL CONTENT: 25%.

pineapple *Ananas cosmosus*, a large exotic tropical fruit, with an aromatic acidic flesh, widely grown in tropical climates. The juice contains a **proteolytic enzyme**, bromelin, similar in action to **papain**, and capable of tenderising tough meat and digesting **gelatine**. A pineapple jelly must be made with **agar** (unless the enzyme is destroyed by heat). Meat can be made so soft that it loses its texture. The pineapple was formerly the emblem of hospitality and carved or sculptured stone models are often found displayed in front of houses and on gateposts. Pineapples are available fresh and canned.
NUTRITIONAL VALUE: carbohydrate 7%, vitamin B complex, vitamin C up to 30mg per 100g, calcium, trace of iron.
ENERGY per 100g: fresh: 30 kcal, 125 kJ. Canned in juice: 46 kcal, 192 kJ.
USES: as a dessert fruit, in fruit salad and other desserts, often served with grilled gammon steaks. Also prepared as a fruit juice.

pine-kernels See **pinon**.

pinole A dried form of Indian corn (**maize**) or other seed, ground, usually cooked with milk and flavoured with vanilla, herbs, sometimes cocoa.

pinon The edible seeds, known as pine-kernels, of the pine tree, *Pinus cembia*, and its variants, which grow all over the world.
USES: widely used in Mediterranean and Middle Eastern cooking, fried and roasted as snacks; an essential ingredient in **pesto** sauce.

pint Imperial measure equal to 568 ml. It is likely to survive in the UK as a measure for bottled milk and beer but is otherwise being replaced by the litre. The American pint is 473ml. See appendix.

pinto bean A variety of kidney bean with a reddish-brown speckled skin which turns pink when cooked. They are much used in Spain in hot dishes, soups and salads. As with other brown, red and black beans they should be boiled for at least 10 minutes before continuing cooking by simmering. See **beans, lectin**.

pip The seed of a fleshy fruit, which often contains **pectin**. Pips also contain cyanogens which may be released in small quantities when the pips are crushed, as in chewing and in **cider**-making, to form the highly poisonous **cyanide** gas.

pipe A large cask for holding wine, usually about 115 gallons or 517 litres.

pipperade A speciality **omelette** of the Basque region of Spain, made with added sweet peppers, onion, garlic and tomato.

pippin The name given to several varieties of dessert **apple** with a sweet aromatic flesh; the most famous is the Cox's orange pippin.

pissaladien A form of **pizza**.

pissenlit A French speciality **salad** made with **dandelion** leaves dressed with seasoned **vinegar** and oil. Fried bacon is often mixed with the salad which is then topped with a sprinkling of chopped hard-boiled eggs. Said to have a **diuretic** effect, hence the name.

pistachio The sweet edible **nut** of the deciduous subtropical tree *Pistachio vera*. Also known as green almond. Highly esteemed for decoration and eating.

NUTRITIONAL VALUE: average: protein 17%, fat 50%, carbohydrate 15%.

ENERGY per 100g: average: 574 kcal, 2402 kJ.

USES: eaten as a dessert nut, in ice-cream and desserts, as a garnish.

pitcher An earthenware vessel used for holding water.

pith The soft material in the centre of stalks, tree trunks, and under the skin of citrus fruits where it is a source of **pectin** and **pectinase**. The pith of the sago-palm produces **sago**.

pitta bread A risen bread originally made in the Middle East. The loaves are small, almost flat and have a large central cavity which can be filled with food such as cheese, meats as a sort of sandwich. It is widely available in the UK.

pizza A savoury dish with a base of **bread** dough topped with a variable mixture of tomatoes, cheese, meat, mushrooms, anchovies, olives.

pizzeria A place where pizzas are made and/ or sold.

plaice A marine flatfish of European waters with good eating qualities.

NUTRITIONAL VALUE: protein 18%, fat 1–2%, vitamin B complex, calcium, iron.

ENERGY per 100g: average: 85 kcal, 356 kJ.

USES: cooked whole or filleted. Suitable for frying, grilling, baking and poaching.

plankton A collective term for primitive plants and animals which drift in freshwater and the sea. They are of fundamental importance, and the first link in the food chain for **fish** and other edible marine life. Excessive growth of plankton may occur in the sea or reservoirs and colour the water. Some are poisonous, such as blue or red algae which periodically proliferate in coastal waters, and when eaten by lobsters and other shellfish, render them unsuitable for human consumption; a ban is placed on any catch from infested waters. A more recent problem has arisen during hot spells in the UK, where sewage effluents and run-offs from farming practices have increased phosphate levels in reservoirs and led to growth of blue algae; this may cause serious symptoms and even the death of animals and birds drinking at the edge of the water. See **food poisoning**.

plantain *Musa pardisiaca*. A variety of **banana** which is larger and has a higher **starch** and lower **sugar** content than the banana more widely available in the UK.

NUTRITIONAL VALUE: protein 1%, carbohydrate 25–30%, vitamin B complex, vitamin C.

ENERGY per 100g: average: 107 kcal, 448 kJ.

USES: for cooking in sweet and savoury dishes, sliced and fried somewhat like potato crisps; also dried and ground to form flour or meal.

plasticisers A range of viscous organic chemical substances used in the manufacture of certain plastics to keep them flexible. They are generally based on phalic, phosphoric or ricinoleic acid and prevent oxidation. Unfortunately they are not harmless and leach readily from plastic films when they are used for wrapping any food containing **fat**. See **clingfilm**.

plonk A popular name for a low-quality **wine**.

plum The stone-fruit of any variety of the hardy *Prunus* family, which includes the wild plum or **sloe**, **damson**, **greengage** and the dessert plum. They are widely available fresh when in season and canned at all times. A sweet variety is dried and known as **prune**.

NUTRITIONAL VALUE: protein 0.6%, carbohydrate 7–9%, vitamin C, calcium.

ENERGY per 100g: average: fresh: 32 kcal, 134 kJ.

USES: depending on variety, as a dessert fruit, stewed and eaten hot or cold, in various desserts, **jams** and **chutneys**, in meat dishes such as rabbit.

poach To cook slowly in water heated to just below boiling point. A method used for eggs and fish, particularly salmon.

poison Any substance, taken into the body by ingestion, through the lungs, by contact with the skin, by injection or bite, which is damaging to health. Many simple food-substances, essential to health in small or even moderate quantities, are poisonous if taken in excess. Small babies and the elderly are more affected by poisons than healthy adults. Poisons abound and the public are at risk from a large number in the home, from garden or wild plants and seeds, those produced by **bacteria** or **fungi**, waste disposal, industry and rubbish washed up on beaches from shipping.

There are reference centres that advise doctors and hospitals on the management of poisons. The responsibility starts with the first person on the scene who should:−

1. Find out the nature of the poison by asking the victim or examining containers, food or source which might identify the poison.
2. Arrange to get the victim to hospital.
3. If unconscious, place the victim on his/her side in the recovery position, remove dentures, hold the mouth open and, if there is any difficulty in breathing adjust or hold the tongue to allow unobstructed air-flow and to prevent any vomit being inhaled.
4. If the lips or mouth are damaged by **acid** or caustics, give water or **milk** to sip gently.
5. Do not attempt to make the victim vomit by giving salt or any other emetic.
6. Keep any vomit, bottles, samples of food or any substance that may help in identifying the poison and send it with the victim to hospital; it may lead to the administration of the correct antidote and so save life.

Food poisoning. The same general principles apply; keep any food samples to help with diagnosis. Replace fluids lost by persistent vomiting or **diarrhoea** by slow and frequent sips of sweetened or rice water with 1 teaspoonful of salt in each pint or half a litre of water, to maintain kidney function.

Drug poisoning. If the victim does not breath naturally apply artificial respiration until admission to hospital.

Alcohol. As for drugs, in addition to the general principles above.

polarimeter An optical instrument for measuring the degree of rotation of polarised light by optically active substances. Light is first passed through a Nicol prism to polarise it, then through the material under investigation and finally through a second Nicol prism which can be rotated to measure the rotation effect of the substance. Used in assessing sugars and some other optically active substances such as **amino acids**. See **invert sugar**.

polarised light Light which according to the vibration theory vibrates in only one plane. Certain substances have the power to reduce vibrations to one plane and polarise it: used in **polarimeters**.

polenta Coarse or fine flour made of ground **maize**; a staple food in Italy.

NUTRITIONAL VALUE: raw: protein 10%, fat 4%, carbohydrate 70%.

ENERGY per 100g: raw: 338 kcal, 1414 kJ.

USES: cooked with water to make a sort of porridge and often eaten with cheese, may be cooled, sliced and fried or grilled.

pollack *Pollachius pollachius*. A non-oily marine fish, similar to **cod**, but considered to be of inferior eating-quality. It is a useful and inexpensive food.

NUTRITIONAL VALUE: protein 18%, fat 1–2%, vitamin B complex, minerals.

ENERGY per 100g: 77 kcal, 322 kJ.

USES: as for cod.

pollan An Irish freshwater **fish** found in Lough Neagh.

pollen Powder, produced by the male part of flowers, which fertilises the seeds. Pollen is specific for each flower and recognisable by its size and shape. It contains proteins, fats, vitamins, minerals, colouring matter and is an essential source of food for bees and some insects. Pollen is available to insects throughout the growing period of the year, from snow-drops in January through to ivy in November and December. Grass pollens are transferred by wind and are the commonest source of allergic rhinitis or hay fever. There is some evidence that regular ingestion of pollen-containing **honey** (comb honey), honey to which pollen has been added, or pollen gathered from bees in pollen-traps may benefit victims of hay fever. Pollen is sometimes sold as a health food.

polony A **sausage** of partly-cooked **meat** and usually hot-smoked, originally from Bologna in Italy.

NUTRITIONAL VALUE: average: protein up to 15%, fat 20%.

ENERGY per 100g: average: 240 kcal, 1004 kJ.

USES: eaten cold with salads and other similar meat products, as a snack on biscuits, in sandwiches.

polydextrose A polymer of **dextrose**. As prepared, it has a pH of 2.5 but is partially neutralised with potassium hydroxide or potassium bicarbonate to a pH of 5.5; it is then almost tasteless and has an energy value of 1 kcal per g.

USES: as a bulking agent, to add viscosity, to compensate for **sucrose** in association with **artificial sweeteners**, and in reduced fat products, where it gives a smooth feeling in the mouth usually associated with a high fat content.

polyethylene See **polythene**.

polyoxethylenes (434–436) Emulsifiers made from **sorbitol** and used for cake-mixes. They can increase the absorption of paraffins and oils.

polyphosphates (544 and 545) These and related compounds are used as **emulsifiers**, stabilisers, and for their water-retaining properties, particularly in frozen poultry and seafood, where they have a reputation for increasing the weight of the product.

polypropylene A plastic material similar to **polythene**; it is **thermoplastic** and water-wettable. It is used for string, bindings and some moulded goods. The string will melt if used for tying up foods to be cooked. It disintegrates slowly on exposure to **ultra-violet light**.

polysaccharides Carbohydrates, which differ from sugar in that they are not crystalline, they are insoluble in water and generally tasteless; but are converted to sugars by **enzymes**. The group also includes the non-starch polysaccharide **cellulose** and **gums** which form **dietary fibre**, collectively known as NSPs.

polythene Also known as polyethylene. A flexible, transparent plastic material which melts at just above the temperature of boiling water. It is used in two forms; as a high density and fairly hard product for bowls, spoons, and semi-rigid containers and a lower density one for storage bags. It can be heat-sealed and the contents may be vacuum-packed. It is suitable for use in a deep-freeze and in temperatures almost up to boiling point of water but should not be used in a microwave oven. It can be used to wrap fatty foods.

polyunsaturated fat See **fat**.

polyvinyl chloride (PVC) A water-repellent **thermoplastic** material prepared in different grades of density for various uses; such as a rubber substitute, for coating fabrics and other materials, washable wallpapers, water-paints, adhesives; they all produce toxic fumes when burnt. A soft flexible grade, containing a plasticiser, is made as a thin sheet known as **clingfilm**, for wrapping foods; the plasticiser can leach out into fat, and should not come into contact with any food made of, or containing, fat, such as cheese, meats.

pomace Crushed apples ready to be pressed for **cider**, or the residue after pressing, which may be used as a source of **pectin**.

pomato A tomato shoot grafted onto a root-stock of potato.

pomegranate Fruit of the small subtropical tree, *Punica granatum*, with a hard skin and sweet juicy interior full of hard seeds. Grown in Mediterranean countries and elsewhere with a similar climate.

NUTRITIONAL VALUE: juice: protein 1%, carbohydrate 18%, vitamin B complex, vitamin C.

ENERGY per 100g: 80 kcal, 335 kJ.

USES: as a dessert fruit after separation of the seeds. The juice, sweetened with sugar is known as **grenadine**. Also used in savoury dishes in Persian cooking. The seeds are dried and used as a condiment in the Middle East.

pomelo Also known as shaddock, a citrus fruit similar to **grapefruit** but larger and with a thicker skin, coarse internal membranes and drier flesh.

USES: as a dessert fruit.

ponceau 4R (E124) A synthetic azo dye (see **colour**) and permitted red food colouring.

Used for crystallised cherries, canned strawberries and other fruits which lose their natural colour in processing. It can cause symptoms in those who are sensitive to aspirin.

Pont l'évêque A delicately-flavoured, soft French cheese which does not keep well and should be stored, well wrapped, in a refrigerator.

NUTRITIONAL VALUE: average: protein 19%, fat 27.5%.

ENERGY per 100g: average: 324 kcal, 1356 kJ.

USES: as table cheese; unsuitable for cooking.

popcorn A snack made from a special hard variety of **maize**. It is produced by rapid heating of the grain and a sudden increase in volume as the pressure builds up, causing it to explode.

poppadoms Saucer-sized discs made with a dough of ground **pulses**, flavoured with herbs and spices, which is rolled out until very thin. They are usually purchased partially prepared to this stage.

USES: cooked quickly to crispness in hot fat, grilled or baked in a hot oven and served as an accompaniment to **curry**.

poppy-seeds Seeds of *Papaver somniferum* from which **poppy-seed oil** is extracted. Opium is prepared from the juice which flows from the seed-head and is not present in the seeds. Used by early Egyptians as food.

USES: usually roasted and used in small quantities, for their flavour, in curries, sprinkled on bread, rolls or cakes.

poppy-seed oil A cooking oil; high in unsaturated **fats**.

NUTRITIONAL VALUE: saturated fat 8%, monounsaturated fat 50%, polyunsaturated fat 35%.

porbeagle shark or mackerel shark. *Lamma nasus*. The most frequently caught shark around the coastal waters of the UK. The flesh is firm and similar to pork, and is probably the best variety of shark to eat. It freezes well.

NUTRITIONAL VALUE: average: protein 18%, fat 2%.

ENERGY per 100g: average: 90 kcal, 377 kJ.

USES: sold as steaks and is most suitable for grilling, frying or baking.

pork Fresh **pig** meat. When **cured** known as **bacon, ham, gammon**. It is forbidden for Jews and Muslims to eat pig meat. See **religious laws**.

NUTRITIONAL VALUE: average: raw: protein 17%, fat 25%, mostly saturated, (amount depends on breed of pig and cut of meat), vitamin B complex, calcium, iron.

ENERGY per 100g: average: raw: 347 kcal, 1452 kJ.

USES: fresh pork is cooked in a variety of ways according to the cut, such as roast joints, grilled or fried chops, fillets, in casseroles, sausages.

porphyra *Porphyra umbilicus* and *lancinata*. A form of seaweed, a red or pink alga, found around the coasts of the UK and collected to make laverbread. See **laver**.

porridge A dish of slowly-cooked ground or rolled **oats**, traditionally eaten as a breakfast dish with milk and, in Scotland, salt, in England, sugar.

porringer A bowl for soup or porridge.

port Fortified wine from the Duoro river valley, inland from Porto in northern Portugal. White and red varieties are made. The wines are carefully blended and matured and the red ports become tawny with age in the barrel. See **geropiga**.

ALCOHOL CONTENT: average 18%.

USES: white port is usually drunk as an apcritif, red at the end of a meal. Also used in cooking dishes such as jugged hare, game casseroles, and in Cumberland and other sauces, jellies.

porter A dark-brown **beer** originally brewed for London porters.

posnet A small cooking-vessel with a handle and legs.

posset A drink made with **milk**, curdled with vinegar, wine or beer. See **curdle**.

potable Safe to drink. Usually refers to water that is free of harmful **micro-organisms** and chemical pollutants, in accordance with standards laid down by the EEC.

potassium Chemical symbol K. An **element** essential for many body functions; most is present within tissue cells. Severe deficiency is associated with weakness of muscles. It is widely available in foods and deficiency is unlikely, unless induced by drugs especially **diuretics**. Excess is excreted by the kidneys and an overdose is unlikely except in kidney failure. Potassium chloride has a salty taste and is used as a **salt** substitute when there are medical reasons for a low **sodium** diet. Potassium iodide is added to salt in **iodine**-deficient areas to prevent **goitre**.

potassium bromate One of the chemical substances known as **flour improvers**; used commercially by millers of flour as an oxidiser in the process known as **ageing** which enhances the baking quality of **bread**.

potassium ferrocyanide and **sodium ferrocyanide (535** and **536)**. Food additives used as anticaking compounds in cake-mixes and **salt**. The poisonous cyanide component is strongly bonded to the iron, which prevents it being toxic in the quantities used.

potassium nitrite (E249 and related nitrates **E250–E252)** Permitted food **preservatives** used in cooked meat products, sausages, cheese and pizzas.

potato The edible tuber of *Solanum tuberosum*, and the same family as the tomato and sweet pepper. Unrelated to the **sweet potato**, although the food value is similar. It is widely grown and one of the most important food sources in temperate and subtropical climates. Potatoes turn green on exposure to light with the development of the heat-resistant poison **solanine**; if this happens they should not be eaten, neither should the tomato-like seed capsules nor the leaves of the plant.

Potatoes are a major source of **carbohydrate**, **vitamin C** and **dietary fibre**. The vitamin C content is highest just under the skin, but falls during storage. They should be peeled thinly or eaten with the skin. Cooking disrupts the **starch**-containing cells, causing the starch to take up water and become digestible. There is some loss of vitamin C in cooking. They should be stored in cool, dark conditions. Many potatoes on sale are dusted with technazine, a chemical substance used to delay sprouting in storage, but it is safe to eat them in their skins if they are washed and lightly scrubbed before cooking.

NUTRITIONAL VALUE: raw, protein 2%, fat 0.2%, carbohydrate 17%, vitamin B complex, vitamin C up to 20mg per 100g, calcium, iron, dietary fibre.

ENERGY per 100g: raw: 74 kcal, 310 kJ. Boiled 76 kcal, 318 kJ.

USES: boiled, mashed, baked or fried as a vegetable, baked in their jackets and stuffed, mixed with other foods in pies, gratin dishes, potato scones, or as a topping, sometimes with cheese.

potato crisps Potato cut into thin slices and rapidly deep fried in oil. Generally sold bagged and may be flavoured to increase the appeal; usually salted.

NUTRITIONAL VALUE per 100 grams: average, protein 3.96%, carbohydrate 34%, fat 10.2%, with small quantities of Vitamin B complex and C.

ENERGY per 100gm: average 234 kcal, 979 kJ.

USES: as a snack, with salads.

potato flour Dried potato, in a convenient form for rapid preparation of cooked mashed potato and useful for thickening soups, casseroles and sauces. It has a low **gluten** content.

potato, sweet See **sweet potato**.

pot-au-feu A large earthenware pot used for cooking stew; also the food cooked in this way.

poult A young chicken or game fowl.

poultry Domestic or farmyard birds usually fowls, chickens; also includes geese and turkeys.

poussin A very young chicken.

praline Almonds cooked with sugar and crushed, used for flavouring and garnishing, as a sweetmeat, filling for chocolates.

prawn A small crustacean but larger than a **shrimp**; both are related to lobsters. In the USA one is called shrimp, the larger, jumbo shrimp. There are many different species worldwide, but most fresh prawns available in the UK are the deep water variety *Pandalus borealis*. Other varieties may be caught in coastal waters such as the common prawn *Palaemon serratus* but this is not usually fished on a commercial basis. Several varieties, are available frozen from the far East where many are farmed. They should be taken from unpolluted waters but as a safety measure should always be cooked before being eaten.

NUTRITIONAL VALUE: protein 20%, fat 2%, calcium, iron.

ENERGY per 100gm: 100 kcal 418 kJ.

USES: as a first course in prawn cocktail, in a variety of fish and savoury dishes, particularly Chinese and Japanese, in soups and as a garnish.

preservation of food Treatment of food by any method which destroys or inhibits growth of all **micro-organisms**, including **spores**, and prevents deterioration by the action of **enzymes** or **oxidation**. Preservation is used for a wide range of food products for short or long term storage. However, even preserved food has a limited life beyond which there is loss of quality, and some risk of toxicity. Manufacturers are increasingly labelling products with expiry dates, often related to storage conditions. Common methods used for preservation are:—

Bottling
Canning
Chemicals including **curing** and **smoking** and use of **alcohol**
Drying including **osmotic pressure** by salt or sugar
Freezing
Irradiation by **x-rays**
Pickling
Sterilisation

For further information see separate headings. Chemical substances approved as food preservatives are listed within the range E200—E290.

preservatives (E200—283) A wide range of food additives which control or destroy the **micro-organisms** responsible for **food poisoning** and others such as **moulds** and yeasts which spoil or alter the taste or character of food. Vinegar, sugar and salt are common food preservatives and not classed as food additives. Other substances known as **antioxidants** also protect against deterioration of foods (listed as food additives within the range E300—321). Preservatives are important for health in protecting against diseases due to food and have economic importance by increasing the shelf-life, so keeping down costs. See appendix.

preserves A term generally applied to products of fruit and sugar which includes all **jams** and fruit **jellies** in which sugar is the preserving agent. It can also apply to pickles and chutneys and some fruits such as peaches, pears, apricots, preserved with vinegar and sometimes sugar.

pressure cooker A cooking-vessel which uses the principle that the temperature reached by boiling water is related to atmospheric pressure.

A pressure cooker is a strongly-constructed container with a lid which can be sealed to resist pressures within and a safety valve which allows steam to escape if the pressure rises above a predetermined point. In this way food can be fully cooked at temperatures 7—15°C (45—59°F) above the normal temperature of boiling water in an open saucepan, thus reducing the cooking time by up to 25%. Correctly used, according to the manufacturer's instructions, pressure cookers are safe, save time, conserve energy, and are most valuable for foods which require a long cooking time, such as the tougher cuts of meat, pulses, preparation of **soups** from bones and carcasses and making **stews**.

Food manufacturers use pressure-cooking for canned and processed foods where high temperatures are required to kill heat-resistant spores of **food poisoning** bacteria. Meat, fish and vegetables are unsuitable for **canning** or **bottling** in the home, as the required conditions cannot be safely met.

pretzel A crisp salted biscuit twisted and formed into a knot.

prickly pear The fruit, also known as Indian fig, of varieties of *Opuntia*. It has a sweet pleasantly acidic flesh. See **nopales**.

USES: the flesh is usually extracted and eaten raw, as a dessert, with lime or lemon juice.

probe See **skewer**.

probe-thermometer See **thermometer**.

processed cheese Cheese in which the ripening process has been halted by heat, and which is then finely ground and mixed with **emulsifiers**. There are many varieties and the final products are modified with colouring, salt and sometimes herbs and spices and usually sold wrapped. Processed cheese was first produced in Switzerland but is now widely available from other sources.

profiterole A small bun made of choux **pastry** filled with cream and served with chocolate sauce.

proof The old measurement of **alcohol** in **spirits**. See **proof spirit**.

proof spirit A mixture of alcohol and water of standard strength by comparison with which spirituous drinks were measured for taxation purposes. Proof spirit contains 49.28% alcohol by weight, which is equal to 57% by volume. In the past, customs officers mixed the spirit to be tested with gunpowder and set it alight; if the gunpowder burnt the spirit was proof or overproof. Today alcohol in **beers, wines** and **spirits** is measured as a percentage by volume.

propane A heavy combustible **gas** with very similar properties to butane.

propionic acid (E280 and related compounds **E281–E283)** Permitted food preservative which prevents **mould** growth. Produced by a natural fermentation process.

propyl gallate (E310 and related compounds **E311–E312)** Permitted **antioxidants**, prepared commercially and used mainly to limit deterioration of fats and fat-containing foods which may become **rancid**.

protein Complex substances, made of **amino acids** which themselves are compounds of carbon, hydrogen, oxygen and nitrogen; some may include **phosphorus** and **sulphur**. Proteins are essential to all animal life and are obtained from a wide range of vegetable and animal sources. Twenty amino acids have been identified, of which eight are essential. They are present in adequate quantities in a mixed **diet** which contains foods such as **dairy products, meat, fish, poultry, bread, pulses**; supplements are not necessary.

During digestion, protein is broken down into amino acids, which can then be absorbed and utilised in the body. It should make up about 10% of **energy** requirements. **Vegetarians** who include dairy foods in their diet should not be short of protein and **vegans** can obtain minimum quantities by including **soya** products.

Protein deficiency, in countries where food shortages are frequent, is associated with a number of deficiency diseases; growth of children is retarded, there may be **anaemia, oedema**, brain and liver damage known as kwashiorkor, which is still prevalent in parts of Africa.

ENERGY: all proteins have a value of 4 kcal, 17 kJ per g.

proteolytic enzyme An **enzyme** which is capable of breaking down **proteins** into **amino acids** so that they can then be absorbed and used by the body. See **pepsin, trypsin**.

prune A dried **plum**; a variety of *Prunus domestica* which, by having a high **sugar** content, dries without fermenting and keeps well. Prunes are rehydrated by soaking in water then cooked by boiling. Vitamin C is lost in the drying process. Prunes should be stored in airtight containers in cool conditions.

NUTRITIONAL VALUE: protein 2.4%, carbohydrate 40.3%, calcium, iron, sodium.

ENERGY per 100g: dry: 161 kcal, 686 kJ. Cooked, unsweetened: 76kcal, 318kJ.

USES: presoaked in water and cooked as stewed fruit, in some meat dishes such as cock o'leekie soup, casseroles.

psittacosis An infectious disease caused by *Clamydia psittici*, which may be carried by birds, particularly parrots and sometimes poultry. It is a serious disease affecting the lungs and producing pneumonia-like symptoms in humans.

PTF See **non-stick**.

ptomaine poisoning An obsolete term; used for **food poisoning** before the bacterial causation was discovered. Formerly it was thought that poisoning was caused by 'ptomaines' which are poisonous substances present in some plants.

ptyalin An **enzyme** present in **saliva** which converts **starches** into **sugar**.

pudding A substantial cooked sweet or savoury dish, often steamed. A sweet pudding can be made with a **sponge** mixture or **suet** dough and flavoured with **jam**, **syrup** or **dried fruit**. Savoury puddings are usually made with suet dough and filled with meat and/or vegetables, such as **steak** and **kidney**, or **bacon** and **onions**. The term is also used sometimes for any dessert.

puff pastry See **pastry**.

pullet A young hen which has completed its first period of laying but before the first moult.

pulp The soft fleshy part of a fruit or plant.

pulque A fermented Mexican drink made from the sap of a flowering shrub, *Agarista pulchra*.

pulse The seed of any leguminous plant such as **pea**, **bean**, **lentil**. Pulses are widely grown for their high **energy** value, low cost and **protein** and **carbohydrate** content. Usually sold dried, they keep well and are a major component of **vegetarian** diets. They retain vitamin B complex and minerals when cooked, but vitamin C is destroyed. Most pulses require soaking for up to 8 hours before cooking but lentils are small enough not to need this.

pumice Porous volcanic rock ground to a powder and used as an abrasive in brass and copper polishes and scouring powders. Available also in small blocks to clean the skin.

pumpernickel A coarse, heavy, dark bread made with rye-flour and baked slowly in a flat tin. See **bread**.

pumpkin The round variety of vegetable **marrow**, *Curcubita pepo*, often reaching a large size. The flesh is yellow and sweet but rather bland; of low food value.
  NUTRITIONAL VALUE: negligible.
  ENERGY per 100g: raw: 16 kcal, 67 kJ.
  USES: boiled or fried as a vegetable, in a variety of sweet and savoury dishes, soups, and in the traditional American pumpkin-pie.

punch An alcoholic drink based on **spirits** and/or **wine**, flavoured with fruit, herbs, spices and often drunk hot.

punt e mes ('point and a half'). An Italian bitter-sweet aperitif flavoured with herbs, quinine and orange.
  ALCOHOL CONTENT: Approximately 15%.

purée Food reduced to a smooth soft mass, free of seeds and stalks, by passing through a sieve. Used as a basis for soups, sauces and a variety of desserts.

purslane *Portulaca oleracia*, the common purslane, also known as pigweed and portulaca. A squat hardy, annual, spreading herb with a slightly sour taste, sometimes used in salads with **vinaigrette** dressing. Used mainly in the Middle East and India. Contains vitamin C.

purslane *Claytonia perfoliata*, a perennial herb, native of North America where it is cultivated as a salad crop. The tender shoots are eaten, usually served with a **vinaigrette** dressing.

Q

quail *Citornix coturnix*. The smallest of the **game**-birds, which is a protected species in the UK. Birds for the table are bred in captivity and are now becoming more widely available in some supermarkets, as are their eggs.

SEASON: none for farmed birds.

NUTRITIONAL VALUE: similar to other game birds.

ENERGY per 100g: 95 kcal, 397 kJ.

USES: usually roasted fresh. The eggs are often used hard-boiled with various salads as a starter or as a dish in hors d'oeuvres.

quart Imperial measure equal to 2 pints, 40 ounces, one quarter of a gallon or 1.14 litres.

quassia *Quassia amara*, a tropical tree. A bitter extract from the wood is used diluted, as a bittering agent to flavour some wines and aperitifs. A related tree, *Picrasia excelsas*, is used for the same purpose. A strong extract can be used as an insecticide or incorporated in adhesive flypapers.

quawrama A Lebanese speciality dish made from overfed fat sheep. The fat is rendered, the meat seasoned and fried, and packed with the fat into an earthenware crock which is then sealed and the meat kept for winter consumption.

queencake A small sponge-like **cake** containing **currants**.

queen of puddings A rich Victorian **pudding**, made with a base of **strawberry** or **raspberry jam** and layered with breadcrumbs, **milk**, and **egg** yolks, cooked to set in an oven and then topped with **meringue** mixture and cooked to crispness.

queen substance See **royal jelly**.

quenelle A form of **dumpling** made with chicken, veal or fish, bound with egg and then put into a small mould or made into an oval shape and lightly boiled; usually served with a **cream** or **velouté** sauce.

quercetin A yellow colouring, known as a **flavone**, which is widely distributed in plants such as onions (in the skin), hops, some flowers and tea. It is stable, withstands cooking and changes in acidity, and can be used for dyeing.

quern A primitive grindstone consisting of a hollowed-out base stone and a hand-held grinding stone. See **grind**.

quiche Traditionally, a savoury open tart from Lorraine in France. It was originally filled with egg custard made with cream and flavoured with smoked bacon but the name is now used for other savoury tarts, mainly those with egg and milk or cream-based fillings.

quick-freezing The commercial process of rapid freezing by exposing the material to a blast of very cold air; used for most frozen vegetables and other foods. The method conserves flavour and **vitamin C**.

quine A small variety of **scallop**.

quinine A bitter-tasting drug extracted from the bark of a tropical tree, *Cinchona calisaya*, and other varieties of it. It was the only effective treatment for malaria until new synthetic drugs were introduced after

World War 1. The malarial parasite has developed resistance to several of these new drugs, hence quinine remains important. It is also used as the bittering agent in tonic water and bitter-lemon drinks but has no medicinal effect in the quantity used.

quinoa Seeds of the half-hardy annual herb, *Chenopodium quinoa*, a native of the Andes. It is a member of the goosefoot family which grows to about 1½m and produces a profusion of very small millet-like seeds, which have been described as vegetable caviar for their character and pleasant flavour. It has relatively recently been introduced in the UK.

NUTRITIONAL VALUE: uncooked: protein 13%, fat 5%, carbohydrate 62%, dietary fibre 4.7%, vitamin B complex.

ENERGY per 100g: uncooked: 347 kcal, 1451 kJ.

USES: as a **gruel**, in cakes, as an alternative to **rice**.

quince The aromatic, large pear-shaped fruit, of the hardy tree *Cydonia oblonga (vulgaris)*, related to the **pear**. The cydonia is closely related to the shrub *Chaenomeles japonica* which produces similar fruit, but smaller and harder which are also sometimes referred to as quince.

NUTRITIONAL VALUE: high in pectin, some protein and vitamin C.

USES: in a variety of preserves, particularly jelly, stewed and used to flavour apples, also in savoury Middle Eastern dishes.

quinoline yellow (E104) Permitted yellow food colouring; a synthetic coal-tar dye. It is used for smoked **haddock** and **scotch** eggs. A related dye, known as Yellow 2G (107), is awaiting approval; both should be avoided by asthmatics and those sensitive to aspirin.

Quorn Trade name for **mycoprotein**.

R

rabbit A small herbivorous mammal introduced into England by the Normans as a source of meat. Rabbits were kept in enclosures called warrens and looked after by a warrener. They later became a serious pest, consuming vast amounts of **grain** and grass at the expense of farmers, until the introduction, in the mid 1950s, of myxomatosis, a virus disease lethal to rabbits and spread by rabbit fleas; this greatly reduced their numbers. The disease does not affect humans. Rabbits remaining are probably resistant to it and, in some areas, numbers have again reached pest proportions. Few wild rabbits are eaten today and most rabbit-meat is from farmed animals or imported carcasses particularly from China.

NUTRITIONAL VALUE: average: raw: protein 20%, fat 4%, vitamin B complex, calcium, iron.

ENERGY per 100g: raw: 125 kcal, 523 kJ.

USES: usually made into casseroles or pies, sometimes roasted.

rabbit-fish A prime sort of **herring**.

rack A method of clarifying liquids, particularly **wine**, by allowing the sediment to settle and drawing off the clear fluid above.

radiation See **irradiation**.

radicchio A small purplish-red **lettuce** usually used in a mixed salad.

radiofrequency cooking See **microwave oven**.

radish *Raphenus sativus*, a hardy, fast-growing annual with a bulbous, slightly pungent, root with edible skin. Most radishes are red, but there are white and black-skinned varieties. They are available throughout the year and the winter varieties are larger, with a stronger flavour. See **mooli**.

NUTRITIONAL VALUE: low in protein and carbohydrate, vitamin C 10–30mg per 100g.

ENERGY per 100g: negligible.

USES: in salads, whole or shredded.

ragi A type of **millet** grown in India.

ragout A **stew** of meat, poultry, fish and/or vegetables; often highly seasoned.

raisin The largest of the dried **grapes**, with a slightly coarser skin than **sultanas**; some are seedless. They store well under dry conditions.

NUTRITIONAL VALUE: protein 2–3%, sugar 25–30%, carotene, vitamin B complex, calcium, iron.

ENERGY per 100g: 108–128 kcal, 451–535 kJ.

USES: in cakes, desserts, chocolates, sweetmeats, mincemeat, for sweetening wine and cream sherry, served with nuts as a snack.

raki A form of **brandy** made in Eastern Mediterranean countries.

ram The male **sheep** (the female is **ewe**).

rambutan *Litchi chinensis*. Also known as **lychee** or nephelium.

ramekin, ramequin or **cocotte** A small earthenware or porcelain pot in which individual portions are cooked and served. The term is also used for the savouries cooked and served in such dishes.

rampion *Campanula rapunculus*, a hardy biennial with a swollen edible root.

USES: the leaves are used as a winter salad

crop; the swollen roots are eaten raw or cooked.

rancid A state of deterioration that occurs in **fats** and oils, associated with an unpleasant smell and taste, due to their breakdown to **fatty acids** and glycerol. All fat-containing foods, including cakes, biscuits, pastry and nuts, are subject to rancidity and keep for only a limited period. Spoilage occurs in the presence of moisture, due to the process of **hydrolysis** which is hastened by **bacteria** and **enzymes** present in the oil and fat; also by **oxidation** processes affecting unsaturated-fat molecules which are therefore more likely to occur with vegetable and fish oils than with animal fats. **Antioxidants** are frequently added to fats, and foods containing them, to prolong shelf-life and delay deterioration. **Food additives** used for this purpose are listed within the range E300–E321 and include **ascorbic** acid, **tocopherol** and related compounds.

All fats and oils should be stored under cool conditions, wrapped, or in airtight containers. Cooking-oil should not be left in the cooking-pan if it is to be used again, but filtered, to remove any impurities, and put into a container as soon as it has cooled; nevertheless it is likely to deteriorate with repeated use and should not be re-used more than two or three times.

rape *Brassica napus.* An annual, widely grown in Europe for its oily seeds. The fields of flowering rape in May are vivid yellow. The flowers have a high **nectar** content and attract bees, which produce from it a near-white **honey** which rapidly crystallises; it has little flavour of its own but is often used to blend with other honeys. Oil is extracted from the seeds and the residue provides high **protein** animal feed. See **rape-seed oil**.

rape-seed oil Oil extracted from the rape seed. It has a high content of monounsaturated **fats**. Some varieties of rape have a high content of a toxic substance, erucic acid, and cooking-oils should be from selected strains and purified for use.

NUTRITIONAL VALUE: saturated fat 7%, monounsaturated 60%, polyunsaturated 33%.

ENERGY per 100g: 900 kcal, 3766 kJ.

USES: as a cooking oil, particularly in Indian dishes.

rare (or blue) Describes very lightly-cooked meat, usually **beef**. Rare meat remains red and is appreciated by many people, but it is not entirely safe to eat and can cause **food poisoning**; ingestion of living **parasites** is also possible, particularly in countries where food is not rigidly inspected.

rarebit A dish of melted cheese served on toast; originally from Wales. The name is a corruption of rabbit.

raspberry A fruit developed from varieties of the hardy wild raspberry, *Rubus indaeus*, of the family which includes blackberry. The berries are soft, delicate and contain many seeds; most are red but some are yellow. They have a pleasantly acidic and characteristic flavour; numerous variations are available with different characteristics and fruiting times. Hybrids include **tayberry**, **wineberry**. They do not travel or keep well. Grown on a large scale for jam or self-picking. They freeze well, retaining their shape and most of their flavour. See **loganberry**.

NUTRITIONAL VALUE: carbohydrate 5–6%, vitamin C up to 30mg per 100g, ENERGY per 100g: 25 kcal, 104 kJ.

USES: eaten raw, in fruit salads and other desserts, for jam, preserves.

raspings Fine bread crumbs used to coat foods which have been dipped in beaten egg prior to frying.

rastrello A boat-shaped spoon designed to remove flesh from citrus fruits, particularly grapefruit.

ratafia An essence made from bitter **almonds**.

ratafia biscuits Biscuits flavoured with **ratafia** and used in **trifles** and other desserts.

ratatouille A vegetable stew of Mediterranean origin. The vegetables, traditionally aubergines, courgettes, onions, sweet peppers, tomatoes, garlic, are cooked in olive oil and their own juices. Ratatouille can be eaten hot or cold, on its own, with meat, pasta, rice.

ravel bread Bread made wholly or partly with **wholemeal** flour.

ravigote A basic **béchamel** sauce with the addition of white wine, onions and herbs. Also refers to **french dressing** with onions, herbs, capers and anchovies.

ravioli Small square envelopes of pasta containing spiced and savoury meat and/or vegetables.

raw beef See **beef tartare**.

rawn The hard **roe** of a female **fish**.

ray See **skate**.

razor-fish *Solen curtis*. A bivalve **mollusc**, shaped like an old-fashioned razor; the shells are found empty on the sand between the tides. The living mollusc is edible, and was formerly eaten raw or cooked; although plentiful it is hard to find and extract from the sand. Common salt sprinkled over the tell-tale hole often brings the mollusc to the surface.
    NUTRITIONAL VALUE: protein 15%, fat 2%, vitamin B complex, calcium, iron.
    ENERGY per 100g: 78 kcal, 325 kJ.
    USES: the risk of **food poisoning** makes it no longer safe to eat raw and all should be cooked.

réchauffé Food which has been reheated, or dishes made with left-over food such as **rissoles**. There is a risk of **food poisoning**, particularly with **poultry**, when the food to be reheated or reconstituted has been incompletely cooked, not been refrigerated soon after cooking, or has been allowed to warm up for some time before being used. Chilled food is now used extensively in large catering establishments, including hospitals, and users of chilled or frozen food have a responsibility to take all precautions against food poisoning. See **hygiene**, **cook-chill**, **cook-freeze**.

rectal feeding Feeding by infusing soluble nutrients by enema into the rectum where up to 2 litres can be absorbed in a day. The feed may include **salt**, **glucose**, **amino acids** and soluble **vitamins**. The method is generally used under medical supervision, where there is inability to swallow or repeated vomiting but no **diarrhoea**.

rectify A term used to describe the purification of alcohol. Rectified spirit is purified ethyl alcohol (**ethanol**).

red beans Red beans of many varieties are widely grown in temperate and tropical climates and frequently dried for storage. They form an important food crop and source of **protein**, particularly for **vegetarians**. All red beans contain a poisonous glucoside, **lectin**, which is destroyed by boiling for 10 minutes. Slow cooking which fails to reach boiling-point will not destroy the poison. Lectins remain viable even when dried beans are stored for long periods. Red beans and most other **pulses** contain **inulin**, a polysaccharide in the complex called **dietary fibre**; in excess this can increase the amount of **flatus** passed.
    NUTRITIONAL VALUE: raw: protein 20%, fat 1–2%, carbohydrate 45%, vitamin B complex, calcium, iron. Cooked: protein 9.7%, fat 1%, carbohydrate 20%.
    ENERGY per 100g: raw: 270 kcal, 1130 kJ. Cooked: 120 kcal, 502 kJ.

USES: in a variety of dishes such as **chilli-con-carne**, vegetarian casseroles, salads.

red cabbage A variety of *Brassica oleracea*, with red leaves.

NUTRITIONAL VALUE: raw: protein 1%, carbohydrate 2.8%, vitamin A, vitamin B complex, vitamin C, dietary fibre.

ENERGY per 100g: raw: 17 kcal, 71 kJ.

USES: cooked as a vegetable, often with apples and vinegar, grated raw in salads, pickled in vinegar.

red colouring Some natural fruit and other food-colouring matter is unstable and tends to be lost in processing; dyes are used to restore lost colour. The original red dye, cochineal, is expensive, and has largely been replaced by synthetic products, listed as **food additives** within the range E120, E122, E123, E127 and E128. Asthmatics and those sensitive to aspirin should avoid them. The dyes are used in canned cherries, rhubarb and strawberries and in cakes, jams, and pies. See **colour**.

redcurrant *Ribes sativum*. A hardy shrub producing clusters of small red, acidic, berries.

NUTRITIONAL VALUE: protein 1%, carbohydrate 4.4%, vitamin C 40mg per 100g.

ENERGY per 100g: 20 kcal, 84 kJ.

USES: in a variety of desserts, as a jelly for serving with meat (traditionally lamb), game, to glaze fruit tarts.

redfish The **sea bream**. Also refers to the male **salmon** at the time of spawning.

redgram Also known as pigeon-pea, dahl, gunga-pea, congo-pea. The seed of a tropical evergreen climber, *Cajanus indicis*, a member of the legume family with pods bearing nutritious pea-like seeds varying from white to black in colour; usually dried and may contain **lectin**.

NUTRITIONAL VALUE: protein 15–20 %, fat 1–2%, carbohydrate 45%, vitamin B complex, minerals.

USES: grown mainly for animal-feed but also used as a **pulse**.

red herrings Herrings which have been heavily salted and smoked. They have generally been replaced by **kippers**, which have a milder flavour.

red mullet See **mullet**.

red pepper See **pepper, red**.

red tide Red colour which appears in coastal waters during hot weather, due to an abundance of a toxic primitive organism on which fish, shellfish, including crabs, lobsters, oysters, feed, rendering them unfit for human consumption. It has been necessary on occasions to ban the sale of sea-food from affected areas until the seas become clear.

reduce To boil down and concentrate flavour. Used for **stock**, **sauces**, **soups** and **gravy**. Commercially this is done in a partial vacuum, which is more economical of heat and associated with less loss of flavour, due to the lower temperatures needed.

reest Scottish term for drying and **smoking** fish.

refrigerants Substances used for cooling. The simplest, a mixture of salt with crushed ice, was commonly used for making **ice-cream** before the introduction of powered freezers. Refrigerants in refrigerators and freezers are contained in a closed circuit. They are easily-liquefied gases which, when compressed, generate heat and are allowed to escape in a heat exchanger; the gases are then allowed to expand with a cooling effect. The majority of domestic refrigerators use a CFC gas such as freon, which is dichlorodifluoromethane, but alternative cooling gases are being developed because CFC gases enter and remain in the upper atmosphere, and if they escape from old or disused refrigerators, they damage the **ozone** layer.

Regulations have been introduced to prevent the escape of CFCs during the disposal of old or faulty refrigerators and freezers, and all should be sent to depots where the CFCs can be recycled.

Commercial refrigeration plants may use ammonia, carbon dioxide or other gases. Some small domestic refrigerators are of the absorption type and use ammonia, in a fully-closed system; dissolved in water it is driven off by heat, becomes compressed, reduced to room temperature in a heat exchanger and allowed to expand, with a cooling effect, in a continuous cycle. There are no moving parts.

refrigerator A cabinet for the storage of food which should be kept at a temperature above freezing but at or below 5°C (41°F). Some refrigerators have a frozen food compartment for storing pre-frozen food for a limited time, but which not suitable for freezing food. See **deep-freeze**.

WARNING. Old refrigerators should only be disposed of through a local authority or other depot where regulations for disposal are adhered to. See **refrigerants**.

regulo A system of numbers used on gas-cooker controls; they represent approximate oven temperatures in the middle of the oven, which are regulated by a thermostat. Temperatures are always higher at the top of the oven and lower at the bottom than those stated (except in fan-assisted ovens, only rarely available in gas-cookers). The heat equivalents are as follows:—

regulo	celsius	fahrenheit
0–¼	110–120°	230–248°
½	120°	248°
1	135°	275°
2	150°	302°
3	160°	320°
4	180°	356°
5	190°	374°
6	200°	392°
7	220°	428°
8	230°	446°
9	240°	464°

Some gas-cookers have a very low oven-temperature setting of about 93°C or 180°F.

release agents Substances used to prevent food adhering to cooking utensils, equipment or to itself. The group includes oils, fats, flour, waxes. See **nonstick**.

religious laws concerning food

Buddhist. Many Buddhists are vegetarians. Their religion preaches against killing, and although eating meat is not forbidden, it is not encouraged. Fish is permitted.

Christian. The Christian religion does not impose any dietary restraints, although historically fish was eaten on Fridays instead of meat. The Protestant Church imposed no restraint whilst the Roman Catholic Church did, but ceased to do so in 1960.

Hindu. Many Hindus are vegetarians. The cow is a sacred animal and beef must not be eaten but other meats are permitted to non-vegetarians.

Jewish. All food must be kosher, that is, all animals must be slaughtered and prepared according to strict Jewish laws, whereby they are killed by cutting all soft tissues in the neck. Beef, mutton, lamb, goat, venison, birds and fish are permitted; meat from pigs, birds of prey, eels, fish without scales and **shellfish** are not permitted. Meat must not be eaten at the same meal as **dairy products** and separate cooking and tableware must be set aside for each type of food. Animal rennet must be replaced by vegetable rennet. Meat must not be cooked with butter and chicken fat is usually used instead. The laws are enforced, particularly in Israel, by Rabbis who regularly inspect hotels and restaurants.

Muslim. Food must be halal: animals

must be slaughtered according to Muslim Law in a similar manner to that used by Jews. Forbidden food is called halam and includes animals dying by accident or incorrectly slaughtered, pig meat, blood, fish without scales, shellfish and alcohol.

Parsee. All meat and alcohol are permitted.

Sikh. All meat except beef is permitted but the animal must have been killed by a single blow to the head. However, the restrictions are not as rigidly adhered to as those of Muslims and Hindus.

relish A sauce, condiment ·or spread with a strong flavour.

remoulade Mayonnaise with added capers, chopped gherkins, herbs, anchovies.

render To clarify or melt **fat** by dry or moist heat and separate it from solid matter. Fat in mammals and poultry is only liquid at body temperature and above and is held in special fat-cells which are disrupted by the application of heat.

rennet A preparation containing the **enzyme** rennin, present in the stomach of mammals and in some plants (vegetable rennet), particularly Ladies' Bedstraw, *Galium verum*, which has the property of coagulating or curdling milk and changing it into **junket**. Only vegetable rennet is kosher. Rennet is used in the first stage of cheese-making before salt is added. Both forms of rennet are available.

rennet apple An old variety of dessert apple.

rennin The **enzyme** in **rennet**.

resin A naturally-occurring gum, mainly extracted from parts of softwoods or leaves of the pine family and used as flavouring in **spruce beer** and **retsina**. The term also includes chemical substances which have the ability to absorb other chemical substances under certain conditions and then release them under others.

These are known as exchange resins and are used in water-softeners, some water purifiers and dish-washers.

retinol The term formerly used for **vitamin A**.

retsina A Greek white **wine** flavoured with **resin**, originally by being stored in resinous pine-wood barrels; various other sources of resin may be used.

revalenta Finely ground **lentils**.

rheum See **rhubarb**.

Rhine wine Light white wine made from grapes grown in the Rhine Valley. It is bottled in brown bottles.

ALCOHOL CONTENT: Around 9% (less than most French wines but a little more than those from the **Mosel** region).

Rhode Island red An American breed of domestic **fowl**.

rhubarb *Rheum raponticum* and hybrids. The common rhubarb was originally introduced to the UK in the 16th century for the laxative properties of its roots. The use of the acidic stalks as an alternative to fruit is comparatively recent. The stalks contain a moderate amount of **oxalic acid** which, although poisonous, is safe in the quantities normally eaten. However, the concentration is high in the leaves and these must never be consumed.

NUTRITIONAL VALUE: negligible quantities of protein and carbohydrate, vitamin C up to 20mg per 100g.

ENERGY per 100g: negligible.

USES: stewed as a dessert, in crumbles, pies, fools and jams (often with ginger). Also sometimes in meat dishes.

Rhudesheimer A white **Rhine wine** from around Rhudesheim in Germany.

Ribena A proprietary syrup of concentrated **blackcurrant** juice with added vitamin C.

NUTRITIONAL VALUE: undiluted: carbohydrate 61%, vitamin C 206mg per 100gm.

ENERGY per 100ml: undiluted: 244 kcal, 1020 kJ. Diluted in 6 parts water: 40 kcal, 167 kJ.

USES: as a drink diluted with water, flavouring desserts, ice-cream.

riboflavin (E101) Permitted orange-yellow food colouring, also called vitamin B2.

rice *Oryza sativa.* A type of grass; one of the most important cereal crops, widely-produced in subtropical and tropical countries and requiring water to flood the fields for its growth. Natural rice is covered in **husk** which is removed to leave brown rice; when this is refined by polishing and the outer coat removed, it becomes the more widely-used white rice but, during this process, most of the valuable **vitamin B** complex content is lost. Dependence on white rice, in countries where it is a staple food, can lead to vitamin B deficiency and the disease known as **beriberi**. Natural brown rice takes longer to cook and has a different flavour from white rice. Long, medium and short-grain varieties are sold for special purposes. The long-grain varieties have a higher **protein** content and the grains remain separate when cooked; short-grain varieties contain dextrins and some sugar, making the grains tend to stick together. All rice lacks **gluten** which is present in **wheat**. It keeps well in dry conditions. See **paella, pilaff, rice (arborio), rice (basmati), rice-flour, rice (ground), rice (parboiled), rice (patna), rice (risotto), rice (wild), rice wine**.

NUTRITIONAL VALUE: white: protein 6.7%, fat 0.7%, carbohydrate 87%, calcium, iron. Brown: protein 7.5%, fat 1.8%, carbohydrate 87%, vitamin B complex, calcium, iron.

ENERGY per 100g: average: raw: 360 kcal, 1506 kJ. Cooked: 120 kcal, 502 kJ.

USES: in many savoury dishes and some desserts and sweetmeats.

rice, arborio A high-quality Italian rice with large oval-shaped grains which are very absorbent and used particularly for **risotto**.

rice, basmati A high-quality Indian long-grain rice, the best of which is aged for a year, to increase its nutty aroma and flavour, before being sold.

rice-flour Flour made from rice and finer than ground rice. It is high in **starch** but does not contain **gluten** and is unsuitable for bread-making.

USES: as a thickener in soups, sauces, mixed with wheat flour in cakes, pastry, short-bread.

rice, ground A coarse flour made from rice.

USES: similar to rice-flour, also as a milk-pudding.

rice-paper An edible light-weight paper made from the pith of the tropical tree, *Fatsia papyrifia*, a native of Taiwan. The pith is softened and rolled out into thin sheets. Used as a base in making macaroons, and other sweetmeats.

rice, parboiled Rice which is steamed in the **husk** to allow the water-soluble **vitamins** of the B complex and other nutrients to diffuse from the outer coat into the grain before final processing to produce white rice; an important process where rice is the staple diet. See **beriberi**.

rice, patna A general term for long-grain rice.

rice, risotto Round or oval-grained rice which is highly absorbent and tends to be sticky when cooked. See **rice, arborio**.

rice-water Water in which rice has been boiled. It contains **carbohydrate**.

rice, wild *Zizania aquatica*. Also known as Canada rice, Indian rice, Tuscarora rice, water-oats, and ziranie. From the tall aquatic grass which grows under similar conditions to rice, and reaches up to 3 m in height. The grain is thin, long and dark-brown, with a finer flavour than rice. The yield is small and it is difficult to harvest, which makes it expensive and regarded as a luxury.

NUTRITIONAL VALUE: average: raw: protein 11.5%, fat 7%, carbohydrate 76%.

ENERGY per 100g: average: raw: 330 kcal, 1380 kJ. Cooked: 110 kcal, 460 kJ.

USES: cooked and used as rice in savoury dishes; often mixed with long-grain brown or white rice.

rice wine Wine made from rice; the liquor being extracted by heat and fermented using a special fungus. In Japan it is known as **saki** or **sake**.

ALCOHOL CONTENT: up to 17%.

ricing The process of forcing cooked starchy foods, such as potatoes, through small perforations in a press designed for the purpose, giving it the appearance of rice. Also cutting food-stuffs into small pieces about the size of rice grains.

rickets and **osteomalacia**. Deficiency diseases in which the bones become soft and subject to deformity. In the growing stages of life it is known as rickets and in the adult as osteomalacia. Both are caused by a lack of **vitamin D** in the **diet**, and compounded by lack of exposure to sunlight. Formerly these were common conditions in slum-dwellers in industrial cities but are now rare. The introduction of margarine, fortified with vitamin D, during the early stages of World War 2 led to a progressive decline in the disease in the UK. It still occasionally affects Asians and the elderly and infirm on restricted diets and with little exposure to sunlight.

Ricotta A very soft, crumbly, white Italian cheese made from **whey**, traditionally with ewe's milk, but often that from cows, sometimes enriched with cream. It ripens quickly and must be eaten fresh.

NUTRITIONAL VALUE: average: protein 10%, fat 15%, carbohydrate 2.5%, lactose.

ENERGY per 100g: average: 185 kcal, 774 kJ.

USES: in many Italian recipes.

Riesling A light German **wine** made from Riesling grapes and sold in brown bottles. A similar wine is produced in other countries from the same grape, such as Yugoslavia and the New World.

ALCOHOL CONTENT: about 8–9%.

rigor mortis The hard contraction of muscles, which occurs after death, due to accumulation of **lactic acid**; in animals it lasts a few days, the duration depending on temperature and state at the time of death. Animals killed under stress develop rigor mortis quickly, due to high lactic acid content of the muscles. The best meat comes from animals and poultry killed in a state of relaxation. Time must be allowed for rigor mortis to pass off, as well as for **enzymes**, naturally present, to cause softening and tenderise the product. In fish the process is over quickly. See **autolysis**, **hanging**.

rind The outer coat of bacon, cheese, lemon and citrus fruits.

ripeness of fruit The state of maturity reached when the natural flavour, texture and aroma are fully developed and the seeds capable of germinating; beyond this point deterioration sets in and the **pectin** content, which is at its peak just before maturity, falls.

risotto An Italian savoury **rice** dish, sometimes flavoured, and coloured with **saffron**, mixed with a variety of vegetables, mushrooms, cheese, onion and herbs, chicken or other meats; sometimes cooked with wine. Best made with a short or oval-grained rice which is highly absorbent giving a slightly sticky result. See **rice**, **arborio**.

rissoles Originally minced meat or fish enclosed in pastry and deep fried. It now describes flattened balls of minced meat and vegetables, flavoured with herbs and coated in **egg** and breadcrumbs and fried. Often made with left-overs. See **réchauffé**, **panada**.

rivet A variety of bearded **wheat**.

roach *Rutilis rutilis*. A freshwater **fish** related to the carp; not a good culinary fish.

roast Historically the term implied cooking in front of a fire, the meat or **carcass** being fixed on a rotating shaft or spit held horizontally, sometimes vertically, in front of, or over, a fire. The high surface-temperatures developed the brown substance known as **melanoidin** which has a characteristic flavour; during cooking the meat was basted with fat. The term is now usually used for cooking meat, poultry, game, potatoes and other vegetables, with fat, in an oven. The traditional method is still used on special occasions when a whole ox, pig or sheep is roasted. See **rôtisserie**.

roasting-jack A clockwork mechanism which rotates a joint of meat suspended on a hook in front of a fire.

robalo *Esox masquinongy*. An American fish, like a **pike** but larger.

rocket *Eruca sativa*. A Mediterranean salad crop with a rather pungent flavour.

rock-salmon Also known as dogfish and huss, small relatives of the **shark** found around the coasts of Europe; varieties include *Sciliorhinus stellar* and *caniculus*. The skeleton is made of **cartilage**, unlike most **fish** which have bones. It has a firm pink flesh, deteriorates rapidly and must be eaten fresh; usually only available from the fishmonger in the winter.
NUTRITIONAL VALUE: protein 18–20%, fat 1%, vitamin B complex, calcium, iron.
ENERGY per 100g: 80–88 kcal, 344–368 kJ.
USES: lends itself to all methods of cooking.

rock-salt Common **salt** in large coarse crystals used in salt-grinders.

rock-samphire See **samphire**.

rocombole *Allium scordoprasum*, also known as sand-leek. A hardy member of the **onion** family which grows wild and is sometimes cultivated for its flavour which is similar to garlic.

roe The eggs of the female **fish**, hard roe, and the sperm of the male fish, soft roe. Both are found within the fish until they spawn, when the female lays its eggs and the male releases the spermatozoa to fertilise them. Roe sold separately is usually that of cod, coley, herring and mackerel; some, such as that from the **shark** is poisonous. It is available fresh, only during the spring, and should be used without delay. **Caviar** is the salted hard roe of the sturgeon. All roe keeps well frozen to −18°C.
NUTRITIONAL VALUE: average: protein 15%, fat, hard roe 1.7%, soft roe 3.0%, vitamin B complex, minerals.
ENERGY per 100g: average: hard: 75 kcal, 315 kJ. Soft: 87 kcal, 364 kJ.
USES: hard roe is usually cooked and eaten cold with salad or in dishes such as **taramasalata**. Soft roe is cooked and eaten hot on toast as a savoury dish, to garnish fish dishes, as fritters, canapés.

roe-deer A small species of **deer**.

roller-dry To dry liquids by passing them over heated rollers; at the final stage the dried product is scraped off. **Milk** loses some of its **vitamins** in the drying process. See **spray-dry, freeze-dry**.

roller-mill The most commonly-used machine for grinding, replacing the old grindstone. The material, usually **cereal**, is passed between a series of pairs of rollers rotating at different speeds and separated by narrowing gaps, the final pair being closest together. It is faster than other methods of grinding but generates heat, which has some effect on flavour and destroys **yeasts** and **moulds**.

roll-mop A **herring** which has been boned, stuffed with onion and spices, rolled up and pickled in **vinegar**.

roly-poly A pudding made with a **suet dough** which is rolled out flat, covered with fruit, jam, or dried fruit, rolled up, traditionally wound in a cloth and steamed or baked in the oven.

root The underground part of a plant responsible for taking up food and water from the soil. The nutrients pass up the stem or trunk to the leaves where **photosynthesis** takes place, building up **carbohydrates** and **proteins** for the growth of the plant. In some plants the processed nutrients are returned to the roots where they are stored. Root **vegetables** such as **carrots, parsnips, swedes, turnips**, are the swollen taproots and only one is produced per plant. Other vegetables such as **potatoes, jerusalem artichokes**, are **tubers**, which are swollen underground branches of roots or stems and several are produced by one plant. All are valuable sources of human and animal food. See also **beetroot, cassava, sweet potato, yam**.

root beer A non-alcoholic carbonated drink made variously with roots of dandelion, extract from the bark of

sarsaparilla, *Sassafras alridum* and or other plants, sometimes oil of **wintergreen**. A popular drink in the past.

root vegetable See **root**.

Roquefort A French **cheese** first made over 1200 years ago from ewe's milk and inoculated with the **fungus**, *Penicillium roqufortii*, giving it a blue appearance and a unique flavour. Like **Stilton**, it is protected by law and must be made of milk from the Larzac breed of sheep and matured in the limestone caves of Cambalou at Roquefort. It does not keep well and is best eaten within a few weeks of purchase. Refrigeration has made it available all the year round. When mature, the rind is orange/yellow and the cheese creamy white, soft with distinctive blue veins and a sharp flavour. See **penicillin**.

NUTRITIONAL VALUE: average: protein 19%, fat 32%, vitamin B complex, calcium, iron.

ENERGY per 100g: average: 364 kcal, 1532 kJ.

USES: as a table cheese.

rosé A **wine** halfway between white and red, made from red grapes. The skins are removed from the fermenting liquor before they have imparted their full colour and tannin content to the **must**. It is also made by blending red and white wines. It is usually sold in clear white bottles.

ALCOHOL CONTENT: 10–11%.

rose-hips The seed pods of species of wild roses containing many seeds and with an acidic flavour.

NUTRITIONAL VALUE: vitamin C up to 150mg per 100g.

USES: during World War 2 to make a syrup as a source of vitamin C, particularly for children; also for preserves in the past.

rose-water An extract, usually from red roses, used to add a delicate flavour to cakes, sponges and desserts, particularly in the Middle East.

rosemary One of several varieties of the aromatic semi-hardy shrub *Rosemarium*. The most common variety, *Rosemarium lavandulaceus*, is grown both for its decorative quality and for its aromatic leaves. The sprigs can be picked fresh all the year round; they can also be dried or frozen.

USES: as a flavouring in a variety of dishes, especially with lamb.

rôtisserie An apparatus for cooking by which **meat** is **roasted** on a rotating shaft or spit in front of, or over, a fire. The original form used power from rising hot air in a chimney, clockwork, a falling weight, or a dog walking inside a treadmill. Electricity has taken over as a source of power and rôtisseries are sometimes incorporated in modern ovens. Small battery-powered spits are available for barbecues. See **roasting-jack**.

Rouennaise Speciality food from Rouen. The best known is Duck Rouennaise; roast duck served with a sauce made of red wine, duck's liver and stock.

roux The basis of most sauces, made with equal parts of flour and melted butter or other fat and gently cooked; for a white sauce it is not allowed to colour, but for darker sauces it is cooked to a golden or brown colour.

rowanberry The fruit of a rowan tree, one of several varieties of *Sorbus* or mountain ash. The fruit is seeded, red or orange in colour, sharp and bitter and contains **sorbic acid**.

USES: usually mixed with apple to make a pungent jelly for eating with **game**.

royale A form of thick custard used to garnish soups. White Royale is made with egg-white and cream and gently cooked, while the whole egg is used for yellow royale. Both are seasoned and cut into shapes to float on the soup.

royal fish See **sturgeon**.

royal jelly Also known as queen substance. The food secreted by worker bees and deposited in specially large cells known as queen cells, leading to the full development of queen bees from eggs which are the same as those which produce worker bees. The extra quantity of food for the grub leads to the bee evolving to full sexual maturity. Royal jelly contains a wide mix of nutrients including **proteins** with essential **amino acids**, **fat**, **carbohydrates**, **minerals** and **vitamins**; the exact composition will vary with the environment, sources of pollen and season. It is claimed to have health-giving properties, but all the substances identified as being present in it are contained in a normal mixed **diet** and the quantity recommended as a **food supplement** of 150mg of jelly per day seems unlikely to contribute to human needs.

rue *Ruta graveolens*, (herb of grace). An evergreen shrub of southern Europe with strongly-flavoured leaves, sometimes used in small quantities as a culinary herb.

rum A spirit distilled from fermented **molasses** and originally made in the West Indies, where each island has its speciality, flavoured with spices, herbs and brown sugar. White rum, known as Bacardi, was first made in Cuba.

ALCOHOL CONTENT: 35–40%.

USES: as an apéritif and in cooking.

rumen The first of the four stomachs of ruminating herbivores such as cows, sheep, goats, from which regurgitated food is chewed; the process is known as 'chewing the cud'. The rumen contains bacteria capable of breaking down cellulose, by enzyme activity, for use as food.

rumkin A drinking vessel.

rumkin A type of **fowl** without a tail.

runner bean *Phaseolus coccineus*. Also known as string bean, scarlet runner. Introduced to Europe from South America, originally as an ornamental climber, now the most widely grown climbing bean in the UK, particularly in vegetable gardens. There are several varieties, with red or white flowers. Although perennial, it is frost tender and grown as an annual in cold climates. It is harvested when young before the seeds are ripe.

NUTRITIONAL VALUE: Protein 0.8%, carbohydrate 1%.

ENERGY per 100g: 7 kcal, 30kJ.

USES: sliced and boiled as a vegetable and in salads.

rusk A light bread, sliced and baked to full crispness. Rusks are given to babies during teething.

russe The name implies of Russian origin. Sometimes used for dishes containing **beetroot**. See **charlotte russe**, **à la russe**.

rust Generally refers to the brown or red oxides of iron that form on iron and steel surfaces. In the culinary sense it is used to describe the hard dry and more strongly-flavoured deep edge of a bacon rasher away from the rind.

rutabaga A variety of **swede**.

Ruthmol Trade name for a **salt** substitute, in which **sodium chloride** is replaced by **potassium chloride** with some **carbohydrate** being added as filler. It can be used where a low **sodium** diet is required by those with high blood pressure, heart or kidney failure. It should be used only under medical supervision, by people who require a diet low in potassium as well as sodium, for example those with kidney failure.

rye A hardy grain-grass, *Secale cereale*, related to **wheat** and **barley** and cultivated for food, mainly in Europe. Rye is subject to a black fungus under damp conditions, producing an alkaloid known as **ergot** which can cause abortions, and gangrene of the limbs, but which has, however, a medicinal use for treatment of **migraine**. The **flour** is dull-grey in colour.

NUTRITIONAL VALUE: protein 6–8%, fat 1–2%, carbohydrate 65%, vitamin B complex, calcium, iron, low in gluten.

USES: mainly for dry crispbread biscuits and **pumpernickel**.

rye-bread Bread made with **rye** flour, sometimes mixed with a high **gluten** flour to make it rise. See **pumpernickel**.

Ryvita Trade name for a crispbread made with **rye**. There are a number of similar products.

NUTRITIONAL VALUE: protein 9%, fat 2%, carbohydrate 66%.

ENERGY per 100g: 320 kcal, 1339 kJ.

S

sabayon A very rich sauce made with egg yolks, sugar and white wine, similar to the Italian **zabaglione** which is made with marsala.

USES: on hot sweets such as Christmas pudding, stewed fruit, as a dessert on its own, served warm or cold, usually in a glass.

sablé A rich biscuit made with equal parts butter and flour and used as a dessert with jam or other filling, or as a savoury with cheese spread.

saccharase An **enzyme** which converts **sucrose** to **glucose** and **fructose**.

saccharides Carbohydrates, the simplest forms are single sugar molecules (monosaccharides), such as **glucose** or **fructose**, and two sugar molecules (disaccharides), such as **sucrose**. **Polysaccharides**, which include **starch**, and the group of non-starch polysaccharides (NSP), form the complex known as **dietary fibre**.

saccharimeter A **polarimeter** calibrated to measure the concentration of **sucrose** solutions by polarised light. See **saccharometer**.

saccharine See **artificial sweetener**.

saccharometer A **hydrometer** or other instrument, calibrated to measure the concentration of sugar in solution by density. See **polarimeter**.

sack The old name for Spanish **wine** (including **sherry**).

sack, burnt A Spanish wine, traditionally heated with a hot poker; it may be spiced.

sacristan Small twisted strips of puff **pastry** rolled out several times, layered each time with castor sugar and baked to caramelise the sugar. Served with ices or fruit salads.

saddle A joint of meat taken from the back (saddle area) of an animal, usually **lamb**.

safflower *Carthamus tinctoria*, also known as saffron thistle. A hardy annual, native of Egypt which can be grown in temperate areas.

USES: the orange-red flowers produce a yellow dye, sold as an inexpensive substitute for **saffron**, but lacking the distinctive flavour.

safflower oil Oil extracted from the seeds of the **safflower**. It is bland in flavour.

NUTRITIONAL VALUE: fat saturated fat 10%, polyunsaturated 75%.

ENERGY per 100g: 900 kcal, 3766 kJ.

USES: for cooking and in salad dressings.

saffron The dried anthers and stamens of the purple-flowered saffron crocus, *Crocus sativus*. They impart a strong yellow colour and have a distinctive flavour. Saffron is often replaced by synthetic dyes or cheaper substitutes, such as **safflower**, which lack the flavour.

USES: in a variety of foods for its colour and flavour such as cakes and buns, rice, Mediterranean dishes, curries.

saffron thistle See **safflower**.

sage *Salvia officianalis*. A hardy **herb** with a strong flavour much used in **stuffing**, with onions, particularly for pork; also with other herbs in a variety of savoury dishes and stuffings.

sago The processed **pith** of the tropical sago palm, *Metroxylon sagu* and some other tropical palms, usually in the form of granules or flakes. The **starch** forms a clear glutinous **gel**, very similar to **tapioca**. Freezing interferes with the gel structure.

NUTRITIONAL VALUE: protein 0.5%, carbohydrate 88%.

ENERGY per 100g: uncooked: 354 kcal, 1472 kJ.

USES: in Asian cooking and in the UK for desserts.

saithe Another name for **coley** or coal-fish.

sake or **saki**. See **rice wine**.

salad A variable mixture of fresh or cooked vegetables, fruits, nuts, pasta, rice, pulses, usually eaten cold but, when the ingredients are cooked, it may be served warm.

salad burnet See **burnet**.

salad cream An emulsion of oil, vinegar or lemon juice with cream, soured cream or yoghurt, sugar and various flavourings.

NUTRITIONAL VALUE: variable: oil content up to 25%, carbohydrate up to 15%. Reduced-fat preparations are now available.

salad dressing Any preparation used to moisten and add flavour to a salad. See **French dressing, mayonnaise, salad cream, vinaigrette**.

salad, fruit A mixture of fresh or cooked fruits served warm or cold as a dessert.

salamander A circular iron plate with a long handle, heated and used to brown meat or pastry.

salami A **sausage** of Italian origin with many local variations; made from pork or beef, then dried and smoked with spices

and herbs. It is sometimes cooked but usually sliced thin and eaten cold as an **hors d'oeuvres**, with **salads**, on pizzas.

salicylic acid See **aspirin**.

saligot French name for **water chestnut**.

saline Water, containing **salt**. 'Normal' saline, used in a medicinal context, contains 0.9% salt and is soothing to wounds and mucous membranes. At this strength it can save life by replacing fluid and salt which are lost by persistent vomiting and/or **diarrhoea**. See **seawater**.

saliva The secretion of numerous glands that drain into the mouth, containing the enzyme **amylase** and the protein **mucin**. Chewing increases the exposure of starches to the enzyme amylase, starting the breakdown to **monosaccharide**. The lubricating property of mucin assists in swallowing. The saliva of the Asiatic swallow is used by the birds to make their nests, which are the basis of **bird's nest soup**.

salmi A stew of **game** birds or **duck**. The birds are first lightly roasted, or browned in fat, then cut into joints and cooked in a rich sauce containing **port** or red **wine** and garnished with **croûtons, fleurons**, parsley, watercress.

salmo The species of fish which includes **salmon, trout** and grayling.

salmon *Salmo salar*. A large, oily, migratory, game-**fish**, of the same family as the trout. The young fry migrates to sea to feed and mature, and returns to its home river to spawn. The Atlantic salmon returns to a European river and the Pacific salmon to a river in North America or Canada. Commercially, salmon are generally caught by netting in the lower reaches of rivers or in estuaries; as a sport, they are caught by rod higher up the rivers. Over-efficient netting, and pollution have reduced the numbers of fish in the rivers considerably. In recent years salmon-farming has flourished in Scottish and Norwegian waters and over 50% of the fish sold in the UK comes from these sources. Most canned salmon is of the Pacific variety. Wild salmon, considered to be superior in flavour and quality are an expensive luxury fish, while farmed salmon are cheaper and widely available. See **canning, smoking**.

SEASON: maximum, in England, Scotland and Wales from 15th January to 31st October but there are local variations. In Northern Ireland 2nd February to 30th October, also with local variations.

NUTRITIONAL VALUE: protein 15–18%, fat (mainly unsaturated) varies from 5–20% according to the species, season when caught, age and part of fish; (it is lowest at the tail end and highest behind the head), vitamin B complex, calcium, iron, iodine. There is no nutritional difference between farmed and wild salmon.

ENERGY per 100g: 105–252 kcal, 440–1054 kJ.

USES: it is best poached and eaten warm or cold, can be wrapped in foil and baked, steaks are often grilled or baked. When smoked it is sliced very thinly as a first course or used in various ways as a snack. Canned salmon is usually eaten cold or in savoury dishes.

salmonella The group of rod-like bacteria that inhabit the intestines of animals and man; some are common causes of **food poisoning**, particularly those which may be present in **poultry** and **eggs**; may also be present in **beef**. They cause the disease known as salmonellosis but usually referred to as salmonella.

salmon-trout or **sea-trout** *Salmo trutta*. A migratory **trout**, and prized game-fish caught in many clean rivers and estuaries. The numbers have been reduced over the years due to over-fishing and pollution.

NUTRITIONAL VALUE: as for **trout** and **salmon**.

ENERGY per 100g: as for trout and salmon.

USES: as for trout and salmon.

salsiccia A generic term for a small Italian sausage, with regional variations; some are **smoked**.

salsify *Tragogon porrifolius*. A native of southern Europe, also known as goat's beard, oyster plant and vegetable oyster. It is a hardy biennial with expanded roots, similar to a parsnip, but longer and more slender. See **scorzonera**.

USES: as a winter vegetable.

salt In the chemical sense, salt is any compound of an acid with a base, such as magnesium sulphate (Epsom salts). Common salt is Sodium chloride and is one of the four natural **tastes** detectable by the tongue. It is essential to all forms of life; not a food but the principal **mineral** in body fluids outside cells and responsible for maintaining their volume and the electrical potential of nerves and muscles. Total salt-intake for humans should not exceed 3g a day and an adequate amount is present in a normal **diet**. Extra salt may be needed for health reasons, for those living and working in a hot humid environment where there is continuous loss of fluid due to sweating, also when there is an abnormal loss of fluid because of severe vomiting and **diarrhoea**.

The average daily intake of salt in the UK is significantly higher than that recommended; an excess, above even 4g a day, under some circumstances, may lead to a build-up of sodium in the tissues, resulting in a collection of fluid known as **oedema**, and predisposes towards a rise in **blood pressure**. Food manufacturers tend to use salt to compensate for lack of natural flavours in processed foods, which can lead to an increased intake. Potassium iodide is added to salt in iodine-deficient areas. See curing, goitre, ruthmol, salt (cooking), salt (sea), salt substitutes, salt (table).

salt, cooking Most salt used in Europe is mined and known as rock-salt. It used to be sold in a block but now it is usually crushed and has added anti-caking agents to make it run freely. See salt, table.

USES: it is essential in cooking, to bring out the flavour of many foods, sweet as well as savoury. In bread-making, gives flavour and also prevents the dough from becoming too sticky. See preservation of food.

salt, sea Sodium chloride which is evaporated naturally from sea-water and contains some other minerals. The crystals are coarse and are ground for use in a salt-mill. Many people consider this superior to common table salt.

salt substitutes Chemical substances which have a salty taste but have part or most of the sodium chloride replaced by potassium or ammonium chloride and used to benefit those who need to reduce their sodium intake. The flavour is similar to, but weaker than that of pure salt. See low-salt, Ruthmol.

salt, table A finely-crystallised form of sodium chloride made free-flowing by anti-caking agents such as magnesium carbonate (504), potassium ferrocyanide (535).

saltpetre See nitre.

samp A coarsely-ground maize of American Indian origin; it also refers to a type of porridge made from it.

samphire Crithmum maritimum, also known as rock samphire and glasswort; a strongly-flavoured perennial with succulent leaves, thriving only near the coast where it grows wild. It is eaten as a salad or pickled.

samshoo A Chinese spirit distilled from fermented rice-water.

ALCOHOL CONTENT: 35–40%.

sander Esox lucius, a German variety of pike, a freshwater fish.

sandwich Named after the Earl of Sandwich in 1762, it was originally a piece of meat placed between two pieces of buttered bread. Now prepared with a variety of sweet and savoury fillings and widely available for snacks and quick meals; sometimes toasted. Open sandwiches have only a base of bread. See smørbrød.

sangaree A West Indian drink made with wine, water, lemon juice, sugar and spices.

sangria A Spanish version of sangaree made with wine, orange and cucumber; the alcohol content is normally less than that of the wine used.

sap The juice produced in a plant, which flows, as part of the food-cycle, through the stalks or trunk between the roots and the leaves, where photosynthesis takes place. A few saps are poisonous, but many have a high nutritional value and are rich in sugars. The sap of the sugar-cane is the most widely used. Maple syrup is the concentrated sugary syrup from the sap of certain maple trees. Some saps are used as a source of drugs and rubber. See agave, coconut, honeydew, jaggery.

sapodillo See naseberry.

sapucaia nut The fruit of the tropical South American tree, Lecythis zabucajo. Sometimes sold as an alternative to brazil nuts. The shell is fragile and the kernel has a sweet and more delicate flavour then the brazil nut.

NUTRITIONAL VALUE: protein 18%, fat 50%, mostly unsaturated, vitamin B complex, minerals.

ENERGY per 100g: 522 kcal, 2184 kJ.

USES: as a dessert nut; in sweetmeats, cakes and desserts.

saracen corn See buckwheat.

sardel A fish similar to a **sardine**.

sardine *Sardinia pilchardus*, a small **pilchard**. A strongly-flavoured oily **fish** related to the **herring**, caught in large numbers off the southern coasts of Europe, particularly in warmer waters. Sold fresh or canned. See **canning**.

NUTRITIONAL VALUE: average: protein 18%, fat 18% mainly unsaturated, vitamin B complex, vitamin D, calcium, iron.

ENERGY per 100g: average: fresh: 282 kcal, 1170 kJ. Canned in oil, fish only, 217 kcal, 906 kJ.

USES: a valuable food, eaten fried or grilled when freshly caught, cold or grilled on toast when canned, as sardines, or later when bigger, as **pilchards**.

sargus A variety of sea **bream**.

sarrasin Seeds of *Fagopyrum esculenta*, also known as **buckwheat**.

sarsaparilla An extract from the root of one of several South American varieties of climbing plants known as smilax, once credited with medicinal properties but now discounted. It has been used as a flavouring for drinks such as **root-beer**, but is now believed to be harmful to the liver and rarely used.

saskatoon The shadbury, a large pear-shaped **citrus** fruit.

sassafras oil Oil extracted mainly from the root bark of a hardy deciduous tree *Sassafras albidum;* used in the past for its medicinal properties as a stimulant. Sometimes confused with **sarsaparilla**.

satsuma A seedless variety of **tangerine**.

NUTRITIONAL VALUE: vitamin C up to 50mg per 100g.

USES: eaten fresh as a dessert fruit or in fruit salads and other desserts.

saturated fats See **fats**.

saturated solution A solution containing the maximum amount of a soluble substance that can be dissolved in the fluid medium. The concentration varies with temperature. Salts dissolve above the saturation point by heating but will crystallise out as the fluid cools.

sauce A dressing to pour over food. There is a very wide range of sweet and savoury sauces, sometimes thick in consistency, sometimes thin, ranging from basic white sauce, which can be flavoured with vanilla, to accompany stewed fruit, parsley or cheese for fish or vegetables, to the more complicated sauces made with egg yolks and butter, such as hollandaise to accompany fish. See **roux**.

USES: to enhance or add flavour to plain food, to make rich food more digestible, to enhance the appearance of food by adding colour or texture or as an integral part of a dish.

saucepan A vessel, generally cylindrical, with a long handle, and usually a lid, for use when cooking in liquid or sometimes fat, on a source of direct heat such as a **hob**. Originally made of iron, later enamelled, copper, and now also aluminium, stainless steel, glass. Many are specially treated to give a **non-stick** surface. See **inductive hob**.

sauerkraut Cabbage, finely sliced, slightly salted and fermented by the action of lactose-fermenting **bacteria** naturally present on the leaves, over a period of 5–10 days depending on temperature. A common dish in Europe, particularly Germany, it is often flavoured with **juniper berries** or **caraway seeds** and eaten raw or cooked. The **lactic acid** produced gives it an acidic taste and acts as a **preservative**. It is available canned or freshly prepared and sold by weight in some delicatessens.

saurel See **horse mackerel**.

sausage. A preparation of minced or chopped meat, including fat, (most commonly pork but also beef, liver, blood, poultry) usually mixed with various cereals or bread and seasoned. The mixture is extruded into tubes of varying diameter and length (**sausage-skins**) according to type, from the small chipolata to various forms of salami. The term covers two types, those sold uncooked, by far the most common in the UK, and others, mostly of continental origin, with a high meat content supplied ready to eat, such as **salami, saveloy**.

Sausages generally contain **preservatives** acceptable under EEC regulations. Some sausages contain elements of the carcase not normally available and not meat in the strict sense, such as gristle and connective tissue, and used to extend the meat content. **Mechanically-recovered meat** has been used but is no longer acceptable in the UK. See **black pudding, frankfurter, liver sausage, polony, sausage and mash, toad-in-the-hole**.

sausage-meat Meat prepared for sausages but sold in bulk; for use mainly in **stuffings**. It should always be purchased from a reliable source.

sausage-skins These are traditionally prepared from the intestines of sheep, pig or cattle which have been cleaned, and scraped to remove fat and muscle, producing an even, thin tube. Nowadays skins are made more economically from reconstituted **collagen**, processed and extruded into continuous thin-walled tubes.

sauté Fried quickly and lightly usually in a **sauté-pan**, which allows the contents to be shaken and tossed while cooking.

sauté-pan A shallow **saucepan** which can be used for frying, but deeper than a **frying-pan**.

sauternes A sweet, white **wine** from the Bordeaux area of France, made from grapes which have been dried naturally, by being affected on the vine by the fungus, botrytis. This gives the wine a high alcohol content but leaves some sugar unfermented.

ALCOHOL CONTENT: 14%.

USES: as a table wine.

savarin A yeast-cake made in a ring mould, sometimes containing fruit and nuts, and soaked in hot sugar-syrup when cooked; often flavoured with brandy or rum.

saveloy A small smoked **sausage**, of Italian origin, bought cooked and ready to eat. Originally made with pigs' brains, but now of cured pork, well-seasoned and with herbs and spices.

savory An aromatic herb (similar to **thyme**, but with a stronger and more peppery flavour); either *Saturiea hortensis*, a tender annual with a delicate flavour or

Saturia montana, a hardy perennial variety regarded as inferior to *hortensis* and with a stronger and more peppery flavour.

USES: to add flavour to meat and fish dishes, in stuffings, and cooked with green beans.

savoy A hardy winter **cabbage**.

saxin Tradename for a brand of saccharine. See **artificial sweeteners**.

scad See **horse mackerel**.

scald To immerse briefly in boiling water. The process reduces the number of **micro-organisms** present and delays deterioration but does not sterilise. Scalding also loosens the skins of fruit, such as peaches, tomatoes, and the feathers of poultry and bristles of pig so that they can be removed easily.

scallops *Pecten varius, Pecten maximus* and other varieties. Large bivalve **molluscs** with a pair of saucer-shaped plates. They are dredged from the sea-bed of coastal waters.

NUTRITIONAL VALUE: protein 25%, fat 1–2%, vitamin B complex, calcium, iron.

ENERGY per 100g: 165 kcal, 418 kJ.

USES: usually sauted in butter or cooked in a sauce, and served in the shell.

scampi *Nephrops norvegicus*. Also known as Norwegian prawn, Dublin Bay prawn or langoustine. A small variety of **lobster** of which only the tail is eaten.

NUTRITIONAL VALUE: protein 20%, fat 3%.

ENERGY per 100g: 120 kcal, 502 kJ.

USES: traditionally fried in batter as a fish or main course and served with sauce tartare.

schnapps Gin made in Holland.

schnitzel A cutlet of **veal**.

schooner A large glass for **sherry**, usually holding about 80ml. See **copita**.

scomboid Name given to fish related to the **mackerel**.

scone Originally a Scottish speciality. A form of bread or cake made with wheat flour, oatmeal, barley or potato, with fat and soured milk or buttermilk. The 'loaf' is circular, about 20cm in diameter and flat and is traditionally cut into four triangles after baking. English scones are smaller, about 5cm diameter, made with flour, milk (sometimes sour) and fat. Both kinds are usually served with butter or cream and jam.

scone, drop A scone made with flour, milk and egg and cooked on a **griddle**.

scorzonera *Scorzonera hispanica* or black salsify; a native of southern Europe and similar to **salsify** but with a blackish skin.

USES: as a winter vegetable.

scotch egg A hard-boiled **egg** shelled, enclosed in a covering of **sausage-meat**, dipped in beaten egg, rolled in breadcrumbs and cooked in the oven or deep-fried. Commercial products may be coloured with **quinoline** yellow (E104).

scotch kale A hardy variety of the *Brassica oleracea*, the cabbage family, with bright green curly leaves and more strongly-flavoured than other members of this family.

NUTRITIONAL VALUE: vitamin A, vitamin B complex, vitamin C, calcium, iron.

USES: boiled as a winter vegetable.

scramble To cook with continuous gentle stirring at a low temperature, particularly **eggs**. The traditional process does not destroy **salmonella** if it is present in the egg but temporarily suspends its growth, as in **pasteurisation**. Eggs cooked this way are generally safe for healthy adults but, unless they are well-cooked and not runny, should be avoided by young children, pregnant women and the elderly and infirm.

scrapie See **bovine spongioform encephalopathy**.

screwpine See **kewra**.

scrumpy See **cider**.

sea bream See **bream**.

sea-cucumber A sausage-shaped primitive marine animal related to the sea anemone; it is edible after preparation by soaking, opening up, cleaning out and cooking for several hours.

sea-date *Mytilidia lithodomus*. A marine bivalve, a type of **mussel**, resembling the date fruit in appearance; requires the same precautions as mussel to avoid **food poisoning**.

seafood Any food gathered from the sea such as **fish**, **crustaceans**, **molluscs** and edible **seaweed**. Seafood should be gathered from uncontaminated waters and is from time to time the source of **food poisoning**.

sea-kale *Crambe maritime*. A hardy plant found wild in sandy soils near coasts. It is cultivated as a vegetable and eaten for its leaf-stalks which need to be forced, with light excluded, to make them tender and delicate in flavour.

season To flavour with salt, spices, herbs.

season A legally defined period during which the hunting, shooting and fishing of certain game birds, animals and fish are permitted.

seasoned flour Flour which is prepared ready for use, seasoned with salt and pepper, sometimes with mixed herbs.

sea-salt See **salt, sea**.

sea-urchin *Echinus esculentis*. Related to the starfish in the class *Echyndermata*. Sea-urchins are globular, with a hard skin and many spines, inhabiting the coasts of southern Europe and warm seas, where they are found on rocks and the sea-bed.
USES: the **roes**, which must be fresh, are eaten raw, cooked with scrambled egg or in sauces.

sea-water Sea-water contains an average of 3.5% **sodium chloride**, but varies above or below this level, depending on evaporation in enclosed seas or inflow from rivers. Sea-water will extract water from the tissues of humans and must never be drunk, even in extremes of thirst. It can be used for cooking. Many countries depend on evaporation of sea-water in salt pans for their supply of salt. Desalinated sea-water is used where normal water supplies are very limited.

seaweed Marine algae which grow on rocks in shallow coastal waters. An important source of **agar** and **iodine**, some are used as food. See **carrageen, kelp, laver**.

sec Describes **wines** which have a low sugar content and are known as dry; the opposite of sweet.

selenium A **trace element** which has an important role in protecting cells from damage by oxidation. There is no evidence that deficiency occurs when a normal mixed **diet** is eaten; most of the selenium comes from cereals and the rest from meat and fish. Supplements are not required, except under unusual circumstances in which there is a deficiency in natural sources; any excess is normally excreted in the urine.

self-raising flour See **flour**.

semolina Particles left behind after milling hard wheat; when cooked the granules give a coarse texture.
NUTRITIONAL VALUE: uncooked: protein 10.5%, fat 2.5%, carbohydrate 71%.
ENERGY per 100g: uncooked: 330 kcal, 1380 kJ.
USES: milk-pudding, **gnocchi**, soups, also made into a variety of sweets in the Middle East.

serviette A table-napkin.

sesame *Sesamum indicum*, a tropical and subtropical annual plant with a long history of cultivation for its seeds.
NUTRITIONAL VALUE: protein 20%, fat 50%, carbohydrate 16%, vitamin B complex.
ENERGY per 100g: 594 kcal, 2485 kJ.
USES: the seeds are sprinkled on bread and rolls, as a garnish on savoury and some sweet dishes, pulped as **tahina**; also in halva, a Turkish sweetmeat made with honey.

sesame oil Oil, with a strong flavour, extracted from **sesame** seeds.
NUTRITIONAL VALUE: fat, saturated 15%, monounsaturated 40%, polyunsaturated 45%.
USES: as a cooking oil, sometimes trickled onto pasta dishes, pizzas for added flavour; also used in the manufacture of soap.

seville orange The acidic and bitter fruit of the evergreen subtropical tree, *Citrium* *aurantium*, known as melangol, bigaradier and khush. The pith has a high **pectin** content. The tree is used as a rootstock for grafting sweet oranges because it is disease-resistant.

NUTRITIONAL VALUE: vitamin C up to 50 mg per 100g, high in pectin.

USES: the whole fruit is used to make **marmalade**, an essential oil extracted from the skin is used in the liqueurs **curaçao** and **cointreau**, the zest and juice are used as flavouring in desserts and savoury dishes, and the petals of the flowers are the source of oil of neroli used as a flavouring and in perfumes.

shad An oily fish similar to a **herring**.

shaddock See **pomelo**.

shallot *Allium ascalonicum*. A member of the **onion** family, but smaller and with a milder flavour.

shandy A mixture of beer with ginger beer or lemonade.

shark The largest of a group of cartilaginous fish, with firm meaty flesh. The relatively small **porbeagle** shark *Lamna nasus* which frequents the UK coastal waters is the best to eat. Shark roe is poisonous.

NUTRITIONAL VALUE: average: protein 18%, fat 2%, vitamin B complex, calcium, iron.

ENERGY per 100g: average: 90 kcal, 377 kJ.

USES: as steaks grilled, baked or fried. Oil is extracted from the liver as a source of **vitamins A** and **D**.

sharon fruit See **persimmon**.

Sheffield plate High quality silverplate made by bonding together a sheet of copper between two sheets of pure silver; named after the city where it was first produced in 1743 and for which it became famous. The plate was worked in the same way as pure silver. It was superseded in 1840 by electroplate, which is less durable but less expensive. It was used for ornamental and table silverware.

shellac (904) A naturally-occurring resin obtained from the lac insect, *Laccifer lacca*, native of India. Classed as a food additive and used as a glazing agent on cake decorations and sweetmeats.

shellfish A term which includes **molluscs**, and **crustaceans**.

sherbet A fruit-flavoured drink, also an effervescent powder used for making a drink or a type of water-ice.

sherry A fortified **wine** made in Jerez in Spain; only wine from that area can correctly be called sherry, but it is much copied elsewhere. The three principal types are fino and manzanilla (very dry), amontillado (medium dry), and oloroso (sweet). Some sweet sherries are sweetened with the juice of dried grapes. See **geropiga**.

ALCOHOL CONTENT: Fino 15.5%, Amontillado 16–17%, Oloroso 18–20%, 'British sherry' is made from imported grape juice, has an alcohol content of 15% and is not a true sherry.

shigella A group of **bacteria** responsible for **dysentery**.

shin Meat from the foreleg of an animal below the shoulder.

shortbread A Scottish speciality cake made with butter, flour and sugar, traditionally pressed flat into a wooden mould, turned out onto a baking tray and baked to a crisp golden brown and cut into various shapes. See **petticoat tails**.

shortening One of a number of fats, used with flour, to make a product which is crisp after baking, particularly **pastry** and biscuits. The fats, chosen for this purpose have a low melting-point and the ability to disperse readily; they have a high proportion of saturated fats. Lard and butter have been traditionally used, but today special shortening fats, based on hardened vegetable oils, are also used, of which some are mixtures containing 50% polyunsaturated fats.

shoulder Meat which includes the shoulder-blade (scapular) and shoulder-joint. See **hand**.

shred To slice thinly.

Shrewsbury cake A form of **shortbread**.

shrimp The smallest of the **crustaceans** with edible tails. *Crangon crangon* and *Pandalus montagut*, are the commonest species found round the coasts of the UK. Other varieties of shrimp are imported frozen from the Far East, where they are plentiful in the warmer seas and generally farmed. All shrimps should be cooked. See **prawn**.

NUTRITIONAL VALUE: protein 20%, fat 2%, vitamin B complex, minerals.

ENERGY per 100g: cooked: 107 kcal, 478 kJ.

USES: as a first course with salad, in a variety of fish and savoury dishes, as a garnish.

sieve A simple vessel with a gauze or a perforated bottom, of metal or plastic; used for separating solids from liquids, reducing lumps to produce an even powder or distribute powder or fine granular products evenly, to aerate flour. Simple mechanically-assisted sieves are available and quicker to use. See **moulin-légumes**.

Sikh See **religious laws**.

silicates (552–556) Inorganic compounds of silica from natural sources, such as rocks; including salts of aluminium, calcium or magnesium with a variety of uses as food additives, for dusting and as anti-caking agents in salt, chewing gum, rice and sweetmeats.

silicones (900) Organic compounds of silica used as food additives for their anti-foaming and anti-sticking properties on paper and cooking utensils.

silver (E174) A fairly soft precious metal. It is easily worked by beating, pressing or casting and takes a high polish with a warm appearance. It is the best conductor of heat and electricity and resistant to many corrosives except common salt, sulphur in the air and sulphur-containing foods such as eggs. Silver eggcups and spoons may be gold-plated to protect against sulphur damage. Silverware of any sort should never be left in contact with salt and only cleaned or polished with an agent specially prepared for the purpose.

Silver has bactericidal properties and **micro-organisms** will not grow on its surface; some surgical appliances are still made of it. It is used for high-class tableware, such as sugar bowls, tea and coffee-pots and cutlery, but the high cost of sterling silver prevents wide use. Items of British silver are usually hallmarked to identify the year, maker and place of manufacture and to confirm the purity of metal used.

It is also used for surface coating of sugar-coated dragees and is recognised as an **additive**. See **Sheffield plate**, **silver (electroplated)**, **silver (german)**.

silver, electroplated A thin layer of pure **silver**, electrically deposited on a base metal, copper or brass, which has first been electroplated with nickel; known as EPNS. A1 plate is the highest grade, having the greatest thickness of silver and lasting well, when used with care, but does gradually wear through to the nickel. EPNS accounts for the great majority of 'silver-ware' in daily use. Contact with salt rapidly corrodes the surface.

silver, german A hard-wearing nickel alloy resembling **silver** and capable of taking a high polish but without the warm quality of the appearance of pure silver. Used for less expensive ware and as a base for electroplating with pure silver.

silver plate See **Sheffield plate**, **silver (electroplated)**, **silver solutions**.

silver solutions Proprietary solutions available for home silver-plating of articles made of copper, nickel, bronze or brass or worn silver-plated pieces. Only a thin layer of silver is deposited, giving a satisfactory visual effect but often too thin to wear and no substitute for electroplating.

simmer To cook in a liquid at just below the boiling point, usually 90–98°C (194–208°F).

simnel cake A rich fruit cake, often spiced, and covered with **marzipan**; associated with Easter.

sippets Small triangular pieces of toast placed round a dish of **mince**, to make it look attractive and as a contrasting flavour.

sirloin A choice cut of loin of **beef**. The name is credited to King Charles 11 who liked the cut so much that he knighted it 'Sir Loin', however, it is more likely to have come from the French, surlonge, meaning, over loin.

NUTRITIONAL VALUE: See **beef**.

ENERGY per 100g: average: 313 kcal, 1310 kJ.

USES: for roasting on the bone or boned and rolled, cut into slices as steaks for frying or grilling.

skate *Raja batis* is the best of many varieties of this flatfish, related to the **shark**, caught for the table. It has a kite-like shape and tough skin on the upper surface, which is difficult to remove before it is cooked. Only the 'wings' are eaten and the flesh is firm. It deteriorates quickly and should only be eaten if its freshness is assured.

NUTRITIONAL VALUE: average: protein 20%, fat 1–2%, vitamin B complex, calcium, iron.

ENERGY per 100g: average: 94 kcal, 393 kJ.

USES: lends itself to all methods of cooking.

skewer A thin shaft of metal or wood with many uses in cooking, such as holding meat or poultry together in preparation for cooking and as a probe to determine the state of the food being cooked, or defrosted; the hole left after withdrawal allowing juices from the inner parts of **meat** or **poultry** to be examined; the red colour changes to colourless when cooking is complete. In cakes it is an indication that they are cooked, when a skewer pierced into it comes out clean with no mixture adhering to it. The ease of penetration is a guide to the completion of cooking of vegetables and detection of ice if defrosting. Long flat skewers are used for impaling pieces of food being prepared for **kebabs**. Metal skewers should be made of well-galvanised steel or stainless steel. Wooden skewers are rarely used today.

skillet The American term for a **frying pan**; also a saucepan with a long handle, sometimes with three legs, used for cooking over an open fire.

skiver Another name for a **skewer**.

sling A sweetened drink made with a **spirit** such as **rum** or **gin**.

slivovicz A spirit distilled from fermented plums; mainly made in Eastern European countries.

ALCOHOL CONTENT: 35–40%.

sloe Fruit of the wild plum, *Prunus spinosa;* also known as blackthorn. The fruit is acid and astringent. Mainly used for making **sloe-gin**.

sloe-gin A liqueur made by bottling pricked **sloes** with sugar and **gin** for 3–6 months, then pouring the liquid off the sloes. It has a red colour and pleasant acidic flavour.

ALCOHOL CONTENT: 25%.

sloke See **laver**.

slow cooker An electrically-heated earthenware pot with a lid, designed to cook the contents at, or just below, boiling point for long periods. Used for cooking cheaper cuts of meat, poultry, vegetables such as **pulses**, stews, soups, stock; also for sweet and savoury steamed puddings. It is important that the temperature should rise to boiling point for part of the time, to destroy **food poisoning** organisms and **lectin** if red, black or brown beans are included. Some of the most virulent food poisoning organisms have heat-resistant spores and food should either be eaten shortly after cooking or cooled quickly and refrigerated.

smelt See **sparling**.

smilax See **sarsaparilla**.

smoke-point See **fat – effects of heat, safety in use**.

smokies Small **haddock** or **whiting** which are brined and hot-smoked, over wood and wet sawdust, from Arbroath in Scotland. They must be eaten fresh, hot or cold, as they do not keep for long, even when chilled. See **smoking**.

smoking The **preservation of food** by exposing it to smoke from burning wood or wood-shavings in a restricted air supply; this produces **preservatives** in the form of tars, **phenols** and aldehydes. The process gives food a characteristic flavour. Cool-smoking is used for **bacon, ham, haddock** and **herring** and they require cooking before they are eaten to ensure destruction of any residual **bacteria** or **parasites**; ham is often cooked before sale. Hot-smoking cooks the food and is used for **mackerel**, sometimes haddock, which can then be eaten as sold. Although **salmon** is cool-smoked it is considered safe to eat without being cooked.

None of the effective chemicals present in smoke are listed among preservatives approved under EEC regulations, as they are theoretically capable of causing cancer. However, smoking has been practised for centuries and is so widespread that it is permitted for historical reasons; its effectiveness in preventing **food poisoning**, and as a preservative are together considered to outweigh the risks of consuming smoked food, in moderation.

smørbrød A Scandinavian term for **hors d'oeuvres** and other delicacies served on pieces of bread.

smörgåsbord A Swedish-style buffet where a variety of savoury and other dishes are set out for self-service.

snack A small meal, which may be little more than a few mouthfuls, taken in place of, or between, main meals.

snail French – escargot. A **mollusc**. Snails have been eaten since Roman times when they were considered a luxury and reared on a mixture of meal and wine. There are a number of edible species but the one most favoured today is the large *Hellix Pomata* or Roman snail. They are now being farmed in the UK, mainly for export to France, where they are a popular delicacy; the best are fed on vine leaves.

USES: after a salting process to remove the slime, they are plunged into boiling water, removed from their shells and cooked. They are usually served replaced in their shells with garlic butter.

snipe *Gallinago gallinago* in the UK and *Capella media* in Europe and Asia. Small game-birds similar to **woodcock** and considered a delicacy. Care must be taken to cook them thoroughly, to destroy any food poisoning **bacteria**.

SEASON: 12th August to 31st January in England, Scotland and Wales, 1st September to 31st January in Northern Ireland.

NUTRITIONAL VALUE: average: protein 18%, fat 2–3%.

ENERGY per 100g: average: 94 kcal, 393 kJ.

USES: best fresh, undrawn and roasted or spit-roasted, also split, flattened and grilled, or casseroled.

snoek *Thirsites atun*, the Australian barracouta. An oily fish which is a relative of the **tuna** and mackerel; found only in the southern hemisphere. It was available canned in the UK in the 1950s but is unlikely to be found now. See **snook**.

snook *Centropomus undecemales* or common snook, a **pike**-like fish found only in tropical Atlantic and Pacific waters. Not available in the UK.

soap An alkaline **salt** of **fatty acids**, formerly made by boiling animal fat with wood-ash. Sodium hydroxide is used to produce hard, and potassium hydroxide soft, soaps. Soap is inactivated in the presence of soluble calcium or magnesium salts present in hard **water, sea-water**. It is a fat-solvent and acts by reducing the surface tension of water; it is now often replaced by synthetic **detergents** for cleaning and clothes washing.

sockeye *Onchorhynchus nerka*. The blue **salmon** of the Pacific. The fish has a redder flesh and slightly lower fat-content than the Atlantic salmon.

NUTRITIONAL VALUE: protein 15–18%, fat 8–16%, variable with season and part of fish (see **salmon**), vitamin B complex, vitamin D, calcium, iodine.

ENERGY per 100g: 132–216 kcal, 552–904 kJ.

USES: mainly for canning.

soda-syphon An apparatus for making or dispensing **soda-water**. Originally a two-tier glass bottle strengthened with wire mesh. Water was put into the lower container and a dry mixture of acid and sodium bicarbonate into the upper chamber of the apparatus which was then sealed. The mixture gave off carbon dioxide when the appliance was inverted to wet the powder, the carbonated water being drawn off as required, by a long tube controlled by a lever-operated valve. This apparatus is now obsolete and has been replaced by a single vessel charged from a miniature cylinder of compressed gas.

soda-water Originally a slightly alkaline mineral water containing small quantities of **bicarbonate of soda**. Now used to describe water containing **carbon dioxide**, dissolved under pressure to create a fizzy drink. Sometimes it is made at home in a **soda-syphon**, but more often bought in strong plastic or glass bottles.

sodium See **salt**.

sodium alginate (E401) Similar uses to **alginic acid** *(E400)*.

sodium bicarbonate See **bicarbonate of soda**.

sodium bisulphite See **Campden tablets**.

sodium carbonate A white alkaline crystalline **salt** of carbonic acid and sodium, commonly sold as **washing-soda**. It has no place in cooking but is useful in solution for softening water for washing, removing **tannin** from the inside of stainless steel and china tea-pots, cleaning other cooking-ware and for degreasing blocked sinks. It dissolves **aluminium**, most glass and the glaze on old china over a long period, giving a cloudy or roughened surface. Purified sodium carbonate (**food additive** No. 500) is used commercially, or as the milder **bicarbonate of soda** (also 500) in baking powder.

sodium chloride See **salt**.

sodium citrate (E331 and related compounds **E332, E333, E334)** Prepared from **citric acid** and used as an **antioxidant**, **emulsifying** agent and to limit curd formation in milk.

sodium ferrocyanide (535) Used as an anti-caking agent in packaged salt. Although cyanide is a powerful poison, it is so firmly bound to the iron that ferrocyanide is stable and has very low toxicity.

sodium lactate (E325) Food additive used to enhance the antioxidant effect of other substances. Prepared from lactic acid.

sodium pectate (E440) Similar to **pectin**, sharing the same additive number.

sodium phosphate (E450) and related phosphates, all coded E450. Used as **stabilisers** and **emulsifiers**.

soft water See **water**.

sol A chemical term to describe a suspension of **colloid** in water.

solanine A poisonous and heat-stable glucoside which develops when **potatoes** turn green on exposure to light, or have begun to sprout. It is also present in the leaves and in the green tomato-like fruits that develop on potato plants which must not be eaten.

sole *Solea solea* and other varieties. The name refers to several marine **flatfish** of excellent eating quality. See **Dover sole**, **lemon sole**.

solera A system by which wines of different ages produced in the Jerez district of Spain are used for blending **sherries**.

sorbet A frozen dessert made with water, sugar, fruit juice, and sometimes beaten egg-white and gelatin. Commercially-made sorbets contain **additives** to stabilise the mixture, which limits ice-crystal formation and gives a smooth texture.

sorbic acid (E200) A mild acid, which occurs naturally in the fruits of the sorbus

(mountain ash); used as a **preservative** to prevent the growth of **moulds** and **fungi** in food.

sorbitol (E420) A higher **alcohol**, with a sweet taste, present in some fruits or made synthetically; it is less sweet than **sucrose** and poorly absorbed. It is prepared as a white crystalline powder and used as a **sugar** substitute by people with diabetes.

sorghum A genus of annual grasses, a number of which are grown for their food seeds, such as African corn, millet, Kaffir corn, Egyptian rice corn, Guinea corn, Sudan grass. Probably the most important of the African food crops. Other members of the group are grown for their sweet sap, the most important of which is **sugarcane**.

NUTRITIONAL VALUE: protein 10%, fat 3%, carbohydrate 70%, vitamin B, minerals.

ENERGY per 100g: 344 kcal, 1440 kJ.

USES: ground into a meal for a type of porridge, as a flour for unleavened **bread**, or made into local beers in Africa. Widely grown in USA as animal feed, and is the main constituent of birdseed in Britain.

sorrel *Rumus acetosa*, a hardy perennial **herb** with an acidic flavour due to its **oxalic acid** content. It is usually cultivated for culinary use, as wild varieties are inferior in flavour.

USES: in soups, sauces, particularly to accompany fish.

soubise A purée of onions in a white sauce, for serving with mutton, or mixed with rice as a stuffing.

souchet A fish-soup flavoured with onions and thickened with potatoes.

soufflé A light, fluffy, sweet or savoury dish made with **eggs**. Can be baked in the oven and eaten hot or set with **gelatine** and eaten cold. See **salmonella**, **food poisoning**.

soup A nutritious liquid obtained by boiling meat, poultry, fish and/or vegetables in stock, water and/or milk; there are many variations. A wide range of commercial products is available, canned, dried for reconstituting with water, or in cartons ready to use. Dried soups tend to have a high **salt** and **monosodium glutamate** content, but low-salt preparations are available.

sourdough A leaven for **bread**, made by activating the natural **yeasts** present on grain. Modern high-speed milling generates heat which may kill yeasts and only stone-ground **flour** is likely to retain living yeast. A flour and water mix is allowed to ferment in a warm place and is then used as a starter for bread-making. The **dough** kept back from each batch is the sourdough and used to maintain the cycle. Undesirable **bacteria** and **moulds** may also be activated by this process and can spoil the result. Commercially-made yeasts are now readily available and used in preference, for their reliability and consistency.

soured cream Single cream which has beeen soured commercially by the action of lactic acid fermenting bacteria, usually *Streptococcus lactis*. It has a thick consistency and an acidic flavour.

NUTRITIONAL VALUE: average: protein 2.5%, fat 18%, carbohydrate 4%.

ENERGY per 100g: average: 188 kcal, 787 kJ.

USES: as a basis for dips, in soups, sauces, casseroles, in a variety of sweet and savoury dishes, spooned over fruit, vegetables.

souring agent Any acidic substance used in cooking. Many foods are made more acceptable to the palate if they are slightly acid, in a pH range of 4–5. The commonest acidic substances used are fruit acids, especially lemon juice, **citric acid**, **vinegar**, and **lactic acid**; **yoghurt** and **sorrel** are also used.

souse To steep or **marinate** and cook in spiced **vinegar** or **wine**, as with soused **herrings**.

sous-vide A method of food-preservation developed in France and increasingly used because it gives products a long life. Food is precooked at a temperature which kills heat-resistant **micro-organisms**, sealed in a vacuum pack to avoid **oxidation**, and refrigerated until sold or used.

southernwood *Artemisia abrotanum;* also known as Old Man and Lads' Love. A hardy herbaceous shrub which grows wild, but is also cultivated. Formerly used as a **herb** for the pleasant flavour of its leaves and occasionally for flavouring cakes.

soya bean *Glycine hispida*, a **bean** which requires a warm climate to grow. It has a long history of cultivation in China, and is now widely grown in North America and the Far East. It has the highest **protein** content of all beans, up to 40% dry weight, and can be processed and spun or extruded, when it is known as Textured Vegetable Protein (TVP). It has little flavour of its own but absorbs other flavours well. See **soya flour, soya milk, soya oil, tofu**.

NUTRITIONAL VALUE: average: cooked: protein 12.4%, fat 6.4%, carbohydrate 9%, vitamin B complex, carotene, calcium, iron.

ENERGY per 100g: average: cooked: 141 kcal, 590 kJ.

USES: as a meat substitute, it is a valuable food for **vegetarians** and **vegans**, in feed for cattle, poultry and farmed fish.

soya curd Same as **tofu**.

soya flour Flour milled from **soya beans**. It contains **amylase** and has the nutritional values of soya beans.

USES: as a limited substitute for wheat-flour; it is not suitable for bread-making.

soya milk The product of the extraction of **soya bean** by water.

NUTRITIONAL VALUE: protein 3%, fat 1%, carbohydrate 1%, vitamin B complex, minerals.

USES: for cooking, but it is not acceptable as a true milk-substitute; it can be given to babies but with added nutrients, for vegetarian yoghurt and cheese, curdled to make **tofu**.

soya oil One of the cheapest vegetable oils, extracted from **soya beans**; the flavour is considered by some to be unattractive.

NUTRITIONAL VALUE: fat saturated 10%, monounsaturated 25%, polyunsaturated 55%.

ENERGY per 100g: 900 kcal, 3766 kJ.

USES: in cooking, for blending with other vegetable oils, as a basis for margarine.

soy sauce A product of slowly-fermented **soya beans** with wheat-flour, taking many months to mature. It was originally used in Chinese and Japanese cooking as a condiment and is now widely available in the UK. Light and more strongly flavoured dark varieties are made.

spaghetti Long thin strands of **pasta** approximately the thickness of a matchstick. It is served with a variety of sauces, particularly **bolognaise sauce**.

spaghetti bolognaise Spaghetti served with **bolognaise sauce**.

spaghetti marrow A variety of *Cucubita pepo*. The fruit is the shape of a rugby football.

NUTRITIONAL VALUE: negligible.

ENERGY per 100g: 30 kcal, 125 kJ.

USES: as a vegetable, cooked whole by boiling, then cut and the flesh loosened with a fork to look like spaghetti, can be stuffed.

sparling Same as smelt and sniff. Name given to several varieties of fish of the family *Osmeridae*. Small fish found only in the upper reaches of the Tay estuary in Scotland and a few other estuaries. It is considered a delicacy, with a smell of cucumber when caught; it is mainly exported.

sparrow-grass The old name for **asparagus**.

spatchcock A small chicken or other bird which is split open, cleaned, flattened and grilled.

spatula A flattened, blunt blade-shaped tool, made of wood, metal or plastic, in varying widths which may be flexible or rigid. It has many uses in the kitchen.

specific gravity Known as Sp.G. The index of measurement of density of a liquid, measured by a **hydrometer**. Pure water is 1.000. Dissolved salts or sugar in it will raise the specific gravity above 1.000, whilst alcohol will lower it to below 1.000. Hydrometers are used in wine-making and to determine the quality of milk. Hydrometers for testing sugar solutions are called saccharometers.

spice Originally referred to any of the highly-aromatic or pungent seeds, bark or roots of a range of tropical shrubs or trees, such as **cinnamon, cloves, mace, nutmeg, pepper, ginger**, widely grown in tropical countries; today it also includes many other dried seeds such as **dill, fennel, lovage**, with similar qualities. Spices are widely used to give character and flavour to food. Highly prized since the time of Elizabeth 1 when they were the main source of trade with the East.

All spices are best purchased in small quantities and freshly ground when required. Those bought ready-ground deteriorate fairly quickly; all should be stored in airtight containers, in the dark and kept cool.

spinach *Spinacia oleracea*, a tender annual,

grown for its leaves; they contain **oxalic acid** but the quantities consumed are unlikely to cause any harm. See **spinach-beet**.

NUTRITIONAL VALUE: protein 5%, carbohydrate 1.5%, vitamin C up to 60mg per 100g, calcium, iron, carotene.

ENERGY per 100g: 30 kcal, 125 kJ.

USES: cooked as a vegetable, in soups and a variety of savoury dishes, forced in darkness for use as a salad.

spinach-beet A biennial variety of *Beta vulgaris* similar to true **spinach**, but easier to grow. It has less oxalic acid than spinach, is moderately hardy and available all the year round. See **Swiss chard**.

NUTRITIONAL VALUE and USES: as for spinach.

spirits The distilled products of fermented fruits, barley and sugars. **Ethanol** is the main constituent in the primary products, but small quantities of higher alcohols are also formed and known as **congeners**. See **fermentation**, **brandy**, **fusel oil**, **gin**, **whisky**, **vodka**.

spit See **roast**.

spitchcock An eel, split open and grilled.

spleen A soft abdominal organ which is important in the production of white blood cells and the destruction of old red cells. Classed as offal but rarely eaten; it would carry a theoretical risk of transmission of **bovine spongioform encephalopathy**.

split pea A dried **pea** separated into halves.

sponge A light cake made of self-raising flour, or flour and baking powder, sugar, egg and sometimes fat such as butter, margarine. They are often layered with jam or other filling and sprinkled with sugar or iced. There are many variations such as angel-cake, battenburg, swiss roll, victoria sponge. Those made without fat, for use with trifles and flans, are often aerated by folding in whipped eggwhite.

All types should be kept in airtight containers; fatless sponges, particularly, become hard if exposed to air. Commercially-made sponges may contain **antioxidants** to prolong shelf-life.

spoon Commonly used as a measure. Ordinary spoons are not made to a standard size, and standard measuring spoons are more accurate. 5ml is equal to a teaspoon (tsp) and 15ml a tablespoon (tbsp).

spore A small reproductive body produced, often in large numbers, by many plants, **fungi**, **bacteria** and protozoa, leading to a rapid increase in the population of the species.

Spores produced by bacteria are of particular importance in the **sterilisation** of food for **canning** and **bottling** because they are resistant to heat at temperatures which would destroy the parent forms, and also to chemicals. They can survive for long periods in the dry state when they are harmless, but can give rise to **food poisoning** when they become moist and conditions are favourable for their multiplication. See **bacillus cereus**, **botulism**.

sprat *Clupea sprattus*. A small oily fish up to 15 cm (6″) long found around European coasts. It is related to the sardine and herring, identified by a row of spiney scales running along its belly.

NUTRITIONAL VALUE (fried): protein 20%, fat 33%, calcium, iron.

ENERGY per 100gm 400 kcal, 1764 kJ.

USES: usually cleaned by splitting open or cleaning through the gills and then grilled or fried whole. Sometimes smoked, salted and served as first course.

spray dry The process of drying liquids by spraying them into a flow of hot air. Used particularly for milk; the process is speeded up if the liquid is concentrated, by evaporation at low pressure, before being sprayed into the hot air chamber. Ease of reconstitution in water of the resultant powder can be improved by wetting it in moist air, allowing it to form small clumps, then redrying in a granular form.

spring chicken A chicken between 2 and 10 months old.

sprout, brussels See **brussels sprout**.

sprouted seeds Seeds which are germinated, and eaten in the cotyledon stage. The most widely used are **mung beans** (bean sprouts), **mustard** and **cress** and **alfalfa**. It is most important not to use seeds which have been chemically protected against **pests**. Most can be grown on any absorbent bed, such as blotting paper, kitchen towel, which must be kept moist.

NUTRITIONAL VALUE: vitamin B complex, vitamin C, carotene, minerals.

ENERGY per 100g: negligible.

USES: eaten raw in salads, often stir-fried as a vegetable, particularly in Chinese cooking.

spruce beer At one time a traditional beer of Scandinavia made by flavouring a strong beer with the top shoots of hemlock spruce *(Picea abies)*. A particular black beer was made this way in Danzig and became famous.

spruce hemlock A member of one of the *Picea* family such as *Picea abies* or *mariana;* used as a source of **resin** for flavouring **spruce beer**. See **hemlock**.

spud Slang term for **potato**.

squash The American name for members of the marrow family, *Cucurbitacae*. Some of the varieties are disc-shaped and rather sweeter than the common vegetable marrow. All have a high water-content and low food-value, but serve as useful additions to the range of vegetables. They store well through the autumn.

USES: as **marrow**.

squid Also known as calamaris. *Loligo vulgaris*, the smaller *Loligo media* and occasionally the giant squid *Arthitcutis* are the varieties found in European waters; they all have ten tentacles. They are encephalopods related to the octopus which has eight tentacles. The species is widely distributed in the seas of the northern and southern hemispheres.

NUTRITIONAL VALUE: protein 15–20%, fat 1–2%, vitamin B complex, calcium, iodine.

ENERGY per 100g: 69–98 kcal, 289–410 kJ.

USES: dipped in batter and fried, casseroled, in a variety of dishes of Mediterranean origin.

stabiliser See **emulsifiers**.

stag A male deer.

stainless steel A range of steel alloys variously compounded with nickel, cobalt, chromium, or vanadium, which confer resistance to corrosion and are selected for their qualities for cutting, toughness or capacity to be formed into shapes by casting, machining, pressing or spinning. Used for cutting-tools, **saucepans**, spoons, forks, bowls, sinks, and other kitchen equipment. Some stainless steels corrode if left in contact with **salt** and/or with another metal, or a stainless steel of different composition, due to electrolytic action.

star anise A **spice**, the seeds of a tropical plant, *Illicnion anisatum* which have a characteristic shape and aniseed-like flavour; widely used in Chinese cooking.

starch A **polysaccharide** (carbohydrate) made by **photosynthesis** in plants and a main source of **energy** in the **diet**. Starches are present in **cereals, pulses,** root **vegetables**, and the pith of certain **palms**. In its natural state, starch is held within plant cells and needs to be released by cooking. It swells in boiling water and is converted to a **gel**; in this state it can be acted upon by enzymes such as **amylase** for conversion to **sugars**. Food starches vary in composition, producing gels which differ in some of their features, some remaining opaque as with the potato, and others semi-opaque as with **cornflour** or transparent as with **arrowroot** and **sago**; the latter, like **tapioca**, is also mucilagenous.

Ice-crystals form when starch gels are frozen and this can alter the character of the gel when thawed out; cornflour breaks down but arrowroot remains stable. If starch is cooked with an acid fruit, some will be converted to sugar, it will also reduce the apparent acidity of fruit, by its gelatinous nature, delaying the onset of **taste**. See **farina**.

star-fruit *Averrhoea carombola*. A striking, tropical seeded-fruit with a yellow edible, soft skin. It is aromatic and juicy with a delicate acidic flavour. It is up to 10cm, long with fluted sides, so that when sliced, it has a star shape.

USES: as a dessert fruit, sliced in fruit salads, as a garnish.

steak Boneless meat, usually beef; either individual portions of prime cuts, such as **fillet**, **sirloin**, rump, selected for flavour and tenderness to be grilled or fried, or tougher cuts needing longer cooking, cut small for **stews**, **casseroles**. Steak is usually stored for a period of up to 14 days to allow **enzymes** naturally present to tenderise the meat by the process of **autolysis**. Steak from older animals is tougher than from younger ones.

The term is also used for portions of pork, sometimes lamb, and large fish such as cod, salmon, shark.

steak tartare See **beef tartare**.

steam To cook by the heat of steam. The food is usually put in a container with a perforated base, which is placed over a saucepan of boiling water; the steam, which, because of its latent heat, is intensely hot, percolates through the holes and heats the contents of the top container. Steam does not agitate food like boiling water and so food particles tend to stay intact; there is also less loss of minerals than by boiling. See **accidents** (burns), **hangi**, **pressure cooker**, **pudding**.

steel A family name for a large group of iron-based materials with special qualities, such as strength, sharpness, and resistance to staining. Sometimes coated with vitreous **enamel**, zinc, **tin** or plastic to resist corrosion. Also refers to an instrument for sharpening knives. See **stainless steel**.

steep To soak for several hours to absorb flavours from a solution, as in marinating, to release flavours present in food substances, or to reduce salt-content. See **marinate**, **marinade**.

sterilisation The process by which all living **micro-organisms** and their **spores** are destroyed by heat, chemicals, **ultraviolet light**, ionising radiation, or removed by **filtration**. Solids may be sterilised by exposing them to moist heat at a temperature of 134°C (273°F) for 3 mins or 121°C (250°F) for 15 mins. If the heat, or the substance, is dry, a temperature of 160°C (320°F) for 1 hour, or 180°C (356°F) for 10 mins, is required.

Chemical sterilising-agents are unsuitable for food but are used for equipment involved in food production. Water supplies are usually sterilised by **chlorine**, or substances which release chlorine. Water may also be sterilised by intense ultraviolet light, under carefully-controlled conditions. Free-flowing liquids may be sterilised by passing them through filters fine enough to hold back micro-organisms.

Acid fruits can be sterilised at a lower temperature than foods that are near neutral. Meat, fish and vegetables for **canning** require high temperatures obtainable only under carefully-controlled conditions, in pressurised containers, which cannot be achieved safely in the home.

Viruses such as those responsible for **bovine spongioform encephalopathy** (BSE), are highly heat-resistant and a cause for concern, as they may not be destroyed by the methods described above.

Most micro-organisms survive freezing which should not be regarded as a method of sterilisation. See **disinfectant, irradiation, pasteurisation, preservatives, scalding**.

steroids A group of naturally occurring chemical substances which includes vitamin D, the sex **hormones** and the synthetic anabolic steroids. They have been used to increase the growth rate of animals and for the chemical castration of poultry to produce capons, but concern that they can enter the food chain has led to their being banned for all food animals and poultry. See **anabolism**.

stew A method of cooking, in liquid, at or just below boiling point (simmering). Used for **meat, poultry, vegetables, fish**, and mixtures of these in water and/or **stock, wine, beer, cider**. Sometimes the meat is first sealed in hot **fat**, and vegetables **sweated** in fat at a lower heat, to extract oil-soluble flavours. Stews containing **red, black** or **brown beans** must be held at boiling-point for at least 10 mins to destroy **lectins**. Also for cooking fruit such as apples, plums, soft fruits in water, wine or the juice of other fruits.

Stilton A prestigious English semi-hard **cheese**. It was originally made in Leicestershire and its manufacture is protected by law. It must be blue or white, cylindrical in shape, and made from full-cream milk from English dairy herds in the region of Melton Mowbray and surrounding areas. Its name derives from the village in Cambridgeshire where the cheese was first

marketed and became well-known. The blue variety is inoculated with the mould, *Penicillium roquefortii* and then allowed to mature for 6 months, forming its own coarse crust. It has a moist, crumbly texture, and does not keep well once it is fully mature. It can be frozen. See **penicillin**.

NUTRITIONAL VALUE: protein 23%, fat 35%, vitamin A, vitamin B complex, calcium, iron.

ENERGY per 100g: 407 kcal, 1703 kJ.

USES: as a table cheese, in soups and some savoury dishes.

stock The liquid produced by prolonged simmering of meat, bones, fish, poultry and/or vegetables. It can be made from foods which may not be suitable to eat because of size, fragmentation or toughness. **Gelatine** is extracted from **bones** and **connective tissues** during long boiling, and poultry and meat stocks will form a jelly when they are cold. The fat in these stocks tends to float to the surface and solidify when cold and can then be removed easily.

Stock is an ideal breeding-ground for **food poisoning bacteria**, and is readily contaminated; if not used at once, it should be cooled quickly, within one and a half hours, and refrigerated. Kept at less than 5°C (41°F) it is safe for 2–3 days, otherwise it should be frozen to −18°C (−0.5%F).

stock cubes Tablets of concentrated flavouring, usually bonded together with fat and used for **soups, stews and casseroles**. The commonest are meat, chicken, fish and vegetable based. The meaty flavour was originally derived from meat, but the high cost of production has lead to the extensive use of **yeast** extracts, and **monosodium glutamate**. The main value of stock cubes is to strengthen existing flavours, rather than to provide the main source of flavour, and many have a high salt (**sodium**) content. Other forms of flavouring used for the same purposes include stock granules, liquid concentrates, **Bovril**, **Marmite**, OXO.

stockfish Dried unsalted cod, hake or other fish.

stomach The expanded muscular organ which, in mammals, receives food and starts the digestion of **proteins**, by secreting **hydrochloric acid** and **pepsin**. The stomach of animals is known as **tripe** and has little flavour; it is classed as **offal**. See **rennin, rennet, rumen**.

stone The hard-cased seed known as the **kernel** found in members of the *Prunus* family which includes almonds, apricots, cherries, damsons and plums, avocado pear. The centre of the kernel is sometimes eaten, or used for flavouring.

stout A strong black **beer** made with dark **malt** from a high-roasted **barley**. Made famous by Guinness and much copied.

strainer A vessel with a woven-wire, nylon-gauze or perforated metal or wooden base, used to separate lumps and large particles from liquids such as tea, coffee, sauces. Generally smaller than **sieves** but with a similar function. The mesh or size of perforations is selected for the specific purpose. Extra-fine versions are classed as **filters**. Conical strainers are used for sauces. See **moulin-légumes**.

strawberry A unique soft fruit from a small hardy perennial plant of the *Fragaria* family; the fruit is not strictly a **berry** but a fleshy fruit with external seeds. Modern strawberries have been bred from the American wild strawberry, *Fragaria Virginiana*. It is the first fruit to ripen in the summer in the UK and has a delicate aromatic flavour; it is propagated easily from the many runners which root readily. The seeds present on the surface do not produce plants compar-

able to their parent. The fruit is best eaten within 24 hours of picking and should be bright red and firm.

It loses colour in **canning** and artificial red colouring such as E127 or 124 is usually added. Frozen strawberries retain their colour and most of their flavour when they are thawed, but become soft and lose their shape and texture.

NUTRITIONAL VALUE: protein 0.6%, carbohydrate 6.2%, vitamin C up to 60mg per 100g, calcium.

ENERGY per 100g: 25 kcal, 105 kJ.

USES: as a dessert fruit on its own and in a variety of other desserts, for **jam**, usually with added **pectin** in the form of a concentrate or lemon.

strudel A form of pastry cake or dessert made of strong flour, egg and water dough rolled or stretched out very thinly and spread with melted butter and fruit or jam, then rolled up and baked immediately. Savoury strudels can be made with cheese or other filling.

stuffing Also known as forcemeat and filling. Various mixes of cereals, breadcrumbs, **onion, mushrooms, sausagemeat**, minced meat, fats, herbs, spices and egg are used to place inside a roll of meat or cavity of a bird before cooking, or cooked in the form of balls and served separately. Used to enhance the flavour and extend the quantity of food. Vine-leaves can be wrapped round a stuffing and envelopes or tubes of pasta stuffed, as with **ravioli** and **cannelloni**. Stuffing poultry for roasting can prevent the internal carcass temperature reaching the level required to destroy **salmonella** and this requires particular attention.

sturgeon *Acipenser ruthenus*. A large fish found in temperate estuaries and rivers of Eastern Europe. A variety, *Acipenser sturio* sometimes caught in British estuaries and rivers, has been made, by an act of parliament, a Royal fish and becomes the property of the crown. It is best known for the eggs of the female known as **caviar**.

sucking-pig A piglet about 4 weeks old, cleaned and roasted whole; served traditionally on festive occasions.

sucrose See **sugar**.

sudan grass See **sorghum**.

suet Fatty tissue taken from around the **kidneys** and **omentum** of animals, usually cattle. It is soft at blood heat, but quite hard at room temperatures. It is generally processed to remove solid matter (connective tissue) and shredded and coated with flour to prevent sticking. Suet is composed of saturated and monounsaturated fats with very little polyunsaturated fat. Vegetable suet is now available, made with hardened fat but not necessarily containing less saturated fat than suet of animal origin.

USES: for suet **puddings**, Christmas pudding, **dumplings**, suet **pastry**.

sugar The term sugar is usually used to indicate the disaccharide sucrose, which is made up of one molecule each of the simple sugars (monosaccharides) **glucose** and **fructose**, but also includes fructose, glucose and **lactose**. All sugars are widely distributed in nature and are converted from **starches** by the action **enzymes**, naturally occurring in the ripening of fruits and vegetables. They are present in high concentration in **maple syrup**, **sugar-cane**, **sugar-beet**, the **nectar** of flowers and **honeydew**.

For starches to be absorbed and used by the body, they are converted, after cooking, during the process of digestion, into sugar, by the enzyme **amylase**. The sugar, **lactose**, is responsible for the sweetness of milk. Glucose, fructose and sucrose, but not lactose, can be fermented by **yeast**. The sweetness of sugars varies, from fructose which is the sweetest, through sucrose

and glucose to lactose, the least sweet. There is no chemical difference between sugar extracted from the sugar-cane or that from sugar-beet.

Sugar in high concentration acts as a preservative by an osmotic pressure effect, preventing the entry of water, which is essential for growth of all living matter, into **bacteria**. This process is responsible for the keeping properties of honey, jams and other sweetened preserves. Sugar is used not only for its sweetness when added to food but also to give it a special character by its bulk and viscosity.

All sugars can lead to dental **caries** (cariogenic) by providing a medium for the growth of acid-forming **bacteria** in the mouth. There is no evidence that a high-intake of sugar in the diet is specifically associated with a higher incidence of **diabetes**.

Sugar is a pure **energy** food with no associated fibre; the attractive taste it gives to some food encourages an unbalanced **diet** and an excessive intake of calories. As well as the pure product, sugar is contained in many processed foods such as sauces, soups, baked beans, desserts, chocolate, snacks and drinks. See **artificial sweeteners**.

Domestic sugar is sold in a variety of forms:

White refined sugars

Caster. A finely crystalline form, used for sprinkling on fruit, cakes, in some desserts and cake-making.

Cube or lump. Sugar formed into small cubes for sweetening tea, coffee, and other hot drinks; also for rubbing on the zest of citrus fruits to extract oils for flavouring.

Granulated. The common crystalline form, coarser than caster; the cheapest and most widely used.

Icing. Sugar finely ground to a powder and used for icings, fondants, dusting cakes and sweetmeats and in desserts which are not cooked, because it dissolves easily.

Pectinated. Granulated or preserving sugar with added **pectin**. A relatively new introduction, particularly for jam-making when the fruit has a low pectin content such as strawberry.

Preserving. Formed of coarser and less-even crystals than granulated sugar; used for jam-making, jelly-making and other preserves, because it does not form a mass at the bottom of the pan and requires less stirring to avoid burning.

Brown sugars

Barbados. A dark-brown, moist, fine-grained sugar, originally from Barbados, with a strong distinctive flavour. Used in cooking where the flavour is complementary to the main ingredients such as some cakes, puddings, chutneys, sauces.

Demerara. A crystalline raw sugar, named after the region of Guyana where it originally came from. Sometimes it is refined white sugar, that has been dyed brown or mixed with molasses. Used to sprinkle on porridge, cereals, in coffee, cakes, some meat dishes.

Golden granulated. A natural unrefined cane-sugar, lighter in colour than demerara. It is used as white granulated sugar.

Muscovado. A moist, dark-brown, fine-grained, raw cane-sugar, rich in natural molasses. It is used mainly in cooking.

Soft brown. Moist, fine-grained sugars ranging in colour from light to dark brown and having a distinctive flavour. Most of those sold today are made from refined white sugar with added molasses or even dyed.

Coffee crystals. Large slow-dissolving crystals used for sweetening coffee. They may be white, brown or multi-coloured.

NUTRITIONAL VALUE: carbohydrate 100%.

ENERGY per 100g: 375 kcal, 1569 kJ.

sugar-beet A variety of *Beta vulgaris*, a large root-vegetable grown for its high sugar content of up to 20%. Extensively cultivated in Europe and temperate climates as a source of **sugar**.

sugar-candy A course sugar made by suspending pieces of string in a strong solution of sugar which recrystallises on the string as the water evaporates.

sugar-cane *Saccharum officinarum*, a tall tropical grass; native of the East Indies, with a sweet **sap** which is an important source of **sugar**. It is chemically identical to sugar prepared from **sugar-beet**. See **carbohydrate**.

sugar-snap pea or **sugar-pea** See **pea**.

sugar syrup Sugar dissolved in water and reduced by boiling. The concentration may be varied according to use but a stock syrup of 1kg sugar in ½ l of water will keep well at room temperature or in a refrigerator.

USES: making confectionery, stewing fruit, ice-creams, sorbets, icings, sauces.

sulphited The term used to denote that a product has been exposed to **sulphur dioxide** in some form, to preserve natural colours in dried fruits such as apricots, peaches. The process also destroys micro-organisms and insect pests.

sulphur An element present in many **proteins** and part of the structure of living cells and some **enzyme** systems. It is widely distributed in plants and deficiency does not occur. It accounts for the dark discolouration of **silver** exposed to egg and atmosphere polluted by the burning of hydrocarbons such as coal, oil.

sulphur dioxide (E220, also sulphite compounds **E221−E227)** A compound which releases sulphur dioxide **gas**; it is the most widely used general-purpose food-**preservative**, **antioxidant** and **bleaching** agent. The gas is irritant and dissolves readily in water to produce sulphurous acid, a major pollutant from industry and motor exhausts and the principal cause of acid rain. Sulphur dioxide can destroy **vitamin B1** and, in excess, cause gastric irritation and asthmatic attacks. Boiling removes most, if not all, sulphur dioxide from food substances, but not the sodium content, if used in the form of sodium-containing salts such as sodium sulphite. See **sulphited**.

USES: in the preparation of **dried fruit** such as peaches, apricots and apples, to conserve their colour; to retard **moulds** in **wine** and preserve a wide range of foods such as **sausages**, fruit drinks, desserts, dried soups. It is the active principle in **Campden tablets**.

sulphuric acid (513) A highly-corrosive acid which is too strong to have any place in small-scale cooking or in the home. However, highly-purified and well-diluted, it is safe to consume and is used commercially in the preparation of drinks, as long as suitable safety precautions can be taken.

summer pudding An English speciality made with various mixtures of stewed summer fruit such as redcurrants, blackcurrants, raspberries, encased in slices of white bread, allowed to set under slight pressure for several hours and then turned out and served cold.

sunflower-oil Oil extracted from sunflower seeds. An all-purpose oil with a good flavour.

NUTRITIONAL VALUE: fat, saturated 5%, monounsaturated 25%, polyunsaturated 65%.

ENERGY per 100g: 900 kcal, 3766 kJ.

USES: for all cooking purposes, in mayonnaise, salad dressings, manufacture of soft margarines; also in the manufacture of paints.

sunset yellow (E110) Permitted yellow food-colouring; a synthetic azo dye. Used in commercially-produced soups, sweets, ices, jellies, drinks and jams. Occasionally causes allergic reactions in some people.

surfacients A wide range of substances with an affinity for water, or water and oils. They may be derived from **fatty acids**, or higher **alcohols**, and various forms are used as **emulsifiers**, **stabilisers** and wetting agents. Examples are food **additives E472–492**. Used in a wide range of processed foods from cake mixes, **desserts** to **cheeses**, and as soaps and detergents for cleaning.

surmullet *Mullus surmuletus*. A red **mullet** first appreciated by the Romans.

sushi A Japanese dish of fish, rice, vegetables and a vinegar sauce.

swan The largest member of the family which includes ducks and geese; a protected species, not generally available for consumption.

swan-mussel A large freshwater **mussel**.

sweating The process of low-temperature partial cooking of vegetables in butter, margarine or oil, to extract flavours which are oil-soluble but not water-soluble. Used for root-vegetables, onions, leeks, mushrooms, also some spices and herbs.

swede *Brassica napa brassica*. A member of the cabbage family grown for its large, edible root. Closely related to **turnip** and in Scotland referred to as such.

NUTRITIONAL VALUE: protein 0.75%, carbohydrate 3–4%, vitamin B complex, vitamin C up to 40mg per 100g, calcium, iron, dietary fibre.

ENERGY per 100g: boiled: 14 kcal, 59 kJ.

USES: diced and cooked as a vegetable, sometimes mashed, in stews, casseroles.

sweetbreads The thymus glands and pancreas of young animals, usually calves or lambs; classed as **offal** and regarded as a delicacy. There is a theoretical risk of them becoming contaminated with BSE virus during removal from the animal after slaughter. They must be very fresh and soaked in water to remove blood for use.

USES: braised or fried in a variety of dishes, particularly of French origin.

sweet cicely *Myrrhis odorata*, also known as myrrh, or sweet Spanish chervil. A hardy perennial **herb** with fern-like leaves and carrot-like root. Formerly used for the flavour of its leaves, seeds and roots, somewhat like celery. The leaves were used as a salad crop, the roots cooked and served with vinegar in salads. Not often used today.

sweetcorn A variety of **maize** grown for its relatively high sugar content, to be eaten as a vegetable. It is usually harvested when the cobs are 15–20cms long and before the seeds are ripe. Some are harvested when they are only 5–10cms long and are known as 'baby sweetcorn'. Sweetcorn is available fresh, frozen or canned.

NUTRITIONAL VALUE: average: protein 2.9%, fat 1%, carbohydrate 16%.

ENERGY per 100g: average: 85 kcal, 356 kJ.

USES: best boiled immediately after picking. The cob is often served whole with butter as a first course, the seeds stripped from it as a vegetable or salad, sometimes mixed with sweet peppers, peas. Baby sweetcorn may be eaten whole (including the cob) raw in salads or cooked.

sweet-flag *Acorus calamus*, also known as calamus. A hardy water-loving perennial with greenish-yellow flowers and expanded aromatic roots. An oil extracted from the root is used occasionally in liqueurs and in perfumery.

sweet laurel *Laurus nobilis*, see **bay**. It must not be confused with other laurels which belong to a different family, and are poisonous.

sweet marjoram See **marjoram**.

sweet pepper See **pepper, sweet**.

sweet potato The expanded root of a climbing plant *Ipomoea batatum*, related to bindweed; also known as kumara in New Zealand. Widely grown in tropical climates.

NUTRITIONAL VALUE: protein 1%, fat 0.3%, carbohydrate 20%, vitamin B complex, vitamin C up to 20mg per 100g, carotene.

ENERGY per 100g: boiled: 75 kcal, 314 kJ.

USES: cooked as for the common potato.

Swiss chard A variety of *Beta vulgaris cicla*. Similar to **spinach–beet** but with thick white stalks. Varieties with red leaves and stalks are available.

NUTRITIONAL VALUE: protein 5%, carbohydrate 1.5%, vitamin C up to 60g, carotene, calcium, iron.

ENERGY per 100g: 30 kcal, 125 kJ.

USES: the leaves can be cooked as spinach and the stalks chopped as a separate vegetable with a sauce such as bechamel, cheese, to enhance the flavour; also raw in salads.

swiss roll A fatless sponge baked in a shallow rectangular tin, spread with jam, sometimes cream, and rolled up.

swordfish Several large members of the **mackerel** family with firm flesh. *Istiophorus americanus* (sailfish), *Makaira mitsukurii* (marlin), *Xiphias gladius* (swordfish), all characterised by an extended upper jaw. They are commonest in warm waters, but occasional visitors to European waters.

NUTRITIONAL VALUE: protein 18–20%, fat 15–20%, unsaturated.

ENERGY per 100gm: average: 282 kcal, 1180 kJ.

USES: lends itself to most methods of cooking but is best as steaks, baked or grilled.

T

tabasco sauce A pungent **vinegar** sauce, spiced with hot **red peppers** and matured for 3 years; from a 100-year-old recipe.

USES: a few drops are added for flavouring seafood, chicken, meats, sauces.

tabbouleh A Middle Eastern dish of **bulgar wheat** with additions such as onion, sweet peppers, cucumber, nuts, rice, parsley, and dressed with olive oil and lemon juice; served cold as a salad. It is often available from supermarkets ready to eat.

tablet A compressed slab of any substance, of uniform size, often with an inert bulking agent, providing a precise quantity; often in concentrated form as a sweetener, stock cube, vitamin tablet, chocolate. Also a Scottish sweetmeat, similar to **fudge**. Medical tablets should always be taken as directed.

table d'hôte A term for a meal of two or more courses at a fixed price, with no, or only a limited, choice. See **à la carte**.

tabloid A term coined by the Wellcome Foundation for the first products made in **tablet** form.

tafia A spirit distilled from fermented sugar-cane syrup, similar to **rum**.

ALCOHOL CONTENT: 35–40%.

tahina A smooth paste made with **sesame** seeds. Used mainly in Middle Eastern recipes, especially **humus**.

tai The Japanese sea-**bream**.

talin Tradename for thaumatin. See **artificial sweeteners**.

tallow The rendered fat of cattle or sheep; it is solid at room temperature and high in saturated fats. During purification an oily component, known as oleo, separates out and has been used for the manufacture of margarine, but has now been largely replaced by **vegetable oils**. The residue after purification is used for making candles and soap.

tamale A Mexican dish of crushed **maize** with **meat** and highly seasoned.

tamarind Also known as Indian date. Fruit of the tropical tree, *Tamarindus indica*, which produces rounded pods bearing seeds surrounded by a sticky, acidic, pulp.

NUTRITIONAL VALUE: protein 2%, carbohydrate 70%, vitamin B complex, vitamin C up to 10mg per 100g.

ENERGY per 100g: 460 kcal, 1925 kJ.

USES: the pulp, freed of seeds, may be eaten raw with sugar, used as a souring agent in drinks and sauces and in Indian cooking; it may be dried. Also used medicinally for its laxative properties.

tamis A woollen cloth used to strain liquids such as soups.

tangerine One of several varieties of **orange** developed from *Citrus nobilis*. A sweet and distinctively-flavoured, loose-skinned, fruit with many pips, similar to the seed-less hybrids **mandarin** and **satsuma**.

NUTRITIONAL VALUE: carbohydrate up to 10%, vitamin C up to 60mg per 100g.

tannin An astringent substance present in a wide range of plants and fruits in the form of **tannic acid**; capable of hardening proteins. In tea-leaves and the skin of red grapes it accounts for an important part of the character of **tea** and red **wine**, giving a slightly rough feeling in the mouth. White wine, prepared by fermenting only the juice of white or red grapes is low in tannins. Milk added to tea neutralises some of the tannin and modifies the flavour. Tannins are not harmful in the quantities usually consumed. They are used in the hardening of leather in the process called tanning.

tansy *Tanacetum vulgare.* A hardy perennial **herb** common in the wild or cultivated. It has yellow button flowers and characteristic leaves, which look somewhat like **parsley**. Formerly used in omelettes, stews, puddings and salads for its camphor-like flavour. Now used mainly as a garnish.

tapeworm One of several long flat worms which are parasites in the intestines of animals and humans. Eggs may be ingested by contamination of food from faeces or by handling infected dogs. One variety of tapeworm, *Echinococcus,* produces **hydatid** cysts; these are rare and more likely to occur where there is close contact with dogs in sheep-rearing areas.

tapioca Also known as Brazilian arrowroot, manioc and **cassava**. An almost pure form of **starch**, prepared as granules or flakes, from the expanded root of a tropical perennial plant, *Manihot utillisima.* The root is naturally bitter, due to soluble toxins which must be removed in processing. The starch, heated with water, produces an almost clear sticky **gel** very similar to **sago**, although this comes from the **pith** of a **palm**. Products sold as sago may be tapioca and vice versa.

NUTRITIONAL VALUE: carbohydrate 90%.

ENERGY per 100g: uncooked: 360 kcal, 1506 kJ.

USES: in desserts, with stewed fruit, as a milk-pudding.

taramasalata A Greek savoury dish made with **roe** and **olive oil**, flavoured with garlic, parsley, chopped onions or shallots and seasoning.

tare Historic name for **pulses** and vetches.

taro Also known as eddo and dasheen. The expanded roots of the tropical perennial **herb**, *Colocasia esculenta*, or the similar *Colocasia antiquora.* An important source of food in Asia and Africa and used by the Romans.

NUTRITIONAL VALUE: protein 2%, carbohydrate 25%, vitamin B complex, vitamin C up to 5mg per 100g.

ENERGY per 100g: raw: 102 kcal, 427 kJ.

USES: cooked as a vegetable.

tarragon A perennial aromatic **herb**, *Artemisia dracunculus.* The more tender French variety, which can be grown in the southern half of Europe has a better flavour than the hardier Russian variety.

USES: to flavour chicken and fish dishes, sauces, vinegar, dressings for salads.

tartar Also known as argol. The white deposit which forms on the inside of barrels of maturing **wine** and is collected for the preparation of **tartaric acid**. The term is also used for the concretion which develops on teeth and leads to gum disease and **caries**.

tartare sauce Mayonnaise flavoured with **garlic, herbs, gherkins, capers**. Served with fish, **scampi** and similar dishes.

tartaric acid (E334) Naturally-occurring acid found in **grapes** and a by-product of wine-making. See **acids, tartar, cream of tartar**.

USES: as an antioxidant and acidifying agent in jams, jellies, drinks, confectionery, cheeses.

tartrazine (E102) Permitted yellow food-colouring, a synthetic azo dye. Hyperactivity in some children has been associated with this and other azo dyes, so its use is restricted. See **colour**.

taste The special sensation which a substance causes on contact with the tongue. There are only four basic tastes which can be distinguished by the **taste-buds** in the tongue, namely, sweet, sour, bitter and salt. See **flavour**.

taste-buds The many thousands of sensory nerve-endings present in the tongue and sensitive to the four basic **tastes**.

tayberry A seeded-fruit, a cross between a **raspberry** and **blackberry**. When ripe it is almost black in colour and sweet.

tea The dried leaves of several different plants infused in boiling water to make the aromatic, slightly astringent, drink known as tea. It has mildly stimulating properties, and contains **caffeine** and **tannin**. It was introduced into the western world in the early 17th century by Dutch traders who brought it from China where it had been drunk for many centuries.

The majority of teas derive from varieties of *Camellia sinensis* which are grown as bushes in plantations in China, India, Sri Lanka, Africa, Russia. They require a tropical or subtropical climate with adequate rainfall.

The main differences in **flavour** of teas arise from plant varieties, soil and climate where they are grown, leaf-size and method of processing. Green teas, popular in China and Japan are made from fresh dried leaves, while for black teas, the leaves are bruised and allowed to ferment in air before being dried. Most teas on the market are blended and some have added **essential oils** such as bergamot in Earl Grey tea, or flowers such as jasmine in jasmine tea, to give their characteristic flavour and aroma.

Tea will keep for up to two years if dry and in an airtight container.

The following general descriptions are used for tea, depending on the part of the plant from which the leaves are taken:—
Flowering Pekoe – Top leaf buds.

Orange Pekoe – First open leaf.
Pekoe – Third leaf.
Souchong – Lower leaves.
NUTRITIONAL VALUE: caffeine 1.5–2.5%, the dried leaves give approximately 45–60mg caffeine per average cup of tea. Compare **coffee**. See **tisane**.

teacake Sweetened yeasted **dough** baked as a large bun to be eaten cut open, toasted and spread with butter.

tea-seed oil Oil extracted from the seeds of *Camellia sasangue*, closely related to *Camellia sinensis*. Similar to **olive-oil** and used for cooking in some countries.

tea-substitutes See **tisane**.

technazene A chemical substance applied as a powder to potatoes to delay sprouting during storage. Treated potatoes washed and gently scrubbed are safe to eat in their skins.

teel oil See **sesame**.

tender A characteristic of food indicating that it is soft, easily cut or chewed and associated with the pleasure of eating. Tenderness of **vegetables** lessens with age, but **fruits** tend to be tough when young and become tender as they ripen. Tenderness depends on the nature and proportion of connective tissues present, which in vegetables is **cellulose** and **lignin**. The former is generally, but not always, softened by cooking, but lignin is not affected.

The degree of tenderness in meats is due to the character of the muscle fibres and the amount of **collagen** and **elastin** present. Prolonged boiling softens the collagen causing it to take up water and change to **gelatin**. Meat tends to soften when steeped in a mild acid such as **wine** or **vinegar**, the process being known as **marinading**.

Tenderness in meat may be induced by pounding or multiple piercing with a long thin knife to break up the fibres; also by steeping the meat in a solution of **papain** or other **proteolytic enzyme** such as **bromelin,** or by injecting the solution into the carcass before or after slaughter. See **autolysis, game, hanging, pressure cooking.**

tenderise To make **tender.**

tenderloin The **fillet** of **beef, veal** or **pork** which is considered the tenderest cut; taken from near the lumbar vertebrae.

tequila A Mexican spirit distilled from the fermented sap of the *Agave sisaliana*, a half-hardy member of the lily family. See also **pulque.**

ALCOHOL CONTENT: 35–40%.

terrine An oven-proof vessel of glazed earthenware, china or metal used for cooking a pâté-like dish, also known as a terrine, of meat, fish, vegetables, fruit.

theobromine A mild stimulant present in **chocolate** and **cocoa,** with some similarity to **caffeine** but weaker in action.

thermoduric Descriptive of the group of **micro-organisms** which resist temperatures normally lethal to others. Those, present in milk, resistant to pasteurisation are generally harmless but are indicators of poor **hygiene.**

thermometer A heat-measuring instrument depending on one of the following physical properties.
1. The expansion of mercury, or a high boiling-point alcohol, made visible by a red or black dye, in a glass tube.
2. The unequal expansion of two dissimilar metals bonded together in the form of a strip, ribbon or coil which alters in shape with a change in temperature and connected to a finger moving on a dial.
3. The change in electrical conductivity of special alloys that occurs with changes in temperature, and measured by a meter,

calibrated in degrees of heat, known as an electrical-resistance thermometer.
4. Production of an electrical current which arises on heating one side of a junction of two different metals, known as a thermocouple, the current being measured by a meter calibrated in degrees.
5. Changes in the colour of light emitted by a heated object are measured by a spectrometer; used for very high temperatures for scientific and industrial purposes.
6. The change in cholesterol crystals prepared on a strip to reveal figures as the temperature changes.

Types:

Cooking. A thermometer, based on 1 or 2 above, made with a scale registering temperatures between 75°C and 250°C (167°F–482°F.)

Refrigerator and **freezer.** Usually based on 1 above, using alcohol in the tube, or 2 above with a scale registering temperatures required for safe storage of food from 5°C to −22°C (41°F to −7°F). For remote reading, thermometers based on 3 or 4 above are used.

Sugar. Usually a mercury thermometer, covering the range from about 16°C (60°F) to about 180°C (356°F), to show the temperatures reached by different concentrations of sugar in water and used in the manufacture of sugar confectionery and to determine the setting-point in jam-making.

Probe. A thermometer designed to penetrate the substance being cooked, to show the internal or core temperature, which often varies from the surface temperature. Inexpensive types for home use are usually based on 2 above. For commercial purposes those based on 3 or 4 are more favoured. Core temperature is of great importance when cooking poultry, particularly any that has been previously frozen, in order to ensure that **food poisoning micro-organisms** within the carcass have been killed.

Special thermometers of this type are available for use in **microwave ovens**.

thermopeeling A commercial method of peeling hard-skinned fruit by exposing it momentarily to a very high temperature followed by rapid cooling.

thermoplastic Plastic materials such as **polythene**, **polypropylene**, **PVC**, which melt and can be moulded into shapes for bowls, handles. Such plastics distort with heat and should not be used for carrying, or be immersed in, very hot liquids.

thermosetting Descriptive of a plastic which is liquid until it has been heated and then sets and cannot be remelted. Used for plastic spoons, handles, saucepan knobs, electrical equipment. The first of these generally-used plastic materials was **bakelite** which is still used.

thermostat A device for maintaining a predetermined temperature in ovens, heating systems, washing machines and refrigerators. Thermostats, which depend on one of the principles used for thermometers, operate an on/off switch for electrical appliances, or a form of tap to control flow in gas appliances.

thiamine See **vitamin B1**.

thickeners (E400—E440, 551) A range of substances used to increase viscosity, to give body to soups, sauces, to reduce the rate of separation of solids held in suspension, and improve texture. **Flour** or **cornflour** are most commonly used in domestic cooking, but a wide range is available for special purposes including:— **agar**, **agglomerated flour**, **arrowroot**, **carrageenan**, **egg-yolk**, **gelatine**, **pectin**, **potato**, silicon dioxide.

thyme *Thymus vulgaris*. The most common of a group of hardy **herbs** with a strong and characteristic flavour which it retains when dried. *Thymus citriodorus*, lemon-thyme which is less hardy is also used. There are many other varieties.

USES: in **stuffing** and for flavouring meat, fish, poultry dishes and sausages. An essential ingredient in **bouquet garni**.

thyroid gland The gland, located in the front of the lower part of the neck, responsible for the production of the hormone thyroxine which regulates the rate of metabolism and contains **iodine** as an essential constituent. Enlargement of the gland, known as **goitre**, has a number of causes.

tiger nut See **chufa**.

tin A soft white, and now expensive metal, extensively mined in Malaysia and formerly in Cornwall. Very little now comes from the latter.

USES: to coat steel, to prevent rusting, and copper vessels to prevent corrosion. The 'tin-can' is made of mild sheet-steel coated with a thin layer of tin and will resist damage by most contents in the absence of air but once opened, corrosion may start and food should not be stored in an opened tin, even in a refrigerator. Because, nowadays, the layer of tin is very thin additional protection is provided by a coat of light-brown lacquer on the inside. **Pewter** is an alloy of tin with antimony, and **bronze** of tin and copper. Tin is the basis of solder, formerly alloyed with **lead**, used for joining seams on tins and joints in water-pipes; all solder must now be lead-free.

tisane Any form of herbal-tea made from an infusion; it may be made from a wide range of fresh or dried leaves or flowers and used as an alternative to **tea**. Tisanes are claimed to have medicinal properties including those made with flowers of the **lime** tree (Linden), leaves of **camomile** (*Anthemis nobilis*), **rosemary**, gorse, **mint**.

toad-in-the-hole Pieces of **sausage** set in a **batter** and baked.

toast Sliced bread exposed to a high temperature in a toaster, grill or in front of a fire, to make it brown and crisp and to bring out flavour from the conversion of **carbohydrates** and **protein** on the surface into **melanoidin**.

toast An expression of congratulations, for the good health and well-being of a person, persons or, sometimes organisation, being honoured on a formal occasion, such as a wedding or dinner, and endorsed by the raising of glasses and drinking (usually wine) by the assembled company.

toastmaster An official at a dinner or banquet who announces the order of events and introduces the proposer of toasts and those who speak in reply.

tocopherol (E306–309) Also known as **vitamin E**.

USES: as an approved **preservative**, in several forms, for its antioxidant properties in processed foods containing fat.

toddy Fermented sap obtained from the coconut and other palms. The term is also used to indicate an alcoholic drink with sugar and hot water.

toffee A sweetmeat made of **sugar** and **fat** sometimes with the addition of milk, nuts, dried fruits and flavouring agents. The ratio of fat and sugar and the temperature used in the cooking determine the hardness of the product. The softer forms are known as **caramel**. Dark toffees can be made with **molasses**.

NUTRITIONAL VALUE: average: fat 15–20%, carbohydrate 70% and variable amounts of protein when milk or nuts are used.

ENERGY per 100g: 400–420 kcal, 1673–1757 kJ.

tofu A white **curd** made from **soya beans** and acidulated water. It is tasteless but absorbs flavours from other foods with which it is mixed. It is now widely available.

NUTRITIONAL VALUE: average: protein 11.5%, carbohydrate 4.5%.

ENERGY per 100g: average: 94 kcal, 393 kJ.

USES: in curries, vegetarian and Japanese cooking and in sauces and desserts.

tomatillo *Physalis ixocarpoa*, a subtropical annual plant, native of Mexico and Southern USA, which produces a small seeded-fruit which can be used stewed or for preserves. Also known as jamberberry.

tomato *Lycopersicon esculenta*. A native of South America, related to the potato. The plant is a half-hardy annual, producing bright red or yellow juicy fruits with a soft, slightly acid, flesh and edible seeds. Although botanically a berry-fruit, it is widely eaten as a vegetable and is available all the year, fresh or canned. It can be grown out of doors in the south of England, but is commercially-grown under glass in the UK or imported. The pigments are stable and resist cooking and bleaching agents. Also available as a concentrated purée for use in cooking.

NUTRITIONAL VALUE: protein 1%, carbohydrate 3%, vitamin A, vitamin B complex, vitamin C up to 25mg per 100g, calcium, iron.

ENERGY per 100g: 20 kcal, 84 kJ.

USES: eaten raw in salads, snacks, cooked in a wide variety of meat, poultry, fish, pasta and vegetarian dishes, in soups, sauces, chutneys, ketchup.

tongue The muscular organ in the mouth responsible for the appreciation of **taste** and the manipulation of food to aid chewing, biting and subsequent swallowing. See **taste buds**.

The tongues of beef animals (known as ox tongue), sheep and pigs are classed as offal. They are available uncooked, pickled, cooked and pressed, or canned.

NUTRITIONAL VALUE: average: cooked: protein 15%, fat 15%.

ENERGY per 100g: 200 kcal, 837 kJ.

USES: boiled and eaten hot, or served cold with salads, in sandwiches.

tope *Galeorhinus galeus*. A small **shark** and occasional visitor to UK coastal waters. It may weigh up to 30kg.

NUTRITIONAL VALUE: average: protein 18%, fat 2%, vitamin B complex, calcium iron.

ENERGY per 100gm: average: 90 kcal, 377 kJ.

USES: as steaks grilled, baked or fried.

torte A rich cake or sweet **pastry** rather like **shortbread**. Useful as a foundation for a chocolate or fruit dessert.

tortellini Small round cases of **pasta** filled with seasoned **meat** and cooked. Similar to the square form known as **ravioli**.

tortilla A thin, flat bread made with **maize** flour, from Mexico.

tot A small drinking vessel holding 1/8th of an ounce (1 dram or 3 ml). Usually refers to a measure of whisky or other spirits.

tournedos A small prime cut of **fillet steak** grilled and seasoned, served with sauces and often liver pâté, or mushrooms.

toxacara A small parasitic worm living in the intestines of dogs (*Toxacara canis*), cats (*Toxacara cati*), or foxes and some small mammals. The eggs of the mature worms, passed in animal faeces, can be transmitted to humans where they mature and invade the tissues. They have been known to damage the liver and cause blindness. Well-fed pets, which do not need to hunt for food are unlikely to be infected. Children are most vulnerable and should wash their hands after handling pets and before eating. As a precautionary measure, pets should be treated regularly with antiworm preparations.

toxins A wide range of harmful substances or poisons produced by living organisms, particularly **bacteria**, **moulds**, plants or parts of them. Many food substances contain toxins in such small quantities that, eaten in normal quantities, they do not pose a threat. Some, such as those in **red beans**, are discussed in the section on **food poisoning**. Many have specific effects on certain organs such as the liver, heart or the nervous system and may have serious, and sometimes fatal, consequences. Some toxins introduced into the body may stimulate the production of antibodies which neutralise their effect. This phenomenon is used in the treatment of some diseases. There are variations in individual tolerance to toxins and some may escape harmful effects in quantities which have serious consequences in others. See **aflotoxins**, **alkaloids**, **lectin**, **preservation**, **tubers**.

toxoplasma A primitive protozoa, *Toxoplasma gondii*, widespread in wild animals, birds, domestic cats and dogs, responsible for the disease known as toxoplasmosis. The commonest source of the disease in humans is the domestic cat and the parasites are spread by handling, or consuming, uncooked or incompletely cooked food contaminated by cat faeces. Children are most vulnerable. The infection may be symptomless but can cause fatigue and the parasite may migrate to the brain and eyes, in rare cases causing blindness. Cats which are fed on processed or cooked food, and do not hunt for food, are unlikely to carry the parasite. Cats should be kept away from food to be served to humans at all times and the rules of **hygiene** observed.

toxoplasmosis See **toxoplasma**.

trace elements Are **mineral salts** which, in very small quantities, are essential to life. They are important in **enzyme** systems but in large quantities may be poisonous.

The list includes **chromium, copper, iodine, manganese, molybdenum, selenium, zinc**.

tragocanth (E413) A gum obtained by incising the stems of several species of the **pea** family which grow as shrubs. Used as an **emulsifier** and stabiliser, **thickener**.

travel − risks of disease The traveller is vulnerable to a wide range of diseases from **parasites**, **micro-organisms** and virus infections picked up from contaminated water, the sea, food and drink where hygiene practices are not satisfactory. Local populations become resistant to infections to which the traveller may not have developed immunity. Immunisation to a range of infections, such as typhoid, paratyphoid, cholera and hepatitis A, may be advised, depending on the country or countries to be visited.

General guidelines to avoid such infection:−

1. Only drink tap-water when purity is assured, as in most EEC countries, otherwise use water sterilised by boiling or by sterilising tablets, or safe bottled water. Avoid ice unless the water used to make it is known to be safe.
2. Only clean teeth in sterilised water.
3. Only eat hot food which has been recently cooked, whenever possible.
4. Avoid salads which may have been washed in polluted water. Peel all fruit. Ice-cream should be regarded with suspicion unless assurances can be given that it is safe. Avoid soft cheeses, pâtés and all shellfish.
5. Children, pregnant women and the elderly are most vulnerable and the effects more severe.
6. Avoid close contact with pets including dogs and cats. Malaria is not a food-borne disease, but is nevertheless prevalent in some countries and precautions should be taken.

A booklet issued by the Department of Health giving advice for travellers is available free from travel agents, DSS Advice Centres and some supermarkets. See **food poisoning, hygiene**.

trawl A bag-shaped net dragged along the seabed from a boat to catch **fish, molluscs**.

treacle The thick, black, sweet, strongly-flavoured, sugar substance extracted during the early stages of sugar-refining. It is not necessarily different from molasses, although the latter term usually implies a substance more used in animal feed or preparation of silage. A more refined, but similar, product known as golden syrup is less strongly flavoured.

NUTRITIONAL VALUE: carbohydrate 70−80%, calcium, iron.

ENERGY per 100g: 263−300 kcal, 1110−1255 kJ.

USES: for sweetening where a strong flavour is required, as in toffee, puddings. Golden syrup may be used as a substitute for sugar in cooked sweet dishes, cakes.

trehala A disaccharide sugar known as mycose, extracted from the cocoon of a beetle found in Turkey, where it is used as a sweetener. It is also found in some fungi.

trevally See **horse mackerel**.

trichinosis or **trichiniasis** A parasitic disease due to a small worm, *Trichinella spiralis*, present in many animals including, dogs, cats, **pigs** and wild animals. The disease is spread by consumption of **meat** or meat products which have not been fully cooked and contain living **parasites**, in the form of larval cysts, which can grow, causing **diarrhoea** and nausea, and later spread through the wall of the intestine to cause muscle pains and malaise. The disease is rare today in the UK and other countries with a high standard of meat inspection and the further safeguard of reliable cooking practices.

trifle A traditional English dessert, based on

sponge-cake soaked in sherry or wine, custard, fruit or jam and covered in cream, decorated with chopped almonds, glacé cherries.

triglyceride A substance made by the combination of a **fatty acid** with **glycerol** (commonly known as glycerine), and the form in which **fat** is stored in the body. Natural oils contain mixtures of triglycerides.

tripe The muscular wall of the **stomach** of a **beef** animal and classed as offal. The pattern of folds varies from one part of the stomach to another and is described as honeycomb, blanket, monk's hood and reed. In the natural state it is brown and tough due to a high proportion of connective tissue. Consumption has fallen owing to the concern over BSE.

NUTRITIONAL VALUE: average: protein about 10%, fat 2%.

ENERGY per 100g: average: cooked: 100 kcal, 418 kJ.

USES: most tripe sold has been bleached in lime and cooked. It requires boiling and flavouring with onions, herbs, stock, tomatoes.

trivet A three-legged platform for cooking-vessels placed beside a fire, or a platform which is attached to a fire-grate to hold cooking-vessels.

trout *Salmo trutta*, and other varieties. All are game-**fish** which inhabit the rivers and lakes of the UK, of the same family as **salmon**. There are 3 types:—

Brown trout. The native wild trout, with white flesh, of rivers and lakes and with no migratory urge.

Rainbow trout. Introduced from New Zealand; it has pink flesh. Used for stocking reservoirs and lakes; it has a migratory habit and so is unsuitable for stocking rivers.

Sea-trout. It has a similar habit to salmon, in that it matures at sea, returning to its original river to spawn. It is nocturnal and generally caught at night. A prized game-fish. See **salmon-trout, trout-farms**.

SEASON: wild brown trout season varies in different localities but the maximum in England and Wales is 1st March–31st October. In Scotland 15th March–6th October. Rainbow trout has no close-season unless specified by local by-laws.

NUTRITIONAL VALUE: protein 15%, fat 5–20%, mostly unsaturated, vitamin D, calcium, iron.

ENERGY per 100g: 105–252 kcal, 440–1054 kJ.

USES: grilled, fried, baked, poached as a fish or main course. Also available **smoked** and eaten cold.

trout farms Both brown and rainbow trout are extensively farmed, accounting for the majority sold in the UK. They are fed on a high-**protein** food based on **soya bean** and fish meal processed in a granular form. Trout farms are situated where there is a plentiful supply of fresh running water. Fish hatcheries are used to restock rivers and lakes to replace fish caught as a sport.

truffle The underground tuberous structures of the family *Tuberales*, the most highly-prized of all **fungi**. The most favoured are *Tuber tubrum* and *Tuber melanospermum* which are found only in Europe. They grow in oak and beech-woods, but are hard to find and extremely expensive to buy. They are a speciality of Périgord in France where dogs and pigs are trained to smell them out and dig for them.

USES: to flavour omelettes, pâté and other dishes; not usually eaten on their own.

truss To secure poultry, game and joints of meat using skewers or string to make them more compact for cooking.

trypsin A **proteolytic enzyme**, secreted by the pancreas into the first part of the small intestine. It is only effective in an alkaline environment and is responsible for most of the digestion of **proteins**.

tryptophan One of the essential **amino acids** present in most **proteins** except **gelatine**. There is an adequate intake from a mixed **diet** so that supplements are unnecessary and excess may be harmful. It assists in the availability of the **vitamin**, niacin, a member of the B complex.

tuber The expanded root or underground stem of certain plants, where food is stored, often multiple as in potato. Tubers have a high content of **starch**, some **protein**, **vitamin B** complex, **vitamin C**, **dietary fibre**, and are a food source of world-wide importance. Some are intensely poisonous, many containing soluble poisons which must be extracted before they can be eaten (**tapioca**, **arrowroot**) and which in others, such as **yam**, are destroyed by heat in cooking. The **potato**, however, develops a stable, heat-resistant poison, **solanin**, when it becomes green in the presence of light or begins to sprout. See **ginger**.

tuberculosis A once common chronic infection due to the *Tubercle bacillus*. Bovine tuberculosis, caught from infected **cows** through contaminated **milk**, causes suppuration in neck glands and diseases of bones and joints. It is now rare in the UK and wherever measures are taken to eliminate infected cows and to pasteurise milk. The disease had a high incidence in children until around 1945 when preventive measures were established. Bovine Tuberculosis might still be caught in some countries from drinking raw milk. The human form of the disease affects principally the lungs and is caught by person-to-person contact and infected sputum.

tuna or **tunny** *Thunnus thynnus* and other varieties. Large migratory, oily, marine **fish**, related to **mackerel**, of great impor-

tance as a widely-distributed food source. It has firm, pink flesh. In the UK it is more readily available canned than fresh.

NUTRITIONAL VALUE: protein 18%, fat 8–18% depending on season, mostly polyunsaturated, vitamin D, calcium, iron.

ENERGY per 100g: 145–434 kcal, 607–1816 kJ.

USES: sold fresh or canned to be eaten hot or cold and included in a variety of dishes.

turbot *Scophthalmus maximus*. A marine flatfish with firm succulent flesh.

NUTRITIONAL VALUE: protein 18–20%, fat 1–2%, calcium, iron.

ENERGY per 100g: 77 kcal, 322 kJ.

USES: lends itself to most methods of cooking except deep-frying.

tureen A large vessel for serving soup, stew or vegetables at table.

turkey *Meleagris gallopavo*. Originally a native of North America, related to guinea-fowl, but is now bred widely and reared as poultry, both for the frozen-food and fresh markets. Large birds can be reared to weigh 25kg or more. Traditionally eaten at Christmas but now available all the year round, as it is possible to breed turkeys to mature at an early age, at a relatively low cost. See **muscle**.

NUTRITIONAL VALUE: protein 18%, fat 10%, vitamin B complex, calcium, iron.

ENERGY per 100g: roast: 189 kcal, 791 kJ.

USES: roasted whole, in casseroles, pies, stir-fries and various other dishes.

turmeric (E100) *Curcuma longa*. A **spice** of the ginger family. The dried rhizome is ground into a powder of a yellow colour with a mild distinctive flavour. See **curcumin**.

USES: for flavouring and colouring curries, rice dishes, mustards and in **piccalilli**.

turnip *Brassica napus*, a member of the cabbage family grown for its large edible root. Closely related to the **swede**.

NUTRITIONAL VALUE: protein 0.75%, carbohydrate 3–4%, vitamin B complex, vitamin C up to 40mg per 100g, calcium, iron.

ENERGY per 100g: boiled: 14 kcal, 59 kJ.

USES: cooked as a root-vegetable, usually diced, in stews, casseroles.

turnip-tops The early green leaf growth from **turnips** and **swedes**.

NUTRITIONAL VALUE: similar to cabbage.

USES: as a vegetable, alternative to cabbage.

turnover A sealed pastry case containing **fruit**, **meat** or meat and **vegetable** mixture. The edges are usually crimped as for **Cornish pasty**.

turtle *Chelonia midas*. The green edible variety of marine turtle; now a protected species, it was formerly a delicacy, particularly as turtle soup.

tutti-frutti An ice-cream sundae with mixed fruits and nuts.

TVP Textured vegetable **protein**. A **meat** substitute prepared from **soya beans** and dried.

NUTRITIONAL VALUE: average: dried: protein 50%, fat 10%.

ENERGY per 100g: dried: 290 kcal, 1213 kJ.

USES: as a meat substitute. It has little flavour of its own but absorbs others, such as from stock, herbs.

typhoid A fever caused by the Typhoid bacillus, *Salmonella typhi*, which, like the paratyphoid bacillus, is a member of the **salmonella** group and only affects humans. The disease is acquired from bacilli present in sewage-contaminated water, from foodstuffs contaminated with faeces or urine of typhoid patients or from **carriers** who continue to excrete the bacilli after they have recovered from the disease. It is not spread by animals. It is a serious disease, with a high mortality if untreated, and starts with an infection of the intestines and spreads throughout the body.

Known carriers must not be allowed to handle food for consumption by others. Immunisation by TAB inoculation is effective and should be given to all travellers to areas where typhoid is prevalent.

tyrosine One of the essential **amino acids** which form the building-blocks of **proteins** and are released by the digestion of protein, to be utilised by the body. The main dietary sources are grain foods and animal products; adequate quantities are present in a mixed **diet**.

U

udder The organ of the cow and mare which contains the milk-producing mammary tissue. It was considered a delicacy in the 17th century and is still eaten today in some parts of Europe. It is cooked by stewing or braising.

ugli Also known as tangelo. A **citrus** fruit, cross between a **grapefruit** and a **tangerine**, which has a thick rough skin and grows to a large size.

UHT Milk sterilised by ultra-high temperature.

ulluco *Ullucum tuberosus*. A low-growing, half-hardy herbaceous perennial with small fleshy expanded **tubers** used as a substitute for **potato**. It can be grown in the UK, but is not generally considered worth cultivating.

ultraviolet light The invisible form of light which has a very short wavelength and the property of destroying living matter. Ultraviolet light radiated from the sun reaches the surface of the earth, and in small doses is essential for the manufacture in the body of **vitamin D**. In large amounts it can be used to sterilise water in equipment designed for the purpose. See **ozone**.

umbles The **offal** of **deer**.

urd bean *Phaseola mungo*. Also known as mung bean. A tropical **legume** with a small green or brown edible seed, usually dried.

NUTRITIONAL VALUE: protein approx 10–12%, carbohydrate up to 45%, calcium, iron. The sprouted bean-shoots contain vitamin C up to 25mg per 100g.

V

vacuum The state within a container when all gas (air) has been evacuated. A vacuum is rarely 100% complete but nevertheless is effective for most purposes; it is increasingly used in packaging, to prevent deterioration of the product by oxidation. Vacuum-packed products, such as coffee, cheese, meat retain freshness and have a prolonged shelf-life, keeping down costs and improving quality. Use of the process has been brought about by the low cost of sealing plastic-film bags, as a vacuum was formerly produced only in glass or metal vessels.

A vacuum also lowers the temperature at which fluids boil, so that water can be extracted to give a concentrate, or produce a fully-dried powder at a relatively low temperature, and flavours are preserved, which might be lost by evaporation at normal air pressure. See **freeze-dry, sous-vide**.

vanilla A flavouring agent found in the pods of a climbing plant, *Vanilla planifolia*, a member of the orchid family which grows wild in Mexico. The pods are picked just before they are ripe and then sun-dried and placed in a closed container to sweat over a period of several weeks, during which the characteristic flavour of the active ingredient, vanillin, develops. Much used in ice-creams, confectionery, desserts and cakes. A pod of prepared vanilla, placed in a jar of sugar, will flavour the whole jar in time. Synthetic vanilla essence is now available but differs slightly in chemical composition from the natural product, being more stable and 3 times as potent, although lacking the same subtle quality.

veal Meat from a calf which is more than 3 weeks old. The **carcass** is bled after the animal is killed so that the **meat** is pale in colour, and tender.

NUTRITIONAL VALUE: raw: protein 15%, fat 11%, vitamin B complex, iron.

ENERGY per 100g: raw: 160 kcal, 669 kJ.

USES: roast, casseroled, fried, grilled. See **schnitzel**.

vegan A strict **vegetarian** who excludes **dairy products** as well as **meat** and **fish**. A vegan **diet** may be lacking in certain food substances essential for growing children and also in **iron**.

vegetable The edible leaf, stalk, root or seed of a plant. Most vegetables are cultivated and also include some flowers such as **broccoli, cauliflower**, and some **fruits** eaten as vegetables including **tomato, cucumber, marrow, peppers (sweet), aubergines**. They play a major role in the diet, providing **dietary fibre, vitamins, minerals, protein** and energy, as well as adding interest and flavour to other food.

Root-vegetables have a high **carbohydrate** content, seeds, such as **pulses** are high in **protein**, providing sufficient for **vegetarians**. Many vegetables also have a high vitamin A, vitamin B complex, vitamin C and mineral content; most should be cooked in the minimum of water, as quickly as possible, to preserve vitamins and minerals. The water should have a pH below 7 to preserve vitamin C. Sprouted seeds, such as bean-sprouts, have a high vitamin C content and can be eaten raw in salads or stir-fried.

vegetable gelatine A jelly-like substance extracted from certain seaweeds. See **agar**.

vegetable oil See **oil**.

vegetable parchment A type of paper which has been treated with sulphuric acid to alter its character allowing it to prevent sticking; it is used for placing under cakes, biscuits, during cooking.

vegetable pear See **chayotte**.

vegetable rennet See **rennet**.

vegetable spaghetti See **spaghetti marrow**.

vegetable suet Suet made from hardened vegetable oils. It has a similar high-content of saturated **fat** to that in beef suet.

vegetarian One who never eats meat, poultry or fish but whose diet includes all foods of vegetable origin, cereals, pulses, fruit. Most vegetarians also eat dairy products such as milk, cheese, eggs. See **vegan**.

velouté A white **sauce** thickened with egg-yolk and **cream** using **stock** in place of milk.

venison The meat of **deer**, classified as **game**. It is dark in colour, has a low fat-content and is usually hung to make it tender. Venison is becoming more widely available as a result of deer-farming.
NUTRITIONAL VALUE: average: protein 18%, fat 8.5%, vitamin B complex, calcium, iron.
ENERGY per 100g: average: 150 kcal, 628 kJ.
USES: roast, casseroled, grilled, fried, in pies.

verbena *Lippia citriodora*, a small shrub, the leaves of which are used as a source of an **essential oil** with a strong lemon flavour and smell. It is used more for giving perfume to detergents and soaps than for adding flavour to food. A very similar essential oil, obtained from a tropical grass, *Andropogon citrata*, is used to flavour lemon tea.

verjuice The juice of an unripe **fruit**.

vermicelli Pasta which has been extruded in thin threads, finer than **spaghetti**, and used for savoury and sweet dishes.

vermouth A fortified **wine** flavoured with herbs and spices and generally taken as an **apéritif**. The original and best-known makes are Martini and Cinzano. Available dry or sweet and white or red. There are many copies.
ALCOHOL CONTENT: 17%.

véronique Garnished with white grapes: usually fish or chicken.

Vichy A town in France famous for its mineral water.

vichyssoise A **soup** made with chicken stock, leeks, potatoes, onions and cream, and served chilled.

Victoria sponge A basic cake made with equal quantities of flour, butter, sugar and eggs, often sandwiched with jam when cooked.

victuals Provisions.

vigneron A grower of wine grapes.

vinaigrette An unstable emulsion of **vinegar** and **oil**, seasoned with pepper, salt and mustard, sometimes flavoured with herbs. Used as a salad dressing and with fish and some meat dishes.

vine Any climbing plant. Examples of crops which grow on vines are **grape**, **pea**, **hops** but most commonly means grapevine.

vine-leaves Leaves of the grapevine, *Vitis vinifera*, used after blanching to wrap round savoury mixtures, both to keep them intact during cooking and to give a delicate and subtle flavour. Leaves which have been sprayed against **pests** and **fungi** should not be used. Dishes made in this way are often described as stuffed vine-leaves or dolmas (of Greek origin).

vinegar A liquid containing 4–6% **acetic acid**. It is prepared from fermented liquor by the action of *Acetobacter aceti*, which has the property of converting **ethanol** into acetic acid. The source of the liquor depends on what is available in the locality, the commonest being fermented **cider, cereal, malt, molasses** and **wine**. A range of **spices, herbs** and flavourings are used for different specialised vinegars. Some vinegar is prepared from synthetic acetic acid. Malt is the general-purpose vinegar used as a **preservative** and in **pickling**. Wine vinegars are more delicate and preferred for use in **salad dressings**, cooking, sauces, tenderising meat. See **balsamic vinegar**.

vinho verde A Portuguese white **wine**, prepared to be drunk young.

vintage The gathering of **grapes** for **wine-**making.

vintage year When circumstances of sun and rainfall are at their best for grape-growing and the production of high quality wine.

violet *Viola odorata*. The petals of this sweet-smelling wild flower are often crystallised in sugar and used for cake ornamentation, retaining their colour and delicate smell.

viscosity The resistance of a liquid to flow: thus a high viscosity is an essential feature of some syrups, sauces and soups and also holds solids in suspension, maintaining an attractive appearance, as in **jams**. Viscosity increases as the temperature falls and decreases as it rises. A large number of agents are capable of increasing viscosity. See **starches, thickeners**.

vitamins A group of chemical substances which have no energy value on their own but, nevertheless, are essential for growth, repair and health; their importance is indicated by the consequences of their deficiencies. Vitamins are widely dispersed in nature and adequate quantities are available in a broadly-based diet, which includes **dairy products, cereals**, green and root-**vegetables, pulses, fruit**; **vegetarians** can usually obtain sufficient quantities from a balanced **diet** even without **meat, fish** or **poultry**. Vitamins which play the most important roles are:–

Vitamin A (retinol). An oil-soluble vitamin required for normal growth and health of tissues. Much of the vitamin is formed in the body from **carotene** and is available in dairy products, fish, leaf and some root vegetables and pulses, with a very high level in liver. There are negligible quantities in meat and poultry. Vitamin A deficiency is likely to occur only with severely restricted diets, usually in areas of poverty, and results in dryness of the skin and eyes and may cause blindness and stunt growth in babies and children. A gross excess may, rarely, cause deformities in babies; women who are pregnant, or might become pregnant, are advised to avoid excessive intake of liver and vitamin A supplements. Growing children require relatively slightly more for their weight than adults, but supplements are not usually needed. The usual source of added vitamin A is fish-oil which also contains vitamin D.

Vitamin B. A complex of water-soluble vitamins, found particularly in cereals such as wholemeal products (but not in highly purified flour), yeast and yeast extracts, meat. The principal members of the group are:–

Thiamine (Vitamin B1). Controls the **metabolism** of fats, carbohydrates and alcohol. Requirements do not change significantly throughout life and supplements are not usually required, even in pregnancy. Requirements are related to carbohydrate intake and increase with a high energy output, but this is normally supplied by the food taken. Alcoholics are particularly at risk of deficiency because of their usually restricted diet, but requirements would be covered by including wholegrain foods. Vitamin B1 deficiency impairs metabolism and causes a disease called **beriberi** which is rare nowadays in developed countries.

Riboflavin (Vitamin B2). Concerned in the use of **oxygen** by tissues both in man and other forms of life. It is the most widely-distributed of the vitamins in all natural foods, and adequate quantities are present in a mixed diet which includes milk and some dairy products. Deficiency is rare and there is no need to supplement intake during pregnancy and lactation. In the unlikely event of deficiency, symptoms include soreness of the corners of the mouth and tongue, changes in the skin and the appearance of blood vessels in the cornea.

Niacin. A vitamin which is closely related to **nicotinic acid** and nicotinamide. It is widely represented in natural foods and the amount available in the body is associated with the intake of the **amino acid, tryptophan**, present in most food. The vitamin is involved in metabolism and energy expenditure. In the unlikely event of deficiency, there is an increased sensitivity of the skin on surfaces exposed to sunlight, diarrhoea and disturbances of the nervous system, the condition being known as **pellagra**. Deficiency is likely only with severe food deprivation. It was formerly common in communities largely dependant on maize and other cereals.

Vitamin B6. A vitamin involved in **protein metabolism** which is widely-available in foods and synthesised by **bacteria** normally present in the large bowel, so that shortages are rare. There is no need to increase intake during pregnancy or lactation. An excess has been associated with disturbances of sensation.

Vitamin B12. Closely involved with folic acid, with which it is required for normal formation of red blood cells and essential for normal function of nerves:

the vitamin is found only in foods of animal origin, including dairy products, fish, and also in yeast, with a particularly high content in liver. Dietary deficiency causes the condition known as pernicious anaemia; this condition also occurs in certain individuals who lack a particular substance, known as intrinsic factor, normally present in the stomach and which is needed for the absorption of vitamin B12 from the intestine.

Folic acid. Essential for the formation of normal red blood cells and the health and regular replacement of the cells lining the intestines. It is widely represented in nature and present in all green vegetables, yeasts, and foods which are also rich in other members of the B group and vitamin C. Folic acid can be destroyed by heat and by some food **preservatives** which contain nitrates and by nitrates in water supplies. It is low in processed foods and reduced by cooking. Intake must be maintained during pregnancy and lactation, so that supplements are often given. The elderly, dependant on a narrowly based diet, often become deficient.

Pantothenic acid. Involved in metabolism and energy production. It is so widely present in food that deficiency has not been reported and supplements are never required.

Biotin. Involved in metabolism of **fat** and **glucose**; widely distributed in nature and manufactured by bacteria normally present in the large intestine. Deficiency can cause soreness of the tongue, loss of appetite and dermatitis; it has not, however, been reported, except in the unusual case of food fanatics who consume large quantities of egg-whites which inactivate the vitamin.

Vitamin C (ascorbic acid, E300). A water-soluble vitamin essential for the health of the teeth, gums and general well-being. It is an **antioxidant** and so has a role in limiting the breakdown of food substances into toxic products. Present in fresh fruits, green vegetables, most root-vegetables and sprouted seeds. There are high concentrations in the sweet pepper, blackcurrants, citrus fruits and fresh milk which has not been exposed to sunlight. It is destroyed by **alkalis**, prolonged cooking, in the drying of fruits and **canning**. Deficiency causes **scurvy**, a disorder associated with bleeding of the gums, bleeding into and under the skin (giving the appearance of bruising), and anaemia; it was, at one time, common among sailors during long distance voyages and is prevented by taking **lemon** or **lime** juice. The intake of vitamin C should be well-maintained during pregnancy and lactation, and by the elderly who are at risk because of their reduced diet. Requirements are higher for smokers.

Vitamin D. An oil-soluble vitamin closely related to calciferol and ergosterol which is manufactured in the skin, by the action of moderate exposure to sunlight. It is concerned with **calcium** metabolism and formation of bones and teeth. It is widely-distributed in nature in eggs, oily fish, liver and fish-liver oil. By law, **margarine** and some other foods, must include added vitamin D to compensate for lack of sunlight during the winter. Deficiency causes **rickets** in growing children, with deformity of the long bones, ribcage and pelvis, and poor teeth. In adults there is softening of the bones known as **osteomalacia**. Excessive doses can cause calcium to be deposited around joints and the formation of kidney stones. Requirements increase during pregnancy and lactation. At risk of deficiency are those who have a restricted diet and lack exposure to sunlight. Deficiency was common until about 1940, particularly in Scotland, when supplements became mandatory in the UK in certain basic foods. Fish-liver oils are the usual source of supplements.

Vitamin E. An oil-soluble vitamin important for its protective **antioxidant** properties, limiting the breakdown of some fats into toxic substances, which may be associated with an increased risk of arterial disease and some cancers. Widely used in fats, and foods containing fats, as a preservative. It is widely distributed in grain foods, vegetable oils, eggs, but there is little in most vegetables, fruits and highly-purified white flour. Adequate quantities are obtained from a mixed diet which includes some whole-grain products and deficiency is rare, even when there are food shortages. It can be stored in the body, so that supplements are not required. It is not known to be toxic even in high doses. See **tocopherol (E306–309)**.

Vitamin K (Phyloquinone). An oil-soluble vitamin which aids the clotting of blood; widely distributed in natural foods such as green vegetables, pulses, cereals and can be manufactured by intestinal bacteria. Deficiencies are rare and supplements not required.

vodka A spirit distilled from fermented rye or potatoes; it has little flavour and is almost pure **ethanol** and water. It is the alcoholic drink least likely to cause a hangover, owing to the absence of **congeners**. ALCOHOL CONTENT: 40%.

vol-au-vent A small puff **pastry** case with a savoury filling.

waffle A preparation made of **batter**, baked in a hinged waffle-iron giving it a lattice-like appearance. It is an American speciality and is often served in the USA as a breakfast food with **maple syrup**.

walnut *Juglans regia*. The fruit of the large, hardy, slow-growing, deciduous tree, native of Europe and Asia. The ripe nut is encased in a hard shell which can be split into equal halves. The **kernel** has a convoluted surface divided by fibrous membrane.

NUTRITIONAL VALUE: protein 10.5%, fat 51.5% (high in unsaturates), carbohydrate 5%, dietary fibre 5%.

ENERGY per 100g: 525 kcal, 2197 kJ.

USES: as a dessert nut, in a variety of sweetmeats, cakes, desserts. Picked when immature they can be pickled.

walnut-oil Oil extracted from the walnut, with a delicate nutty flavour.

NUTRITIONAL VALUE: 10% saturates, 67% polyunsaturated, 18% monounsaturated.

ENERGY value per 100g: 900 kcal, 3766 kJ.

USES: mainly in **vinaigrette** dressing; it can also be used as a cooking-oil but is expensive.

washing-soda See **sodium carbonate**.

water A clear, colourless, odourless, tasteless liquid, with a neutral **pH** in its purest form. Main sources are springs, lakes, rivers, bore-holes (wells), desalinated sea-water. There are many variations of mineral content, acidity and purity. In the UK most piped-water is passed through filter-beds of sand and clarified with aluminium or iron salts and chlorinated. Rain-water is soft but water collected in catchment areas where there is limestone or rock containing magnesium, such as dolomite, is hard. Hard water is resistant to lathering (frothing) with soap due to the presence of **calcium**, **magnesium** or other salts, held in solution, which react with soap, forming an insoluble deposit. Temporary hardness (caused by **calcium bicarbonate**) is reduced by boiling and appears as a deposit of lime (calcium carbonate) in kettles and water-pipes. Permanent hardness (caused by **calcium sulphate**) is resistant to boiling, but can be reduced by adding a mild **alkali** such as **sodium carbonate**, or using **water-softeners**. Hard water is not in any way harmful; it may indeed be associated with a lower risk of heart disease and strokes and it protects **lead** water-pipes, thereby reducing the risk of lead dissolving out into drinking water. Soft water contains minimum quantities of minerals; it lathers well with **soap** but is capable of dissolving **lead** from water pipes. See **water-filter**, **water-sterilisation**, **mineral water**.

water balance The balance between total water intake in food and drink, together with conversion of food and other substances into water by oxidation in the body, and water loss, by evaporation through expired air from the lungs, mucous surfaces, skin, and water excreted from the body by the kidneys and in the faeces. Water in the average adult is 65–70% of body-weight. It is recommended that an adult should have, in addition to water in food, at least 1.5 litres (3 pints) of liquid a day, increasing the amount in hot weather and when highly active, to maintain an urine output of at least 1 litre a day. **Sea-water** must never be drunk whatever the thirst. See **dehydration**.

water chestnut Most commonly the **tuber** (not as the name implies, a nut) of a Chinese sedge-plant *Eliocharis tuberosa*. It has a crisp texture even when cooked and is only available canned in the UK. A similar species is the South American Jicana. The seeds of *Trapa natans*, which grows in ponds and lakes in southern Europe, and *Trapa singhara*, an important food source in Kashmir, are true nuts and sometimes known as Jesuit's bread.

USES: the first-mentioned variety is used in many Chinese dishes and can also be mixed with vegetables such as green beans.

watercress Varieties of *Rorippa nasturtium-aquaticum*, pungent freshwater aquatic plants, cultivated in special beds in clean water and available all the year. Wild watercress should not be eaten, as the water in which it grows may be contaminated with any of the **food-poisoning organisms** or **parasites**.

NUTRITIONAL VALUE: protein 2%, vitamin A, vitamin C up to 60mg per 100g, carotene, iron.

ENERGY per 100g: 15 kcal, 63 kJ.

USES: in salads, soup, as a garnish.

water-filter Apparatus for removal of suspended matter in water. Those generally on sale have filters capable of retaining **bacteria** but might not necessarily hold back viruses, such as those causing **hepatitis A** and **poliomyelitis**, so they are not a substitute for **water-sterilisation**. If not used and maintained in accordance with manufacturer's instructions, water-filters may act as stores of infection and cause the very diseases they are intended to prevent.

water melon *Citrullus vulgaris*. A member of the *Cucurbitaceae* family, which requires warm conditions for growth; cultivated around the Mediterranean and in tropical countries. It is larger than the common melon and characterised by having black seeds evenly distributed in the flesh and not confined to a central cavity. The flesh is crisp, has a high water content, but very low food value.

USES: as a dessert fruit.

water-oats See **rice − wild**.

water-purifier A **water-filter** that is also capable of removing impurities such as **heavy metals**, odours, viruses, excess of chlorine, nitrates and other chemicals present in water supplies. Purifiers use exchange resins, the effectiveness of which depends on the system employed, the nature and degree of water pollution and the correct replacement of expendable parts, which have a limited life. Manufacturer's instructions must be followed, as the apparatus itself may sometimes become a source of pollution if not correctly maintained. Some claim an improvement in drinking-quality of water by their use, but this is a matter of personal taste; there is no evidence that they improve health in countries which have a high standard of piped-water.

water-softener Apparatus for reducing the content of **calcium** and **magnesium** salts in hard water usually by using exchange resins. Water-softeners should not be used where there are **lead** pipes. Water can be made soft for washing (but not drinking) by using **sodium carbonate**.

water-sterilisation The destruction of all living matter in water. For practical purposes water suspected of, or containing living matter, can be made safe for drinking and cooking, but not necessarily 100% sterile, in the home or when travelling, by boiling or by introducing **chlorine** with water-sterilising tablets based on **chloramine**. Piped water-supplies are rendered safe by the introduction of chlorine. There is sometimes a faint smell of chlorine in piped-water, which is harmless and dispersed by heat; equipment which exposes water to intense ultraviolet light is also used commercially. There have been recent outbreaks of water-borne diarrhoeal diseases due to strains of **giardia** and **cryptosporidia**, which are relatively resistant to **chlorine**. In such cases water suppliers usually warn consumers to boil tap-water for use until the danger has been overcome.

whale-meat Meat of the largest living mammal, now a protected species. Somewhat like beef, it was eaten up to and during World War 2 but should not be available today, to conserve the species.

wheat The most important and widely-grown **cereal** crop, that has been cultivated in Eurasia for thousands of years, but not introduced into the western world until the early 16th century when it was taken to America by the Spaniards. There are many different varieties suited to different climates and it is a staple cereal worldwide. In the UK, the variety *Triticum activum* is the most commonly grown for **bread**-making, *Triticum turgidum* for biscuit-making and cooking; *Triticum durum* is the high-protein hard wheat grown for **pasta**-making in countries where the hot, dry summers are suitable for its cultivation. See **flour**.

wheatgerm The embryo of the wheat-grain and separated from it during the milling of white **flour**. It is sold as a separate product and has a good flavour.

NUTRITIONAL VALUE: protein, 29.4%, fat 10.8%, carbohydrate 32.6%, vitamin B complex, vitamin E.

ENERGY per 100g: 346 kcal, 1448 kJ.

USES: in bread-making, as an addition to breakfast cereal, sprinkled on fruit, in yoghurt.

wheatmeal See **flour**.

wheat, puffed A **cereal** subjected to a

commercial process which heats it, and then explodes it, by the sudden release of pressure, producing a characteristic blown-up appearance. The same process is used for **rice**, and also **maize**, when it produces **popcorn**.

whelk *Buccinum undatum*. A marine **shellfish** similar to **snail**. Widely distributed in coastal waters. In Scotland the term is used for **winkle**.

NUTRITIONAL VALUE: protein 20%, fat 2%, iron, calcium.

ENERGY per 100g: 90 kcal, 377 kJ.

USES: cooked by boiling and eaten cold.

whey The liquid residue of cheese-making after the solids and most of the **fat** have been separated to form **cheese**.

NUTRITIONAL VALUE: protein 1%, lactose 4–5%, fat 1–2%.

ENERGY per 100g: 30 kcal, 125 kJ.

USES: in the manufacture of **Ricotta** cheese and some processed cheeses, low-fat butter substitutes. Most of the whey produced is fed to farm stock.

whip To stiffen a substance by agitating it with a fork or **whisk**; usually applies to **cream**.

whisk To agitate one or more substances such as egg-white, eggs and sugar, in order to increase the bulk and stiffness by the incorporation of air. It implies a lighter result than beating. See **beat**.

whisk An instrument, of which there are many variations, for whisking or whipping, such as the pear-shaped wire cage or balloon whisk or an electrically powered machine. The balloon whisk is considered by many to be superior for eggs.

whisky (the American and Irish spelling is whiskey). A liquor distilled from fermented malted **barley**-mash and other **grains**. Originally made in pot-stills in small distilleries, it is now more often made in continuous patent stills. It is traditionally matured in used **sherry** casks to give flavour and colour. In Scotland it must be distilled twice, whilst in Ireland it is distilled three times. By law, in the UK, it must be matured for at least 3 years before being sold. High quality malt whiskies are left in casks for 12 years or more. See **congeners**, **distil**.

The principal varieties are:−

Blended whisky. A blend of **malt** and pure grain whiskies; the most widely distributed type.

Bourbon whiskey. The original Kentucky Whiskey made from **maize** corn and other grains and matured in charred oak barrels.

Grain whisky. Made mainly from unmalted grain and mixed with malted barley, which converts some of the maltose into malt by the action of free maltase enzyme. Most is made in continuous patent stills and used for blending.

Irish whiskey. Made in a similar way to grain whisky but in large pot-stills.

Pure malt whisky. Made wholly from malted barley, distilled in pot-stills and traditionally heated over peat fires. The type of peat, and the character of the water contribute to the special qualities of Scotch Malt Whisky which are unequalled elsewhere.

Rye whiskey. Made from fermented rye liquor together with barley.

ALCOHOL CONTENT: 30−40% by volume.

whisky liqueurs See **drambuie, Irish mist**.

whitebait The fry (young) of **herring** and **sprat**, up to 50mm in size, caught in shoals in river estuaries in Europe. In other parts of the world the fry of other fish such as sardines, sand-eels, blennies, gobies are caught in the same way. They are generally cooked whole without being gutted.

USES: usually served as a first course coated in flour and deep fried, or they may be stir-fried and spiced.

whitecurrant *Ribes sativum* (variant). A hardy shrub bearing small clusters of white acidic berries. Not as readily available as blackcurrants and redcurrants.

NUTRITIONAL VALUE: protein 1.3%, carbohydrate 5.6%, vitamin C 40mg per 100g.

ENERGY per 100g: 25 kcal, 105 kJ.

USES: not widely used but can be cooked as, or with blackcurrants and redcurrants.

whiting *Merlangus merlangus*. A small member of the **cod** family. Usually available only in autumn and winter. It is sometimes smoked.

NUTRITIONAL VALUE: protein 16−18%, fat 0.5−1.0%, vitamin B complex, minerals.

ENERGY per 100g: average: 75 kcal, 314 kJ.

USES: grilled, baked or poached.

wholemeal See **flour**.

whortleberry See **bilberry**.

wienerwurst A **sausage** used for **hot dogs**; may be indistinguishable from the **frankfurter** sausage.

wild rice See **rice, wild**.

wine The fermented juice of the **grape** and sometimes other **fruits**. Wine-making has a history extending back to biblical days. Widely used to give pleasure, for ceremonial purposes and to enhance cooking both by virtue of its own flavour and because alcohol extracts flavours which are insoluble in water. The strength of alcohol (**ethanol**) present in wine depends on the sugar content of the fruit at the time of harvesting, type of yeast used and the duration of **fermentation**. Fermentation ceases naturally, either when all fermentable sugar has been converted to alcohol, or when the alcohol strength is too high for the yeast to work.

Grape wines are usually made only from 100% fruit, but the addition of limited amounts of sugar is allowed in some wine areas. The process is known as **chaptalization**. White wines are made from juice separated from the skins and therefore have a low **tannin** content. Red wines are fermented in the presence of the skins and have the characteristic astringency of **tannic acid**. Rosé wines are fermented for part of the time in the presence of the skins (although some are a mixture of red and white wines). White wines can be made from red grapes using only the juice of the grape. Special yeasts are used in the production of **Champagne**.

There are major differences in the quality of wines, from variations in the quality of fruit used, climate, soils in which the vines grow, yeasts used and the manner in which the wine is made. Many wines are skilful blends of different grapes and vintages, the purpose being both to obtain the high qualities expected in the best wines and a comparable standard from year to year. Pure, unblended vintage wines of high quality are costly, while cheaper blended wines are rougher and lack the fine flavours. White wines and light reds, such as Beaujolais are generally drunk young whilst the richer red wines are kept, initially in casks of oak and later in bottles, improving in quality as they mature.

Connoisseurs are careful to select wines to accompany particular foods; traditionally stronger red wines with red meats and cheese, light white wines with poultry, fish, and sweet white wines with desserts. There is today a tendency to make a personal choice of wine, rather than choosing traditional wines.

Wines made with strongly flavoured fruits such as blackberry, gooseberry, elderberry, are made with juice diluted with water and sugar added to provide the required strength of alcohol, but they cannot match the quality of grape wines.

The current laws on drinking and driving are changing drinking habits; thus low-alcohol and alcohol-free wines are becoming available.

ALCOHOL CONTENT:
  white wines: 7–13%.
  red wines: 10–14%.
  champagne: 12–13%.
  low-alcohol wines: 1–2%.
  fortified wines: 14% and over.

Strong and fortified wines keep well, but wines with an alcohol content below that which prevents further fermentation need to be dry, that is without free sugar, or filtered to remove any **yeasts** and other **micro-organisms**.

STORAGE: all wines should be kept in airtight sealed containers, the corks being kept moist with a cap to prevent evaporation and the bottles stored on their sides in dark, cool conditions with minumum changes in temperature. Corks should not be allowed to dry out, leak, nor develop moulds which may contaminate the wine and make it unpleasant to drink. **Lead** capsules, used over the tops of bottles to prevent the corks drying out may leave a deposit of lead around the neck of the bottle, which should be wiped before serving. Wines may contain permitted additives, such as **sulphur dioxide (E220)**, to prevent late fermentation or growth of moulds, but this does not have to be stated on the label.

corked wine The term used for wine which has become tainted by the flavour of moulds growing around a cork. This occurs when the cork shrinks due to drying out and a slight seepage of wine occurs. For this reason corks are capped to prevent drying out and wine bottles are stored on their side.

wine, fortified Wine to which brandy is added to raise the concentration of alcohol above 14%. Typical examples are **sherry**, **Madeira, port**; others are flavoured by herbs and spices, such as **vermouth** and **campari**.

wine, sparkling Effervescent wine. Some

sparkling wines are made by the **Champagne** process of re-fermentation in the bottle, but less expensive ones are made either by re-fermentation in bulk or by adding carbon dioxide to the wine, under pressure.

wineberry *Vaccinia myrtillis*. See **bilberry**.

wineberry *Rubus phoeniculasius*, a seeded-fruit related to the **raspberry** and **blackberry**, characterised by bright red stems covered in soft bristles. The fruit is similar to a raspberry, but more conical and usually smaller, bright red in colour with a pleasantly acid flavour. Grown in gardens but rarely commercially.

wine yeasts Yeasts present on the surface of all fruits are strains of *Saccharomyces cerevisiae ellipsoideus* and were formerly the source of yeasts for fermentation. Wild yeasts are unreliable and today most wines are made from carefully selected cultures, chosen to bring the best out of the **grape** for the type of wine being made. **Sulphur dioxide (E220)** is used to inhibit wild yeasts and moulds before inoculation with the selected one.

winkle *Littorina littoria*. A marine gastropod, also known as periwinkle. In Scotland the term means a **whelk**.
NUTRITIONAL VALUE: protein 11%, fat 2%, calcium and iron.
ENERGY per 100g: 57 kcal, 238 kJ.
USES: cooked and eaten cold as a snack.

wintergreen Aromatic oil extracted from *Gaultheria procumbens*, a small evergreen herb related to the heath family. Used more in the past as a flavouring agent. It contains methyl salicylate and has medicinal properties.

wood alcohol Originally distilled from wood; contains **methanol** (methyl alcohol), the most poisonous of the alcohols. See **methylated spirit**.

woodcock *Scolopax rusticola*. A **game**-bird widely distributed throughout Europe and Asia, similar to the **snipe** but with a more bulky body and considered better to eat. Usually eaten during the autumn.
SEASON: 1st October–31st January; in Scotland, 1st September–31st January.
NUTRITIONAL VALUE: average: protein 18%, fat 2–3%.
ENERGY per 100g: average: 90 kcal, 377 kJ.
USES: roasted, grilled, casseroled.

Worcester sauce A sauce, first made by Lea and Perrins, a firm of chemists, in 1837 for a customer, to a recipe he provided. He failed to return to collect the sauce and it remained forgotten for many years until it was tasted, by which time it had developed an exceptional quality. It is now world-famous and the recipe remains a trade secret. It is widely used either as a sauce in its own right, or to add to other sauces for flavouring and for marinating.

wort The soluble extract of malted **barley** before the addition of **hops**, used in the first stage of **beer**-making.

X

xantham gum (E415) A preparation made by polymerising **carbohydrate** in a bacterial fermentation process.

USES: commercially as a thickener and stabiliser in desserts, fruit pies, fillings, sauces.

xanthoma See **cholesterol**.

xanthophyll Yellow pigment drived from **carotene**, which accounts for the yellow colour of flour. Pure white flours are bleached with such agents as **nitrogen peroxide**.

xerophalmia A condition of dryness of the eyes and degeneration of the cornea which can lead to blindness, due to deficiency of **vitamin A**.

X-rays See **irradiation**.

xylose A complex sugar found in plants, less than half as sweet as sucrose.

Y

yam The name given to a range of tropical and subtropical plants which have swollen roots or stalks with a high food value; the group includes **sweet potato, cassava**, potato-yam and other members of the family *Dioscoreaceae*, and *Colocasia antiquorum*, known as dasheen and **taro**. Most contain poisons which are destroyed by heat in cooking.

NUTRITIONAL VALUE: similar to **potato**. ENERGY per 100g: boiled: 76 kcal, 318 kJ. USES: eaten as potatoes or used for extraction of **starch**. In some countries the main source of **carbohydrate** in the **diet**.

yeast *Saccharomyces*. A family of single cell-organisms related to **moulds**, widely dispersed in nature, present in the air and on the surface of **fruits, grains**, and capable of fermenting **carbohydrate** with the formation of **carbon dioxide** and **alcohol**.

Yeasts are essential for the baking of **bread** and for brewing and wine-making. Originally all fermentation was dependant on natural yeasts but these have been replaced by pure cultured yeasts, free from wild yeasts and moulds, to improve quality. Strains are selected for the particular purpose, with different characteristics for baking, brewing and types of **wine**. **Champagne** yeasts can ferment up to 15% alcohol, whilst others are usually no longer active when the alcohol level reaches 12–13% even if there is still some sugar available. The fermentation process is dependent on the **enzyme, zymase**, present in yeast, which converts **sugar** into alcohol. Dried yeast and yeast frozen to −18°C (−0.5°F) remain viable for several months.

Varieties used: bread making: *Saccharomyces cerivisae*.

beer, ale and stout: *Saccharomyces cerevisae* (top fermenting strains).

lager: *Saccharomyces cerevisae* (bottom fermenting strains).

wines: *Saccharomyces cerevisiae elipsoideus*.

cider and perry. *Saccharomyces apiculatus*.

Surplus yeast from the brewing industry is dried and used as animal feed, providing a protein content of 50%, and for making **yeast extract**.

yeast extract Concentrated water-soluble component of yeast, usually a by-product of the brewing industry; prepared by autolysis, using caustic soda which is neutralised with hydrochloric acid, forming sodium chloride, which accounts for its high salt content. It has a strong meat-like savoury flavour.

NUTRITIONAL VALUE: average: protein 45%, vitamin B complex.

USES: as a flavouring agent for soups, casseroles, pies. It forms the basis of a number of proprietary preparations such as **Marmite**, **Bovril**, OXO, and **stock** cubes.

yoghurt A sour **milk** product, originally produced in Eastern Europe, made by inoculating sterilised milk with *Lactobacillus bulgaricus* and *Streptoccus thermophilus*. The organisms grow at a temperature of 40–45°C (104–113°F), converting **lactose** to **lactic acid** and thickening the milk. Yoghurt will not form if the milk contains any residual antibiotics, and it should be free of other organisms; dried milk powder can be regarded as sufficiently free of **bacteria** to make a reliable yoghurt, but fresh milk should be sterilised by boiling.

The quality of yoghurt depends on the concentration of milk **proteins** and the time and temperature of incubation, small variations leading to differences in acidity and thickness. The tendency to cut down on the intake of dairy **fats** has led to the manufacture of low-fat yoghurts made from skimmed milk, usually with added dried skimmed milk powder to increase thickness. Yoghurts may be flavoured with fruit, nuts, and some are pasteurised after manufacture to prevent further activity of the bacteria.

Yoghurt can be made at home, using a special starter culture or a with a small amount taken from fresh commercial unpasteurised yoghurt. The milk is heated to a temperature of 42–45°C (108–113°F), inoculated, and kept at about this temperature until it produces a good yoghurt in 5–7 hours. Bio-yoghurt is made using subcultures of bacteria normally present in the healthy human intestine and claimed to be better in restoring natural bacteria, particularly after they have been disturbed by treatment with antibiotics; such benefits have yet to be confirmed.

NUTRITIONAL VALUE: Protein 8%, fat 2–10%.

ENERGY per 100g: 48–122 kcal, 200–510 kJ.

USES: as a dessert, for enhancing the flavour of soups, stews, curries, mixed with mayonnaise and salad dressings to reduce their fat content.

yolk index A measure of the freshness of an egg calculated by comparing the depth of the yolk with its diameter at the base when the egg is broken on a flat surface. The greater the ratio of depth to breadth, the fresher the egg.

Yorkshire pudding A savoury, baked batter pudding served, by tradition, in Yorkshire, before roast beef, with gravy made of the juices from the meat. However, it is more commonly served as an accompaniment to the beef.

Z

zabaglione A classic Italian dessert made with egg yolks, **marsala** wine and caster sugar, gently heated until it just thickens and then cooled in the glasses in which it is to be served. The French equivalent is **sabayon**.

zapote See **naseberry**.

zedorria *Curcuma zedoaria*. A tropical **herb**, related to **ginger** with expanded roots and a somewhat camphor-like flavour, used in Indonesian and Malaysian cooking.

zest The outer skin of **citrus** fruits, which contains the **essential oils** responsible for the characteristic flavour of the fruit. Most citrus fruit sold, has been coated in wax, containing fungicidal **preservatives**; while it is unlikely that a harmful amount of these would be eaten, it is a wise precaution to scrub the fruit with warm water and rinse well before use, although this will only remove some of the wax.

USES: grated or in thin parings to give flavour to bland fruits, puddings, savoury dishes and drinks, crystallised for cakes and sweetmeats.

zigamia aquatica See **rice, wild**.

zinc A **trace element** present in most tissues; an important constituent of **enzymes** with a wide range of functions which include the control of the metabolism of **proteins**, **carbohydrates** and **fat**. Deficiency causes retarded growth and defects in the skin, intestinal mucosa and interferes with the immune system. The richest natural source is red **meat**; it is also present in **cereals** but some is lost in refining processes. Although the requirement is higher in pregnancy, this is covered by a normally mixed **diet**.

zucchini See **courgette**.

zymase An **enzyme** present in **yeast** responsible for the conversion of **glucose** to **alcohol**.

zymogens The precursors of **enzymes** which are activated by substances known as kimases.

Appendix

The following tables are approximations for guidance only. For the majority of recipes they are accurate enough for measurements in any given recipe to be made in either system or a mixture of two. It is however safer to use only one or the other and there is less chance of making mistakes. In a few instances, particularly with strong spices, the measurement must be very accurate.

MEASUREMENT BY WEIGHT
APPROXIMATE FIGURES FOR COOKING

METRIC	IMPERIAL	IMPERIAL	METRIC
5 g	0.25 oz	0.25 oz	5 g
10 g	0.5 oz	0.5 oz	10 g
25 g	1 oz	1 oz	25 g
50 g	2 oz	2 oz	50 g
100 g	4 oz	4 oz	100 g
160 g	6 oz	6 oz	160 g
220 g	8 oz	8 oz	220 g
325 g	12 oz	12 oz	325 g
450 g	16 oz (1 lb)	1 lb	450 g
550 g	1 lb 4 oz	1 lb 4 oz	550 g
650 g	1 lb 6 oz	1 lb 8 oz	675 g
900 g	2 lb	2 lb	900 g
1200 g	2 lb 10 oz	3 lb	1340 g
1500 g	3 lb 5 oz	3 lb 8 oz	1580 g
2000 g	4 lb 7 oz	4 lb	1800 g

MEASUREMENT BY VOLUME
APPROXIMATE EQUIVALENTS FOR GUIDANCE

METRIC	IMPERIAL	IMPERIAL	METRIC
5 ml	1 teaspoon	1 teaspoon	5 ml
10 ml	2 teaspoons	2 teaspoons	10 ml
15 ml	1 tablespoon	1 tablespoon	15 ml
30 ml	1 oz	1 oz	30 ml
60 ml	2 oz	2 oz	60 ml
100 ml	3.5 oz	3.5 oz	100 ml
120 ml	4 oz	4 oz	120 ml
150 ml	5 oz	5 oz	150 ml
200 ml	7 oz	7 oz	200 ml
250 ml	9 oz	9 oz	250 ml
300 ml	11 oz	11 oz	300 ml
400 ml	14 oz	14 oz	400 ml
500 ml	18 oz	18 oz	500 ml
750 ml	27 oz	20 oz	560 ml
1000 ml	35 oz	30 oz	840 ml
		40 oz	1140 ml

TEMPERATURE CONVERSIONS

CELSIUS	FAHRENHEIT	CELSIUS	FAHRENHEIT
−25.0°	−13.0°	60.0°	140.0°
−23.0°	−9.5°	65.0°	149.0°
−18.0°	−0.5°	70.0°	158.0°
−15.0°	6.5°	75.0°	167.0°
−10.0°	14.0°	80.0°	176.0°
−5.0°	23.0°	85.0°	185.0°
0.0°	32.0°	90.0°	194.0°
5.0°	41.0°	95.0°	203.0°
10.0°	50.0°	100.0°	212.0°
15.0°	59.0°	110.0°	230.0°
20.0°	68.0°	120.0°	248.0°
25.0°	77.0°	140.0°	284.0°
30.0°	86.0°	160.0°	320.0°
35.0°	95.0°	180.0°	356.0°
40.0°	104.0°	200.0°	392.0°
45.0°	113.0°	220.0°	428.0°
50.0°	122.0°	240.0°	464.0°
55.0°	131.0°	260.0°	500.0°

USEFUL TEMPERATURES

CELSIUS

−29.0°	(−22°F)	Commercial long term storage of food
−18.0°	(−0.5°F)	Domestic deep freeze
−15.0°	(5°F)	Mixture of ice and salt
0.0°	(32°F)	Water freezes
5.0°	(41°F)	Maximum recommended temperature for refrigerator
40.0°	(104°F)	Temperature for making yoghurt
60.0°	(140°F)	Egg protein starts to coagulate. Yeasts and parasites destroyed
80.0°	(176°F)	Minimum temperature for bottling acidic fruits
★100.0°	(212°F)	Water boils
104.0°	(220°F)	Temperature boiling jam should reach for setting. Most plastics melt
120.0°	(248°F)	Average temperature reached inside a pressure cooker
121.0°	(250°F)	Minimum temperature for bottling vegetables and meats
121.0°	(250°F)	Bacteria and viruses destroyed after 13 minutes exposure in moist heat
134.0°	(273°F)	Bacteria and viruses destroyed after 3 minutes exposure in moist heat
154.0°	(309°F)	Maillard reaction becomes rapid
160.0°	(320°F)	Bacteria and viruses destroyed after 1 hour's exposure in dry heat
165.0°	(329°F)	Fat may start to smoke
180.0°	(356°F)	All bacteria and viruses destroyed after 10 minutes exposure in dry heat
184.0°	(363°F)	Sugar browns
230.0°	(446°F)	Fat may ignite spontaneously
1093°	(2000°F)	Red heat
1650°	(3000°F)	Gas flame

★ The temperature at which water boils falls by 1° (2°F) for every rise in altitude of 300m (1000ft)

COMPARATIVE COOKING TEMPERATURES

DESCRIPTION	CELCIUS	FAHR	GAS MARK
Cool	107–121°C	225–250°F	0–0.5
Very slow	121–135°C	250–275°F	0.5–1
Slow	135–149°C	275–300°F	1–2
Very moderate	149–163°C	300–325°F	2–3
Moderate	170–190°C	350–375°F	4–5
Moderate hot	204°C	400°F	6
Hot	218–233°C	425–450°F	7–8
Very hot	246°C	475°F	9

HEAT AND ENERGY

1 Therm	=	100,000 British Thermal Units (BTU) Obsolete 1992.
	=	29.3 kWh
1 kWh	=	0.034 therms
1 litre domestic heating oil	=	10.25 kWh
1 kcal (kilocalorie)	=	4.184 kJ (kilojoules)
1 MJ (megajoule)	=	1000 kJ
Protein	=	4.0 kcal, 17 kJ per g.
Fat	=	9.0 kcal, 37 kJ per g.
Carbohydrate	=	3.7 kcal, 15.48 kJ
Alcohol	=	7 kcal, 29.2 kJ

Note. The figures quoted may vary slightly, as different sources may attempt to take account of the amount of useable energy, and this differs from one sample to another. Biological products are themselves subject to wide variations, depending on season, environment and age at time of gathering. Food science can never be a precise exercise.

AVERAGE pH VALUES OF SOME COMMON FOODS

The full range of pH values lies between 1 and 14. Each unit represents a tenfold change: thus black coffee is 10 times as acid as evaporated milk and a lemon over 10 times as acid as an orange.

Gastric juice	1.5–3.0	Peaches	3.7	Corned beef	5.9
Lime juice	2.3	Pineapple	3.7	Tuna	5.9
Lemon juice	2.4	Tomato	4.3	Peas	6.0
Pickles	2.7	Banana	4.6	Sardines	6.0
Rhubarb	3.1	Black coffee	5.0	Evaporated milk	6.0
Apricots	3.2	Cabbage	5.2	Pork, processed	6.1
Grapefruit	3.2	Carrots	5.2	Chicken	6.2
Plums	3.4	Parsnips	5.2	Butter	6.2
Strawberries	3.4	Baked beans	5.3	Salmon	6.4
Raspberries	3.6	Spinach	5.4	Milk	6.9
Orange juice	3.7	Potatoes	5.5	Egg white	7.6

Tap water varies from 5–9 depending on catchment area.

The pH value may be roughly estimated by the use of test papers, such as those sold for checking the pH of garden soil. More accurate estimations can only be carried out using a special pH meter, such as that supplied by Jencoms Scientific, Industrial Estate, Stambridge Rd, Leighton Buzzard. LU7 8UA. Cat No H35/26. which is accurate to 0.1 pH.

All the tables on the following pages are taken from "Manual of Nutrition" Reference Book 343 published by HMSO and reproduced by kind permission.

Crown Copyright reserved

Biology is not a precise science and it must be emphasised that nutritional values are variable. All biological products, both of plant and animal origin, differ according to exact variety (even though known as the same product), season, environment and age at harvesting.

There are also variations in quantities of nutrients that are accessible for use by the body, variations from one individual to another in their ability to utilise the same product and the use of alternative methods of assessment by different sources. This does not mean that a particular source of figures is incorrect. All figures should be taken as a working average.

ACCEPTABLE WEIGHT RANGES

	Height (without shoes)		Weight (without clothes)	
	ft in	cm	lb	kg
Men	5 5	165	121–152	55–69
	5 6	168	124–156	56–71
	5 7	170	128–161	58–73
	5 8	173	132–166	60–75
	5 9	175	136–170	62–77
	5 10	178	140–174	64–79
	5 11	180	144–179	65–80
	6 0	183	148–184	67–83
	6 1	185	152–189	69–86
	6 2	188	156–194	71–88
	6 3	191	160–199	73–90
Women	4 11	150	94–122	43–55
	5 0	152	96–125	44–57
	5 1	155	99–128	45–58
	5 2	157	102–131	46–59
	5 3	160	105–134	48–61
	5 4	163	108–138	49–62
	5 5	165	111–142	51–65
	5 6	168	114–146	52–66
	5 7	170	118–150	53–67
	5 8	173	122–154	55–69
	5 9	175	126–158	58–72
	5 10	178	130–163	59–74

Prepared from data published in the Royal College of Physicians' Report on Obesity, 1983.

AVERAGE ENERGY REQUIREMENTS PER DAY
PER KILOGRAM OF BODY WEIGHT

Age	Male		Female	
	kcal	kJ	kcal	kJ
0–12 months	50	210	50	210
1–10 years	40	167	50	210
Adult	25	105	24	100
Over 60	Requirements fall by approximately 0.13% per year			

AVERAGE RESTING ENERGY REQUIREMENTS

	Weight	Resting energy requirements per day			
	kg	Total		Per kg	
		kcal	kJ	kcal	kJ
Infant 1 year	10	500	2,100	50	210
Child 8 years old	25	1,000	4,200	40	170
Adult woman	55	1,300	5,400	25	100
Adult man	65	1,600	6,700	25	100

ENERGY REQUIREMENTS

For an average 25 year old man weighing 65 kg (10 stone)

	Average energy expenditure	
	kcal/min	kJ/min
Everyday activities		
Sitting	1.4	6
Standing	1.7	7
Washing, dressing	3.5	15
Walking slowly	3	13
Walking moderately quickly	5	21
Walking up and down stairs	9	38

Work and recreation

Light

Most domestic work
Golf
Lorry driving   2.5–4.9   10–20
Light industrial and assembly work
Carpentry, bricklaying

Moderate

Gardening
Tennis, dancing, jogging
Cycling up to 20 km per hr   5.0–7.4   21–30
Digging, shovelling
Agricultural work, non-mechanized

Strenuous

Coal mining, steel furnace work
Squash, cross country running   7.5 and over   Over 30
Football, swimming (crawl)

TOTAL ENERGY REQUIREMENTS

The dietary energy required by an individual who is neither gaining nor losing weight exactly equals the energy expended on maintenance and physical activity. In practice this balance is achieved over periods of a few days, with remarkable accuracy: an excessive intake of only 10 kcal each day would be equivalent to a weight gain of about 1 lb (0.5 kg) every year.

	kcal	MJ
8 hr asleep at 1.1 kcal per min	530	2.2
8 hr at work		
6 hr sitting at 1.4 kcal per min	500	2.2
2 hr standing and walking averaging 2.5 kcal per min	300	1.2
8 hr non–occupational activities		
2 hr 15 min travelling, averaging 1.7 kcal per min	230	0.9
15 min washing and dressing, at 3.5 kcal per min	50	0.2
1½ hr light domestic activities, averaging 3 kcal per min	270	1.2
3 hr sitting, eating, reading, watching television, at 1.4 kcal per min	250	1.1
30 min squash, averaging 7.5 kcal per min	230	0.9
30 min gardening, averaging 5 kcal per min	150	0.6
Total energy expenditure	2,510	10.5

Because of individual variations, the diet of any particular sedentary worker may provide more or less energy than this; the average intake of a group of such people would, however, be expected to be close to this value.

COMPOSITION OF COMMON FOODS

FATS

Typical fatty acid composition of some foods as bought

	Fat g per 100g edible portion	Fatty acids, per cent of fat by weight[1]		
		Saturated	Monounsaturated	Polyunsaturated
Milk, cows'	3.9	64	28	3
Milk, human	4.1	48	39	8
Cheese, Cheddar	33.5	63	27	4
Eggs	10.9	31	39	11
Beef, average	27.4	41	47	4
Pork, average	25.5	35	42	15
Chicken	12.8	30	45	20
Liver, lambs	6.2	28	29	15
Mackerel	22.9	20	49	20
Butter	82.0	68	23	4
Margarine, hard	81.0	39	47	10
Margarine, soft	81.0	30	41	26
Margarine, polyunsaturated	81.0	17	27	52
Corn (maize) oil	99.9	13	25	58
Blended oil	99.9	8	52	36
Potato crisps	35.9	34	40	21
Peanuts, roasted, salted	49.0	21	38	37
Biscuits, chocolate	27.6	65	26	4
Chocolate, milk	30.3	58	33	4

[1] The total percentage of fatty acids is less than 100 because of the glycerol and other fatty compounds which are present. To calculate the total fatty acid content of a food, multiply the percentages of the various types of fatty acid by the amount of fat. Thus the total polyunsaturated fatty acid content of 100g of beef is $\frac{1}{100} \times 27.4 = 1.1$g.

Vitamin D content of selected foods, μg per 100 gm edible portion

Milk, whole	0.03	Herring and kipper	22.4
Milk, skimmed	0	Salmon, canned	12.5
Milk, skimmed, fortified	0.08	Sardines, canned	7.5
Evaporated milk	4.0	Butter	0.8
Cheese, Cheddar	0.3	Margarine	7.9
Yoghurt, fortified	2.0	Vegetable oil	0
Eggs	1.6	Cornflakes, fortified	2.8
Beef, average	0	Ovaltine, dry	8.7
Liver, average	0.8	Cod liver oil	212.5

The main sources of vitamin D in the diet are, on average, margarine, fatty fish, eggs, breakfast cereals, and butter.

Composition per 100g (raw edible weight except where stated)

No.	Food	Inedible waste %	Energy kcal	kJ	Protein g	Fat g	Carbo-hydrate (as mono-saccharide) g
	Milk						
1	Cream − double	0	447	1,841	1.5	48.2	2.0
2	Cream − single	0	195	806	2.4	19.3	3.2
3	Milk, liquid, whole	0	65	272	3.2	3.9	4.6
4	Milk, liquid, skimmed	0	32	137	3.4	0.1	4.7
5	Milk, condensed whole, sweetened	0	170	709	8.5	10.2	11.7
6	Milk, whole, evaporated	0	149	620	8.4	9.4	8.1
7	Milk, dried, skimmed	0	339	1,442	36.1	0.6	50.4
8	Yoghurt, low fat, natural	0	65	276	5.1	0.8	10.0
9	Yoghurt, low fat, fruit	0	89	382	4.1	0.7	17.9
	Cheese						
10	Cheddar	0	406	1,682	26.0	33.5	0
11	Cottage	0	96	402	13.6	4.0	1.4
12	Cheese spread	0	283	1,173	18.3	22.9	0.9
13	Feta	0	245	1,017	16.5	19.9	0
14	Brie	0	300	1,246	22.8	23.2	0
	Meat						
15	Bacon, rashers, raw	11	339	1,402	13.9	31.5	0
16	Bacon, rashers, grilled	0	393	1,632	28.1	31.2	0
17	Beef, average, raw	17	313	1,296	16.6	27.4	0
18	Beef, mince, stewed	0	229	955	23.1	15.2	0
19	Beef, stewing steak, raw	4	176	736	20.2	10.6	0
20	Beef, stewing steak, cooked	0	223	932	30.9	11.0	0
21	Black pudding, fried	0	305	1,270	12.9	21.9	15.0
22	Chicken, raw	41	194	809	19.7	12.8	0
23	Chicken, roast, meat and skin	0	213	888	24.4	12.8	0
24	Chicken, roast, meat only	0	148	621	24.8	5.4	0
25	Corned beef	0	202	844	25.9	10.9	0
26	Ham	0	166	690	16.4	11.1	0
27	Kidney, pigs, raw	6	86	363	15.5	2.7	0
28	Kidney, pigs, fried	0	202	848	29.2	9.5	0
29	Lamb, average, raw	23	295	1,223	16.2	25.6	0
30	Lamb, roast	0	266	1,106	26.1	17.9	0
31	Liver, lambs, raw	0	140	587	20.3	6.2	0.8
32	Liver, lambs, fried	0	237	989	30.1	12.9	0
33	Luncheon meat	0	266	1,153	12.9	23.8	3.3
34	Paté, average	0	347	1,436	13.7	31.9	1.4
35	Pork, average, raw	26	297	1,231	16.9	25.5	0
36	Pork chop, cooked	26	332	1,380	28.5	24.2	0
37	Sausage, beef, cooked	0	267	1,114	12.9	17.7	15.0
38	Sausage, pork, cooked	0	317	1,318	13.6	24.5	11.2
39	Steak & kidney pie	0	274	1,146	9.3	17.1	22.2
40	Turkey, roast, meat & skin	0	189	793	26.2	9.4	0

Water g	Calcium mg	Iron mg	Sodium mg	Vitamin A (retinol equivalent) μg	Thia-min mg	Ribo-flavin mg	Niacin equivalent mg	Vitamin C mg	No.
49	50	0.2	30	500	0.02	0.08	0.4	1	1
72	79	0.3	40	155	0.03	0.12	0.8	1	2
88	103	0.1	50	56	0.05	0.17	0.9	1.5	3
91	108	0.1	50	1	0.05	0.18	0.9	1.5	4
30	270	0.2	140	123	0.09	0.46	2.3	4.1	5
69	260	0.3	170	125	0.07	0.42	2.1	1.5	6
3	1,230	0.3	510	550	0.38	0.16	9.5	13.2	7
86	200	0.1	80	12	0.06	0.25	1.2	0.8	8
77	150	0.1	70	12	0.05	0.21	1.2	0.7	9
37	800	0.4	610	363	0.04	0.50	6.2	0	10
79	60	0.1	450	41	0.02	0.19	3.3	0	11
51	510	0.7	1,170	198	0.02	0.24	0.1	0	12
56	384	0.2	1,260	270	0.03	0.11	4.2	0	13
48	380	0.8	1,410	238	0.09	0.60	6.2	0	14
51	7	0.6	1,340	0	0.45	0.14	6.5	0	15
34	14	1.3	2,404	0	0.57	0.27	12.5	0	16
55	7	1.9	70	10	0.05	0.23	6.9	0	17
59	18	3.1	320	0	0.05	0.33	9.3	0	18
69	8	2.1	72	0	0.06	0.23	8.5	0	19
57	15	3.0	360	0	0.03	0.33	10.2	0	20
44	35	20.0	1,210	0	0.09	0.07	3.8	0	21
67	9	0.7	75	0	0.11	0.13	9.6	0	22
62	13	0.5	90	0	0.05	0.19	13.6	0	23
68	9	0.8	81	0	0.08	0.19	12.8	0	24
59	27	2.4	854	0	0	0.20	9.1	0	25
67	4	0.6	1,405	0	0.54	0.20	6.3	0	26
80	10	6.4	200	160	0.56	2.58	11.1	6.5	27
58	12	9.1	220	220	0.41	3.70	20.1	11.9	28
56	7	1.4	71	0	0.09	0.21	7.1	0	29
55	8	2.5	65	0	0.12	0.31	11.0	0	30
70	6	7.5	73	19,900	0.39	4.64	20.7	19.2	31
54	8	10.9	83	30,500	0.38	5.65	24.7	18.6	32
54	39	1.0	913	0	0.06	0.15	3.9	0	33
47	14	8.2	762	8,300	0.14	1.32	4.3	0	34
57	8	0.9	65	0	0.49	0.20	8.9	0	35
46	11	1.2	84	0	0.66	0.20	11.0	0	36
48	68	1.6	1,095	0	0	0.14	9.0	0	37
45	54	1.5	1,075	0	0.01	0.16	7.2	0	38
51	47	1.8	402	0	0.12	0.25	4.9	0	39
63	7	0.9	70	0	0.09	0.16	12.2	0	40

Composition per 100g

No.	Food	Inedible waste %	Energy kcal	kJ	Protein g	Fat g	Carbo-hydrate (as mono-saccharide) g
	Fish						
41	White fish, filleted	3	77	324	17.1	0.9	0
42	Cod, fried	0	235	982	19.6	14.3	7.5
43	Fish fingers, raw	0	178	749	12.6	7.5	16.1
44	Herrings, whole	46	251	1,040	16.8	20.4	0
45	Mackerel	40	282	1,170	19.0	22.9	0
46	Pilchards, canned in tomato sauce	0	126	531	18.8	5.4	0.7
47	Sardines, canned in oil, fish only	0	217	906	23.7	18.6	0
48	Tuna in oil	0	289	1,202	22.8	22.0	0
49	Prawns, boiled	0	107	451	22.6	1.8	0
	Eggs						
50	Eggs, boiled	12	147	612	12.3	10.9	0
51	Eggs, fried	0	232	961	14.1	19.5	0
	Fats						
52	Butter	0	740	3,041	0.4	82.0	0
53	Lard, cooking fat, dripping	0	892	3,667	0	99.1	0
54	Low fat spread	0	366	1,506	0	40.7	0
55	Margarine, average	0	730	3,000	0.1	81.0	0
56	Cooking and salad oil	0	899	3,696	0	99.9	0
	Preserves, etc.						
57	Chocolate, milk	0	529	2,214	8.4	30.3	59.4
58	Honey	0	288	1,229	0.4	0	76.4
59	Jam	0	262	1,116	0.5	0	69.2
60	Marmalade	0	261	1,114	0.1	0	69.5
61	Sugar, white	0	394	1,680	0	0	105.3
62	Syrup	0	298	1,269	0.3	0	79.0
63	Peppermints	0	392	1,670	0.5	0.7	102.2
	Vegetables						
64	Aubergines	23	14	62	0.7	0	3.1
65	Baked beans	0	81	345	4.8	0.6	15.1
66	Beans, runner, boiled	1	19	83	1.9	0.2	2.7
67	Beans, red kidney, raw	0	272	1,159	22.1	1.7	45.0
68	Beans, soya, boiled	0	141	592	12.4	6.4	9.0
69	Beetroot, boiled	0	44	189	1.8	0	9.9
70	Brussels sprouts, boiled	0	18	75	2.8	0	1.7
71	Cabbage, raw	43	22	92	2.8	0	2.8
72	Cabbage, boiled	0	15	66	1.7	0	2.3
73	Carrots, old	4	23	98	0.7	0	5.4
74	Cauliflower, cooked	0	9	40	1.6	0	0.8
75	Celery	27	8	36	0.9	0	1.3
76	Courgettes, raw	13	29	122	1.6	0.4	5.0

Water g	Calcium mg	Iron mg	Sodium mg	Vitamin A (retinol equivalent) μg	Thia- min mg	Ribo- flavin mg	Niacin equivalent mg	Vitamin C mg	No.
82	22	0.5	99	1	0.07	0.09	6.0	0	41
57	80	0.5	100	0	0.06	0.07	4.9	0	42
64	43	0.7	320	0.2	0.09	0.06	3.5	0	43
64	33	0.8	67	46	0	0.18	7.2	0	44
57	24	1.0	130	45	0.09	0.35	11.6	0	45
74	300	2.7	370	8	0.02	0.29	11.1	0	46
58	550	2.9	650	7	0.04	0.36	12.6	0	47
55	7	1.1	420	0	0.04	0.11	17.2	0	48
70	150	1.1	1,590	0	0.03	0.03	7.4	0	49
75	52	2.0	140	190	0.09	0.47	3.7	0	50
63	64	2.5	220	140	0.07	0.42	4.2	0	51
15	15	0.2	870	985	0	0	0.1	0	52
1	1	0.1	2	0	0	0	0	0	53
51	0	0	690	900	0	0	0	0	54
16	4	0.3	800	860	0	0	0.1	0	55
0	0	0	0	0	0	0	0	0	56
2	220	1.6	120	6.6	0.10	0.23	1.6	0	57
23	5	0.4	11	0	0	0.05	0.2	0	58
30	18	1.2	14	2	0	0	0	10	59
28	35	0.6	18	8	0	0	0	10	60
0	2	0	0	0	0	0	0	0	61
28	26	1.5	270	0	0	0	0	0	62
0	7	0.2	9	0	0	0	0	0	63
93	10	0.4	3	0	0.05	0.03	1.0	5	64
74	48	1.4	550	12	0.08	0.06	1.3	0	65
91	22	0.7	1	67	0.03	0.07	0.8	5	66
11	140	6.7	40	0	0.54	0.18	5.5	0	67
67	145	2.5	15	0	0.26	0.16	3.4	0	68
83	30	0.4	64	0	0.02	0.04	0.4	5	69
92	25	0.5	2	67	0.06	0.10	0.9	40	70
88	57	0.6	7	50	0.06	0.05	0.8	55	71
93	38	0.4	4	50	0.03	0.03	0.5	20	72
90	48	0.6	95	2,000	0.06	0.05	0.7	6	73
95	18	0.4	4	5	0.06	0.06	0.8	20	74
94	52	0.6	140	0	0.03	0.03	0.5	7	75
92	30	1.5	1	58	0.05	0.09	0.6	16	76

Composition per 100g

No.	Food	Inedible waste %	Energy kcal	kJ	Protein g	Fat g	Carbohydrate (as monosaccharide) g
77	Cucumber	23	10	43	0.6	0.1	1.8
78	Lentils, cooked	0	99	420	7.6	0.5	17.0
79	Lettuce	30	12	51	1.0	0.4	1.2
80	Mushrooms	25	13	53	1.8	0.6	0
81	Onion	3	23	99	0.9	0	5.2
82	Parsnips, cooked	0	56	238	1.3	0	13.5
83	Peas, frozen, boiled	0	72	307	6.0	0.9	10.7
84	Peas, canned processed	0	86	366	6.9	0.7	18.9
85	Peppers, green	14	12	51	0.9	0	2.2
86	Potatoes	10^1 20^2	74	315	2.0	0.2	17.1
87	Potatoes, boiled	0	76	322	1.8	0.1	18.0
88	Potato crisps	0	533	2,224	6.3	35.9	49.3
89	Potatoes, fried (chips)	0	234	983	3.6	10.2	34.0
90	Potatoes, oven chips	0	162	687	3.2	4.2	29.8
91	Potatoes, roast	0	150	632	3.0	4.5	25.9
92	Spinach, boiled	0	30	128	5.1	0.5	1.4
93	Sweetcorn, canned	0	85	379	2.9	1.2	16.8
94	Sweet potato	14	91	387	1.2	0.6	21.5
95	Tomatoes, fresh	0	14	60	0.9	0	2.8
96	Turnips, cooked	0	14	60	0.7	0.3	2.3
97	Watercress	23	14	61	2.9	0	0.7
98	Yam, boiled	0	119	508	1.6	0.1	29.8
	Fruit						
99	Apples	20	46	196	0.3	0	11.9
100	Apricots, canned in syrup	0	106	452	0.5	0	27.7
101	Apricots, dried	0	182	772	4.8	0	43.4
102	Avocado pear	29	223	922	4.2	22.2	1.8
103	Bananas	40	76	326	1.1	0	19.2
104	Blackcurrants	2	28	121	0.9	0	6.6
105	Cherries	13	47	201	0.6	0	11.9
106	Dates, dried	14	248	1,056	2.0	0	63.9
107	Figs, dried	0	213	908	3.6	0	52.9
108	Gooseberries, cooked, unsweetened	0	14	62	0.9	0	2.9
109	Grapes	5	63	268	0.6	0	16.1
110	Grapefruit	50	22	95	0.6	0	5.3
111	Lemon juice	64	7	31	0.3	0	1.6
112	Mango	34	59	253	0.5	0	15.3
113	Melon	40	23	97	0.8	0	5.2
114	Oranges	25	35	150	0.8	0	8.5
115	Orange juice	0	38	161	0.6	0	9.4
116	Peaches	13	37	156	0.6	0	9.1
117	Peaches, canned in syrup	0	87	373	0.4	0	22.9
118	Pears	28	41	175	0.3	0	10.6

[1] Old potatoes   [2] New potatoes

Water g	Calcium mg	Iron mg	Sodium mg	Vitamin A (retinol equivalent) µg	Thiamin mg	Riboflavin mg	Niacin equivalent mg	Vitamin C mg	No.
96	23	0.3	13	0	0.04	0.04	0.3	8	77
72	13	2.4	12	3	0.11	0.04	1.6	0	78
96	23	0.9	9	167	0.07	0.08	0.4	15	79
92	3	1.0	9	0	0.10	0.40	4.6	3	80
93	31	0.3	10	0	0.03	0.05	0.4	10	81
83	36	0.5	4	0	0.07	0.06	0.9	10	82
78	35	1.6	2	50	0.30	0.09	1.6	12	83
70	33	1.8	380	10	0.10	0.04	1.4	0	84
94	9	0.4	2	33	0.08	0.03	0.9	100	85
79	8	0.4	8	0	0.20	0.02	1.5	8–19	86
80	4	0.4	7	0	0.20	0.02	1.2	5–9	87
3	37	2.1	550	0	0.19	0.07	6.1	17	88
44	14	0.84	41	0	0.20	0.02	1.5	6–14	89
59	1	0.8	53	0	0.10	0.04	3.1	12	90
65	10	0.62	9	0	0.20	0.02	1.3	5–12	91
85	136	4.0	120	1,000	0.07	0.15	1.8	25	92
72	4	0.5	270	4	0.04	0.06	1.8	0	93
70	22	0.7	19	4,000[3]	0.10	0.06	1.2	25	94
93	13	0.4	3	100	0.06	0.04	0.8	20	95
95	55	0.4	28	0	0.03	0.04	0.6	17	96
91	220	1.6	60	500	0.10	0.10	1.1	60	97
66	9	0.3	17	2	0.05	0.01	0.8	2	98
84	4	0.3	2	5	0.04	0.02	0.1	5	99
68	12	0.7	1	166	0.02	0.01	0.4	2	100
15	92	4.1	56	600	0	0.20	3.8	0	101
69	15	1.5	2	17	0.10	0.10	1.8	15	102
71	7	0.4	1	33	0.04	0.07	0.8	10	103
77	60	1.3	3	33	0.03	0.06	0.4	200	104
82	16	0.4	3	20	0.05	0.07	0.4	5	105
15	68	1.6	5	10	0.07	0.04	2.9	0	106
17	280	4.2	87	8	0.10	0.08	2.2	0	107
90	24	0.3	2	25	0.03	0.03	0.5	31	108
79	19	0.3	2	0	0.04	0.02	0.3	4	109
91	17	0.3	1	0	0.05	0.02	0.3	40	110
91	8	0.1	2	0	0.02	0.01	0.1	50	111
83	10	0.5	7	200	0.03	0.04	0.4	30	112
94	16	0.4	17	175	0.05	0.03	0.3	50	113
86	41	0.3	3	8	0.10	0.03	0.3	50	114
88	12	0.3	2	8	0.08	0.02	0.3	25–45	115
86	5	0.4	3	83	0.02	0.05	1.1	8	116
74	4	0.4	1	41	0.01	0.02	0.6	4	117
83	8	0.2	2	2	0.03	0.03	0.3	3	118

[3] The vitamin A content of white and yellow varieties may vary between 0 and 12,000 µg

Composition per 100g

No.	Food	Inedible waste %	Energy kcal	kJ	Protein g	Fat g	Carbohydrate (as monosaccharide) g
119	Pineapple, canned in juice	0	46	194	0.5	0	11.6
120	Plums	8	32	137	0.6	0	7.9
121	Prunes, dried	17	161	686	2.4	0	40.3
122	Raspberries	0	25	105	0.9	0	5.6
123	Rhubarb, cooked with sugar	0	45	191	0.5	0	11.4
124	Strawberries	3	26	109	0.6	0	6.2
125	Sultanas	0	250	1,066	1.8	0	64.7
	Nuts						
126	Almonds	63	565	2,336	16.9	53.5	4.3
127	Coconut, desiccated	0	604	2,492	5.6	62.0	6.4
128	Peanuts, roasted & salted	0	570	2,364	24.3	49.0	8.6
	Cereals						
129	Biscuits, chocolate	0	524	2,197	5.7	27.6	67.4
130	Biscuits, plain, digestive	0	471	1,978	6.3	20.9	68.6
131	Biscuits, semi-sweet	0	457	1,925	6.7	16.6	74.8
132	Bread, brown	0	217	924	8.4	2.0	44.2
133	Bread, white	0	230	980	8.2	1.7	48.6
134	Bread, wholemeal	0	215	911	9.0	2.5	41.6
	Breakfast cereals						
135	Cornflakes	0	368	1,567	8.6	1.6	85.1
136	Weetabix	0	340	1,444	11.4	3.4	70.3
137	Muesli	0	368	1,556	12.9	7.5	66.2
138	Cream crackers	0	440	1,857	9.5	16.3	68.3
139	Crispbread, rye	0	321	1,367	9.4	2.1	70.6
140	Flour, white	0	337	1,435	9.4	1.3	76.7
141	Flour, wholemeal	0	306	1,302	12.7	2.2	62.8
142	Oats, porridge	0	374	1,582	10.9	9.2	66.0
143	Rice, raw	0	359	1,529	7.0	1.0	85.8
144	Spaghetti, raw	0	342	1,456	12.0	1.8	74.1
	Cakes, etc.						
145	Chocolate cake with butter icing	0	500	2,092	5.8	30.9	53.1
146	Currant buns	0	296	1,250	7.6	7.5	52.7
147	Fruit cake, rich	0	322	1,357	4.9	12.5	50.7
148	Jam tarts	0	368	1,552	3.3	13.0	63.4
149	Plain cake, Madeira	0	393	1,652	5.4	16.9	58.4
	Puddings						
150	Apple pie	0	369	1,554	4.3	15.5	56.7
151	Bread and butter pudding	0	157	661	6.1	7.7	16.9
152	Cheesecake, frozen, fruit topping	0	239	1,005	5.2	10.6	32.8
153	Custard	0	118	496	3.8	4.4	16.7

Water g	Calcium mg	Iron mg	Sodium mg	Vitamin A (retinol equivalent) μg	Thia-min mg	Ribo-flavin mg	Niacin equivalent mg	Vitamin C mg	No.
77	12	0.4	1	7	0.08	0.02	0.3	20–40	119
85	12	0.3	2	37	0.05	0.03	0.6	3	120
23	38	2.9	12	160	0.10	0.20	1.9	0	121
83	41	1.2	3	13	0.02	0.03	0.5	25	122
85	84	0.3	2	8	0	0.03	0.4	7	123
89	22	0.7	2	5	0.02	0.03	0.5	60	124
18	52	1.8	53	5	0.10	0.08	0.6	0	125
5	250	4.2	6	0	0.24	0.92	4.7	0	126
2	22	3.6	28	0	0.06	0.04	1.8	0	127
5	61	2.0	440	0	0.23	0.10	21.3	0	128
2.2	110	1.7	160	0	0.03	0.13	2.7	0	129
2.5	92	3.2	600	0	0.14	0.11	2.4	0	130
2.5	120	2.1	410	0	0.13	0.08	2.9	0	131
40	99	2.2	540	0	0.27	0.10	2.3	0	132
38	105	1.6	525	0	0.21	0.06	2.3	0	133
38	54	2.7	560	0	0.34	0.09	1.8	0	134
3.0	3	6.7	1,160	0	1.8	1.6	21.9	0	135
1.8	33	7.6	360	0	1.0	1.5	14.3	0	136
5.8	200	4.6	180	0	0.33	0.27	5.7	0	137
4.3	110	1.7	610	0	0.13	0.08	3.4	0	138
6.4	50	3.7	220	0	0.28	0.14	2.9	0	139
14.0	140	2.0	2	0	0.31	0.04	3.5	0	140
14.0	38	3.9	2	0	0.47	0.09	8.3	0	141
8.2	52	3.8	9	0	0.90	0.09	3.3	0	142
11.4	4	0.5	4	0	0.41	0.02	5.8	0	143
9.8	25	2.1	3	0	0.22	0.03	3.1	0	144
8.4	130	1.6	440	298	0.07	0.09	2.0	0	145
27.7	110	1.9	230	0	0.37	0.16	3.1	0	146
20.6	84	3.2	220	0	0.07	0.09	1.3	0	147
14.4	72	1.7	130	0	0.06	0.02	1.2	0	148
20.2	42	1.1	380	0	0.06	0.11	1.6	0	149
22.9	51	1.2	210	0	0.05	0.02	0.4	0	150
67.5	130	0.6	150	78	0.07	0.23	1.8	0	151
44.0	68	0.5	160	0	0.04	0.16	1.7	0	152
74.9	140	0.1	76	38	0.05	0.20	1.0	0	153

Composition per 100g

No.	Food	Inedible waste %	Energy kcal	kJ	Protein g	Fat g	Carbo-hydrate (as mono-saccharide) g
154	Ice cream, dairy	0	165	691	3.3	8.2	20.7
155	Rice pudding	0	131	552	4.1	4.2	20.4
156	Trifle	0	165	690	2.2	9.2	19.5
	Beverages						
157	Chocolate, drinking	0	366	1,554	5.5	6.0	77.4
158	Cocoa powder	0	312	1,301	18.5	21.7	11.5
159	Coffee, ground, infusion	0	3	12	0.3	0	0.4
160	Coffee, instant powder	0	100	424	14.6	0	11.0
161	Carbonated 'ades	0	38	166	0	0	10.0
162	Tea, dry	0	0	0	0	0	0
163	Squash, undiluted	0	98	418	0	0	26.1
	Alcoholic beverages						
164	Beer, keg bitter	0	37	156	0	0	2.3
165	Spirits	0	222	919	0	0	0
166	Wine, medium white	0	89	371	0	0	2.5
167	Cider, average	0	43	180	0	0	2.9
	Miscellaneous						
168	Curry powder	0	325	1,395	12.7	13.8	41.8
169	Marmite	0	179	759	41.4	0.7	1.8
170	Peanut butter	0	623	2,581	22.6	53.7	13.1
171	Soy sauce	0	56	240	5.2	0.5	8.3
172	Tomato soup	0	55	230	0.8	3.3	5.9
173	Tomato ketchup	0	98	420	2.1	0	24.0
174	Pickle, sweet	0	134	572	0.6	0.3	34.4
175	Salad cream	0	311	1,288	1.9	27.4	15.1

Water g	Calcium mg	Iron mg	Sodium mg	Vitamin A (retinol equivalent) μg	Thiamin mg	Riboflavin mg	Niacin equivalent mg	Vitamin C mg	No.
65.7	120	0.3	70	0	0.04	0.15	0.9	0	154
71.8	30	0.1	55	33	0.04	0.14	1.1	0	155
68.1	68	0.3	63	50	0.06	0.10	0.6	0	156
2	33	2.4	2	2	0.06	0.04	2.1	0	157
3	130	10.5	7	7	0.16	0.06	7.3	0	158
98	3	0.1	1	0	0	0.01	0.6	0	159
3	140	4.6	81	0	0.04	0.21	27.9	0	160
91	4	0.1	8	0	0	0	0	0	161
0	0	0	0	0	0	0.9	6.0	0	162
72	11	0.1	35	0	0	0.01	0.1	5	163
93	8	0	6	0	0	0.03	0.17	0	164
68	0	0	0	0	0	0	0	0	165
85	10	0.4	1	0	0	0	0.1	0	166
92	5	0.2	7	0	0	0	0	0	167
9	478	29.6	52	99	0.25	0.28	3.5	11	168
25	95	3.7	4,500	0	3.10	11.0	67	0	169
1	37	2.1	350	0	0.17	0.10	15	0	170
71	65	4.8	5,720	0	0.04	0.17	1.8	0	171
84	17	0.4	460	35	0.03	0.02	0.6	0	172
65	25	1.2	1,120	0	0.06	0.05	0.3	0	173
59	19	2.0	1,700	0	0.03	0.01	0.2	0	174
52.7	34	0.8	840	0	0	0	0	0	175

Dietary fibre content of selected foods as measured by two different methods, g per 100 g edible portion

	Method A	Method B		Method A	Method B
Meat	0	0	Biscuits, rich tea	2.2	2.3
Baked beans	3.2	7.3	Bread, white	1.6	4.1
Beans, haricot, dry	15.1	25.4	Bread, brown	4.3	6.4
Beans, runner	4.4	2.9	Bread, wholemeal	5.8	8.5
Cabbage	2.7	3.4	Flour, white	2.3	4.0
Carrots	2.3	2.9	Flour, wholemeal	8.9	8.1
Potatoes	1.3	1.8	All bran	23.7	26.0
Tomatoes	1.7	1.5	Porridge oats	6.5	7.7
Apples	1.9	2.0	Rice Krispies	0.9	6.0
Bananas	1.1	3.4	Shredded Wheat	9.8	11.2
Raisins	1.7	6.8	Weetabix	9.8	9.3
Nuts, hazel	4.3	6.1	Macaroni	2.6	5.5
Peanuts	6.0	8.1	Rice, white	0.5	3.0
Biscuits, digestive	2.9	5.1	Rice, brown	1.7	4.2
			Spaghetti	2.7	5.6

Method A excludes 'resistant starch' while method B includes it as a part of dietary fibre. It is not yet known whether resistant starch shares all the properties attributed to dietary fibre.

Daily intake and total body content of minerals for a reference man

	Daily intake		Total body content	
Major minerals				
Calcium	1.1	g	1,000	g
Phosphorus	1.4	g	780	g
Sulphur	0.85	g	140	g
Potassium	3.3	g	140	g
Sodium	4.4	g	100	g
Chlorine	5.2	g	95	g
Magnesium	0.34	g	19	g
Iron	16.0	mg	4.2	g
Trace elements				
Fluorine	1.8	mg	2.6	g
Zinc	13.0	mg	2.3	g
Copper	3.5	mg	72	mg
Selenium	0.15	mg	›15	mg
Iodine	0.2	mg	13	mg
Manganese	3.7	mg	12	mg
Chromium	0.15	mg	Less than 2 mg	
Cobalt	0.3	mg	1.5	mg

The following list of additives is taken from 'About Food Additives' reference number PB0552 1991 and reproduced by kind permission of HMSO. Crown Copyright reserved.

FOOD ADDITIVES

ANTIOXIDANTS

Stop fatty foods from going rancid and protect fat-soluble vitamins from the harmful effects of oxidation

E300   L-ascorbic acid — *fruit drinks; also used to improve flour and bread dough*

E301   sodium L-ascorbate

E302   calcium L-ascorbate

E304   6-0-palmitoyl-L-ascorbic acid (ascorbyl palmitate) — *scotch eggs*

E306   extracts of natural origin rich in tocopherols — *vegetable oils*

E307   synthetic alpha-tocopherol — *cereal-based baby foods*

E308   synthetic gamma-tocopherol

E309   synthetic delta-tocopherol

E310   propyl gallate — *vegetable oils; chewing gum*

E311   octyl gallate

E312   dodecyl gallate

E320   butylated hydroxyanisole (BHA) — *soup mixes; cheese spread*

E321   butylated hydroxytoluene (BHT) — *chewing gum*

E322   lecithins — *low fat spreads; also used as an emulsifier in chocolate*

diphenylamine

ethoxyquin — *used to prevent 'scald' (a discolouration) on apples and pears*

COLOURS

Make food more colourful, compensate for colour lost in processing.

E100   Curcumin — *flour confectionery, margarine*

E101   Riboflavin — *sauces*

101(a) Riboflavin-5'-phosphate

E102   Tartrazine — *soft drinks*

E104   Quinoline yellow

E110   Sunset Yellow FCF — *biscuits*

E120   Cochineal — *alcoholic drinks*

E122   Carmoisine — *jams and preserves*

E123   Amaranth

E124   Ponceau 4R — *dessert mixes*

E127   Erythrosine BS — *glacé cherries*

128   Red 2G — *sausages*

E131   Patent Blue V

E132   Indigo Carmine

133   Brilliant Blue FCF — *canned vegetables*

E140   Chlorophyll

E141   Copper complexes of chlorophyll and chlorophyllins

E142   Green S — *pastilles*

E150   Caramel — *beer, soft drinks, sauces, gravy browning*

E151   Black PN

E153   Carbon Black (vegetable carbon) — *liquorice*

154   Brown FK — *kippers*

155   Brown HT — *chocolate cake*

E160(a) *alpha*-carotene; *beta*-carotene; *gamma*-carotene — *margarine, soft drinks*

E160(b) annatto; bixin; norbixin — *crisps*

E160(c) capsanthin; capsorubin

E160(d) lycopene

E160(e) *beta*-apo-8'-carotenal

E160(f) ethyl ester of beta-apo-8'-carotenoic acid

E161(a) Flavoxanthin

E161(b) Lutein

E161(c) Cryptoxanthin

E161(d) Rubixanthin

E161(e) Violaxanthin

E161(f) Rhodoxanthin

E161(g) Canthaxanthin

E162 Beetroot Red (betanin) — *ice cream; liquorice*

E163 Anthocyanins - *yoghurt*

E171 Titanium dioxide — *sweets*

E172 Iron oxides; iron hydroxides

E173 Aluminium

E174 Silver

E175 Gold — *cake decorations*

E180 Pigment Rubine (lithol rubine BK)

Methyl violet — *used for the surface marking of raw or unprocessed meat*

paprika — *canned vegetables*

turmeric — *soup*

EMULSIFIERS AND STABILISERS

Enable oils and fats to mix with water in foods; add to smoothness and creaminess of texture; retard baked goods going stale.

E400 alginic acid — *ice-cream; soft cheese*

E401 sodium alginate — *cake mixes*

E402 potassium alginate

E403 ammonium alginate

E404 calcium alginate

E405 propane-l, 2-diol alginate (propylene glycol alginate) — *salad dressings; cottage cheese*

E406 agar — *ice-cream*

E407 carrageenan — *quick setting jelly mixes; milk shakes*

E410 locust bean gum (carob gum) — *salad cream*

E412 guar gum — *packet soups and meringue mixes*

E413 tragacanth — *salad dressings; processed cheese*

E414 gum arabic (acacia) — *confectionery*

E415 xanthan gum — *sweet pickle; coleslaw*

416 karaya gum — *soft cheese; brown sauce*

432 polyoxyethylene (20) sorbitan monolaurate (Polysorbate 20)

433 polyoxyethylene (20) sorbitan mono-oleate (Polysorbate 80)

434 polyoxyethylene (20) sorbitan monopalmitate (Polysorbate 40)

435 polyoxyethylene (20) sorbitan monostearate (Polysorbate 60)

436 polyoxyethylene (20) sorbitan tristearate (Polysorbate 65) — *bakery products; confectionery creams*

E440 (i) pectin

E440 (ii) amidated pectin

pectin extract — *jams and preserves*

442 ammonium phosphatides — *cocoa and chocolate products*

E460 microcrystalline cellulose — *grated cheese*

alpha-cellulose (powdered cellulose) — *slimming bread*

E461 methylcellulose — *low fat spreads*

E463 hydroxypropylcellulose

E464 hydroxypropylmethylcellulose — *edible ices*

E465 ethylmethylcellulose — *gateaux*

E466 carboxymethylcellulose, sodium salt (CMC) — *jelly; gateaux*

E470 sodium, potassium and calcium salts of fatty acids — *cake mixes*

E471 mono- and di-glycerides of fatty acids — *frozen desserts*

E472(a) acetic acids esters of mono- and di-glycerides of fatty acids – *mousse mixes*

E472(b) lactic acid esters of mono- and di-glycerides of fatty acids – *dessert topping*

E472(c) citric acid esters of mono- and di-glycerides of fatty acids – *continental sausages*

E472(d) tartaric acid esters of mono- and di-glycerides of fatty acids

E472(e) mono-and diacetyltartaric acid esters of mono- and di-glycerides of fatty acids – *bread; frozen pizza*

E472(f) mixed acetic and tartaric acid esters of mono- and di- glycerides of fatty acids

E473 sucrose esters of fatty acids

E474 sucroglycerides – *edible ices*

E475 polyglycerol esters of fatty acids – *cakes and gateaux*

E476 polyglycerol esters of polycondensed fatty acids of castor oil (polyglycerol polyricinoleate) – *chocolate-flavour coatings for cakes*

E477 propane-1, 2-diol esters of fatty acids – *instant desserts*

E481 sodium stearoyl-1-2-lactylate – *bread, cakes and biscuits*

E482 calcium stearoyl-1-2-lactylate – *gravy granules*

E483 stearyl tartrate

491 sorbitan monostearate

492 sorbitan tristearate

493 sorbitan monolaurate

494 sorbitan mono-oleate

495 sorbitan monopalmitate – *cake mixes*

extract of quillaia – *used in soft drinks to promote foam*

oxidatively polymerised soya bean oil

polyglycerol esters of dimerised fatty acids of soya bean oil – *emulsions used to grease bakery tins*

PRESERVATIVES

Protect against microbes which cause spoilage and food poisoning. They also increase storage life of foods.

E200 sorbic acid – *soft drinks; fruit yoghurt; processed cheese slices*

E201 sodium sorbate

E202 potassium sorbate

E203 calcium sorbate – *frozen pizza; flour confectionery*

E210 benzoic acid

E211 sodium benzoate

E212 potassium benzoate

E213 calcium benzoate

E214 ethyl 4-hydroxybenzoate (ethyl para-hydroxybenzoate)

E215 ethyl 4-hydroxybenzoate, sodium salt (sodium ethyl para-hydroxybenzoate)

E216 propyl 4-hydroxybenzoate (propyl Para-hydroxybenzoate)

E217 propyl 4-hydroxybenzoate, sodium salt (sodium propyl para-hydroxybenzoate)

E218 methyl 4-hydroxybenzoate (methyl para-hydroxybenzoate)

E219 methyl 4-hydroxybenzoate, sodium salt (sodium methyl para-hydroxybenzoate) – *beer, jam, salad cream, soft drinks, fruit pulp, fruit-based pie fillings, marinated herring and mackerel*

E220 sulphur dioxide

E221 sodium sulphite

E222 sodium hydrogen sulphite (sodium bisulphite)

E223 sodium metabisulphite

E224 potassium metabisulphite

E226 calcium sulphite

E227 calcium hydrogen sulphite (calcium bisulphite) – *dried fruit, dehydrated vegetables, fruit juices and syrups, sausages, fruit-based dairy desserts, cider, beer and wine; also used to prevent browning of raw peeled potatoes and to condition biscuit doughs*

E228   Potassium bisulphite – *wines*

E230   biphenyl (diphenyl)

E231   2-hydroxybiphenyl (orthophenylphenol)

E232   sodium biphenyl-2-yl oxide (sodium orthophenylphenate) – *surface treatment of citrus fruit*

E233   2-(thiazol-4-yl) benzimidazole (thiabendazole) – *surface treatment of bananas*

234   nisin – *cheese, clotted cream*

E239   hexamine (hexamethylenetetramine) – *marinated herring and mackerel*

E249   potassium nitrite

E250   sodium nitrite

E251   sodium nitrate

E252   potassium nitrate – *bacon, ham, cured meats, corned beef and some cheeses*

E280   propionic acid

E281   sodium propionate

E282   calcium propionate

E283   potassium propionate – *bread and flour confectionery, Christmas pudding*

SWEETENERS

There are two types of sweeteners – intense sweeteners and bulk sweeteners. Intense sweeteners have a sweetness many times that of sugar and are therefore used at very low levels. They are marked with ★ in the following list. Bulk sweeteners have about the same sweetness as sugar and are used at the same sort of levels as sugar.

★acesulfame potassium – *canned foods, soft drinks, table-top sweeteners*

★aspartame – *soft drinks, yoghurts, dessert and drink mixes, sweetening tablets*

hydrogenated glucose syrup

isomalt

lactitol

E421   mannitol – *sugar-free confectionery*

★saccharin

★sodium saccharin

★calcium saccharin – *soft drinks, cider, sweetening tablets, table-top sweeteners*

E420   sorbitol; sorbitol syrup – *sugar-free confectionery, jams for diabetics*

★thaumatin – *table-top sweeteners, yoghurt*

xylitol – *sugar-free chewing gum*

OTHERS

Acids, anti-caking agents, anti-foaming agents, bases, buffers, bulking agents, firming agents, flavour modifiers, flour improvers, glazing agents, humectants, liquid freezants, packaging gases, propellants, release agents, sequestrants and solvents.

E170   calcium carbonate – *base, firming agent, release agent, diluent; nutrient in flour*

E260   acetic acid

E261   potassium acetate

E262   sodium hydrogen diacetate

262   sodium acetate – *acid/acidity regulators (buffers) used in pickles, salad cream and bread; they contribute to flavour and provide protection against mould growth*

E263   calcium acetate – *firming agent; also provides calcium which is useful in quick-set jelly mix*

E270   lactic acid – *acid/flavouring protects against mould growth; salad dressings, soft margarine*

E290   carbon dioxide – *carbonating agent/ packaging gas and propellant; used in fizzy drinks*

296   DL-malic acid; L-malic acid

297   fumaric acid – *acid/flavouring; used in soft drinks, sweets, biscuits, dessert mixes and pie fillings*

E325   sodium lactate – *buffer, humectant; used in jams, preserves, sweets, flour confectionery*

E326   potassium lactate – *buffer; jams, preserves and jellies*

E327   calcium lactate – *buffer, firming agent; canned fruit, pie filling*

E330   citric acid

E331   sodium dihydrogen citrate (monosodium citrate); disodium citrate; trisodium citrate

E332   potassium dihydrogen citrate (monopotassium citrate); tripotassium citrate

E333   monocalcium citrate; dicalcium citrate; tricalcium citrate – *acid/ flavourings, buffers, sequestrants, emulsifying salts (calcium salts are firming agents); used in soft drinks, jams, preserves, sweets, UHT cream, processed cheese, canned fruit, dessert mixes, ice-cream*

E334   L-(+)-tartaric acid

E335   monosodium L-(+)-tartrate; disodium L-(+)-tartrate

E336   monopotassium L-(+)-tartrate (cream of tartar); dipotassium L- (+)-tartrate

E337   potassium sodium L-(+)-tartrate – *acid/flavourings, buffers, emulsifying salts, sequestrants; used in soft drinks, biscuit creams and fillings, sweets, jams, dessert mixes and processed cheese*

E338   orthophosphoric acid (phosphoric acid) – *acid/flavourings; soft drinks, cocoa*

E339   sodium dihydrogen orthophosphate; disodium hydrogen orthophosphate; trisodium orthophosphate

E340   potassium dihydrogen orthophosphate; dipotassium hydrogen orthophosphate; tripotassium orthophosphate – *buffers, sequestrants, emulsifying salts; used in dessert mixes, non-dairy creamers, processed cheese*

E341   calcium tetrahydrogen diorthophosphate; calcium hydrogen orthophosphate; tricalcium diorthophosphate – *firming agent, anticaking agent, raising agent; cake mixes, baking powder, dessert mixes*

350   sodium malate; sodium hydrogen malate

351   potassium malate – *buffers, humectants; used in jams, sweets, cakes, biscuits*

352   calcium malate; calcium hydrogen malate – *firming agent in processed fruit and vegetables*

353   metatartaric acid – *sequestrant used in wine*

355   adipic acid – *buffer/flavouring; sweets, synthetic cream desserts*

363   succinic acid – *buffer/flavouring; dry foods and beverage mixes*

370   1,4-heptonolactone – *acid, sequestrant; dried soups, instant desserts*

375   nicotinic acid – *colour stabiliser and nutrient; bread, flour, breakfast cereals*

380   triammonium citrate – *buffer, emulsifying salt; processed cheese*

381   ammonium ferric citrate – *dietary iron supplement; bread*

385   calcium disodium ethylenediamine-NNN'N'-tetra-acetate (calcium disodium EDTA) – *sequestrant; canned shellfish*

E422   glycerol – *humectant, solvent; cake icing, confectionery*

E450(a)   disodium dihydrogen diphosphate; trisodium diphosphate; tetrasodium diphosphate; tetrapotassium diphosphate

E450(b)   pentasodium triphosphate; pentapotassium triphosphate

E450(c)   sodium polyphosphates, potassium polyphosphates – *buffers, sequestrants, emulsifying salts, stabilisers, texturisers – raising agents; used in whipping cream, fish and meat products, bread, processed cheese, canned vegetables*

500   sodium carbonate; sodium hydrogen carbonate (bicarbonate of soda); sodium sesquicarbonate

501   potassium carbonate; potassium hydrogen carbonate – *bases, aerating agents, diluents; used in jams, jellies, self-raising flour, wine, cocoa*

503   ammonium carbonate; ammonium hydrogen carbonate – *buffer, aerating agent; cocoa, biscuits*

504   magnesium carbonate – *base, anti-caking agent; wafer biscuits, icing sugar*

507   hydrochloric acid

508   potassium chloride – *gelling agent, salt substitute; table salt replacement*

509   calcium chloride – *firming agent in canned fruit and vegetables*

510   ammonium chloride – *yeast food in bread*

513   sulphuric acid

514   sodium sulphate – *diluent for colours*

515   potassium sulphate – *salt substitute*

516   calcium sulphate – *firming agent and yeast food; bread*

518   magnesium sulphate – *firming agent*

524   sodium hydroxide – *base; cocoa, jams and sweets*

525   potassium hydroxide – *base; sweets*

526   calcium hydroxide – *firming agent, neutralising agent; sweets*

527   ammonium hydroxide – *diluent and solvent for food colours, base; cocoa*

528   magnesium hydroxide – *base; sweets*

529   calcium oxide – *base; sweets*

530   magnesium oxide – *anti-caking agent; cocoa products*

535   sodium ferrocyanide

536   potassium ferrocyanide – *anti-caking agents in salt; crystallisation aids in wine*

540   dicalcium diphosphate – *buffer, neutralising agent; cheese*

541   sodium aluminium phosphate – *acid, raising agent; cake mixes, self-raising flour, biscuits*

542   edible bone phosphate – *anti-caking agent*

544   calcium polyphosphates – *emulsifying salt; processed cheese*

545   ammonium polyphosphates – *emulsifier, texturiser; frozen chicken*

551   silicon dioxide (silica) – *anti-caking agent; skimmed milk powder, sweeteners*

552   calcium silicate – *anti-caking agent, release agent; icing sugar, sweets*

553(a)   magnesium silicate synthetic; magnesium trisilicate – *anti-caking agent; sugar confectionery*

553(b)   talc – *release agent; tabletted confectionery*

554   aluminium sodium silicate

556   aluminium calcium silicate

558   bentonite

559   kaolin

570   stearic acid – *anti-caking agents*

572   magnesium stearate – *emulsifier, release agent; confectionery*

575   D-glucono-1, 5-lactone (glucono delta-lactone) – *acid, sequestrant; cake mixes, continental sausages*

576   sodium gluconate

577   potassium gluconate – *sequestrants*

578   calcium gluconate – *buffer, firming agent, sequestrant; jams, dessert mixes*

620   L-glutamic acid

621   sodium hydrogen L-glutamate (monosodium glutamate; MSG)

622   potassium hydrogen L-glutamate (monopotassium glutamate)

623   calcium dihydrogen di-L-glutamate (calcium glutamate)

627   guanosine 5′-disodium phosphate (sodium guanylate)

631   inosine 5′-disodium phosphate (sodium inosinate)

635   sodium 5′-ribonucleotide – *flavour enhancers used in savoury foods and snacks, soups, sauces and meat products*

636   maltol

637   ethyl maltol – *flavourings/flavour enhancers used in cakes and biscuits*

900   dimethylpolysiloxane – *anti-foaming agent*

901   beeswax

903   carnauba wax – *glazing agents used in sugar and chocolate confectionery*

904   shellac – *glazing agent used to wax apples*

905   mineral hydrocarbons — *glazing/coating agent used to prevent dried fruit sticking together*

907   refined microcrystalline wax — *release agent; chewing gum*

920   L–cysteine hydrochloride

925   chlorine

926   chlorine dioxide

927   azodicarbonamide — *flour treatment agents used to improve the texture of bread, cake and biscuit doughs*

aluminium potassium sulphate — *firming agent; chocolate-coated cherries*

2-aminoethanol — *base; caustic lye used to peel vegetables*

ammonium dihydrogen orthophosphate; diammonium hydrogen orthophosphate — *buffer, yeast food*

ammonium sulphate — *yeast food*

benzoyl peroxide — *bleaching agent in flour*

butyl stearate — *release agent*

calcium heptonate — *firming agent, sequestrant; prepared fruit and vegetables*

calcium phytate — *sequestrant; wine*

dichlorodifluoromethane — *propellant and liquid freezant used to freeze food by immersion*

diethyl ether — *solvent*

disodium dihydrogen ethylenediamine-NNN′N′-tetra-acetate (disodium dihydrogen EDTA) — *sequestrant; brandy*

ethanol (ethylalcohol)

ethyl acetate

glycerol mono-acetate (monoacetin)

glycerol di-acetate (diacetin)

glycerol tri-acetate (triacetin) — *solvents used to dilute and carry food colours and flavourings*

glycine — *sequestrant, buffer, nutrient*

hydrogen

nitrogen — *packaging gases*

nitrous oxide — *propellant used in aerosol packs of whipped cream*

octadecylammonium acetate — *anti-caking agent in yeast foods used in bread*

oxygen — *packaging gas*

oxystearin — *sequestrant, fat crystallisation inhibitor; salad cream*

polydextrose — *bulking agent; reduced and low calorie foods*

propan-1, 2-diol (propylene glycol)

propan-2-ol (isopropyl alcohol) — *solvents used to dilute colours and flavourings*

sodium heptonate — *sequestrant; edible oils*

spermaceti

sperm oil — *release agents*

tannic acid — *flavouring, clarifying agent; beer, wine and cider*

Bibliography

About Food Additives, ref PB0552 (Ministry of Agriculture, Fisheries and Food, 1991)

Collins Guide to Tropical Plants (1981)

Dictionary of Nutrition and Food Technology, Arnold E. Bender (1990)

E for Additives, Maurice Hanssen (Thorsons, 1984)

Experimental Study of Food, A.M. Campbell, M.P. Penfield and R.M. Griswold (Constable, 4th edn. 1981)

Food Safety (Food Safety Advisory Centre, 1991)

Food Science, Brian A. Cox and Allan G. Cameron (Hodder and Stoughton, 4th edn. 1986)

Health of the Nation (HMSO 1991. Dietary Reference Values for Food and Nutrients for the United Kingdom, no. 41)

Manual of Nutrition (HMSO no. 342)

Mushrooms and Toadstools, Geoffrey Kibby (Oxford University Press, 1979)

On Food and Cooking, Harold McGee (Harpers Collins, 1991)

Royal Horticultural Society Dictionary of Gardening 5 vols. (Oxford University Press, 1951)

Christian, Glyn. *World Guide to Cheese* (Ebury Press, 1984)

David, Elizabeth. *English Bread and Yeast* (Penguin Books, 1977)
   French Provincial Cooking (Penguin Books, 1960)

Grigson, Jane. *Fruit Book* (Penguin Books, 1982)
   Vegetable Book (Penguin Books, 1980)

Guerard, Michel. *Cuisine Minceur* (Macmillan, 1977)

Hicks, Susan. *The Fish Course* (BBC Books, 1987)

Hom, Ken. *Chinese Cooking* (BBC Books, 1984)

Hume, Rosemary and Downes, Muriel. *Cordon Bleu Cookery Book* (Book Club Associates, 1974)
   Penguin Dictionary of Cooking (1966)

Jaffrey, Madhur. *Indian Cookery* (BBC Books, 1982)

Leeming, Margaret. *A History of Food* (BBC Books, 1991)

Leith, Prue and Waldegrave, Caroline. *Leith's Cookery School* (McDonald & Co., 1985)

Liddell, Caroline. *The Wholefood Cook Book* (Coronet Books, 1980)

Paterson, Margaret. *1001 Ways to be a Good Cook* (Pan Books, 1986)

Rogers, Jenny. *The Taste of Health* (BBC Books, 1985)

Smith, Delia. *Delia Smith's Cookery Course* (BBC Books, 1978)

Stobart, Tom. *The Cook's Encyclopaedia* (Batsford, 1980)

The Dairy Book of Family Cooking, Milk Marketing Board (Ebury Press, 1983)

Eating for a Healthy Heart, Good Housekeeping (National Magazine Company, 1976)